GEOLOGIC TIME SCALE

Era	Period	Epoch	Beginning (Years Ago)
Cenozoic	Tertiary	Pleistocene	1.5-2 Million
		Pliocene	7 Million
		Miocene	26 Million
		Oligocene	37-38 Million
		Eocene	53-54 Million
		Paleocene	65 Million
Mesozoic	Cretaceous		136 Million
	Jurassic		190-195 Million
	Triassic		225 Million
Paleozoic	Permian		280 Million
	Carboniferous		345 Million
	Devonian		395 Million
	Silurian		430-440 Million
	Ordovician		500 (?) Million
	Cambrian		570 Million

Figures are from a Geological Society of London symposium held in 1964.

Anthropology & Education

The major objective of this series is to make the knowledge and perspective of anthropology available to educators and their students. It is hoped and believed, however, that it will also prove valuable to those in other professions and in the several disciplines that comprise the behavioral sciences.

In recent years some educators have discovered that anthropology has much to offer the areas of professional training and educational theory and practice. In its cross-cultural comparisons of human behavior and in its inductive, empirical method of analysis is found a conceptual freshness that is intellectually liberating.

Actually, there are four major areas of anthropological theory which have direct relevance for education. These are the transmission of culture and learning processes; the regularities of behavior and belief which we call culture; the ways in which individuals group themselves for the accomplishment of communal purposes, from which comes organization theory; and the processes by which transformations occur in human behavior and groupings which can be explained by a theory of change. In addition, there are the subject-matter areas of child rearing; community and the relationships among institutions within it; the rites of passage; the cultural categories of social class, ethnic group, age, grading, and sex; and others.

These several areas of theory and substance provide a rich source for this series. For example, there are plans for analyses of the relevance of anthropology to each educational specialty, such as administration, guidance, and curriculum. In another direction, the perspective and method of such areas as social anthropology, applied anthropology, and linguistics in relation to education will be examined. Several studies about educational activities which use anthropological research methods and concepts will appear. Other subject areas for the series include the culture of childhood, comparative educational systems, methods of research, and the exemplification of anthropological theory in subject-matter organization. It is believed that the availability of such a storehouse of knowledge in the several volumes in this series will contribute immensely to the further improvement of our educational system.

Solon T. Kimball, *General Editor*

THE WAY TO MODERN MAN

AN INTRODUCTION TO HUMAN EVOLUTION

Fred T. Adams

TEACHERS COLLEGE PRESS

Teachers College, Columbia University, New York

Design and Illustrations by Gaspar Vilato

Manufactured in the United States of America

Foreword

As long as men of the Western world believed themselves to be created in the image of the one and perfect Divinity there was no earthly reason why they should be curious about their origins. But when the consequences of the systematic study of nature began to contradict the commonly held assumptions and beliefs about a supernaturally created and spiritually ordered universe a few adventurous intellects began to question the long accepted explanations. In the beginning even the validity of the evidence itself was in doubt, but gradually it became clear that it was man who created his own realities, his perceptions of himself.

In this onward march of discovery, questioning, and revision, a little more than a century ago the time grew ripe for a great new synthesis. For that achievement we honor Charles Darwin who gave a new perspective about and for all mankind. He it was who made man a full member of the natural order when he challenged the validity of special creation. But another contribution of even greater importance came when he set the objective of natural science as the discovery of the processes of perpetual transition. In so doing he redirected the focus of thought away from the identification of things to the search for interdependence and change.

It is that perspective which permeates this book's account of how man came to be. The genealogical connections are traced backward into the shadowy reaches of time and forward through the long and tortuous ascent as man's precursors travelled the toilsome route that carried them away from their brutish origins. We can only speculate on that moment in time when first appeared a tool-making and symbol-using creature who eventually in his confident arrogance called himself *Homo sapiens*.

But we encounter much more here than just the details of man's origin and his relation to other species. We also find the dramatic record of the hesitating, erratic, but nonetheless certain steps by which these early scientific discoverers struggled with and finally overcame the intellectual tradition that beclouded their vision. In the process of understanding man's emergence they also forged new processes of thought, the full significance of which are not yet widely understood. Our debt to them is indeed a great one.

The understandings which an author wishes to convey are more clearly grasped if we also know something about him. I first came to know Fred Adams two decades ago when he was a graduate student at the University of Alabama. He impressed me with his keen intellect, his lucid prose style, and his humility. After he had completed his graduate studies at Tulane University, he accepted a teaching position in a small liberal arts college in the South. There he immersed himself in that intimate exchange between teacher and student which such an environment permits. In the classroom he faced the challenge of helping young minds to discover the grandeur contained in the long progression toward humanity. In one way this book is a record of that confrontation. Although the substance he gives us is meaty stuff, he still conveys a sense of wonder in the mystery of creation. Adams also explains the birth trauma of the new ideas about the origin of man experienced by those men of science who slowly labored to new levels of perception.

The book also possesses another distinguishing characteristic which might be overlooked all too easily. In the organization of materials it reproduces the method of enquiry and discovery of the scientists, who raise questions, interpret evidence, and offer conclusions. Thus it carries the reader along the same route as the one which produced each new understanding and encourages him to participate in the process of assembling facts and drawing conclusions about them. In incorporating the method of natural history research in the structure of his argument, Adams has achieved a standard worthy of emulation by all educators.

Solon T. Kimball

Acknowledgements

One of the aims of this work is to communicate to others an appreciation for the ideas and efforts of those who have concerned themselves with the study of man. My own appreciation developed largely because I was exposed to such teachers as Solon T. Kimball, Alec (Jack) Kelso, C. Loring Brace, Marshall T. Newman, and Frank Livingstone.

A number of other people have contributed, directly or indirectly, to the writing of this book. I owe special debts of gratitude to James A. Gavan of the University of Missouri and to the staff and faculty of Wofford College. Dr. Gavan gave freely of his time and criticisms while the book was in manuscript form. A research grant from Wofford College provided me with badly needed time and library resources; and considerable clerical assistance was supplied by Mrs. Mildred Self and her assistants, notably Mrs. Mildred Thompson. Colleagues—especially John Harrington and William Hubbard—were helpful in answering questions and in providing encouragement. Last, but by no means least, I should like to thank my wife Margaret for her unwavering confidence and support.

The following publishers were kind enough to allow me to use materials from their books: The Macmillan Company; Prentice-Hall, Inc., Encyclopaedia Britannica, Inc. (*The Great Ideas Today*); The World Publishing Company; Alfred A. Knopf, Inc.; Harper & Row, Publishers; and John Wiley and Sons, Inc.

Fred T. Adams

Contents

Figures

I

INTRODUCTION: EVOLUTION AND EVIDENCE

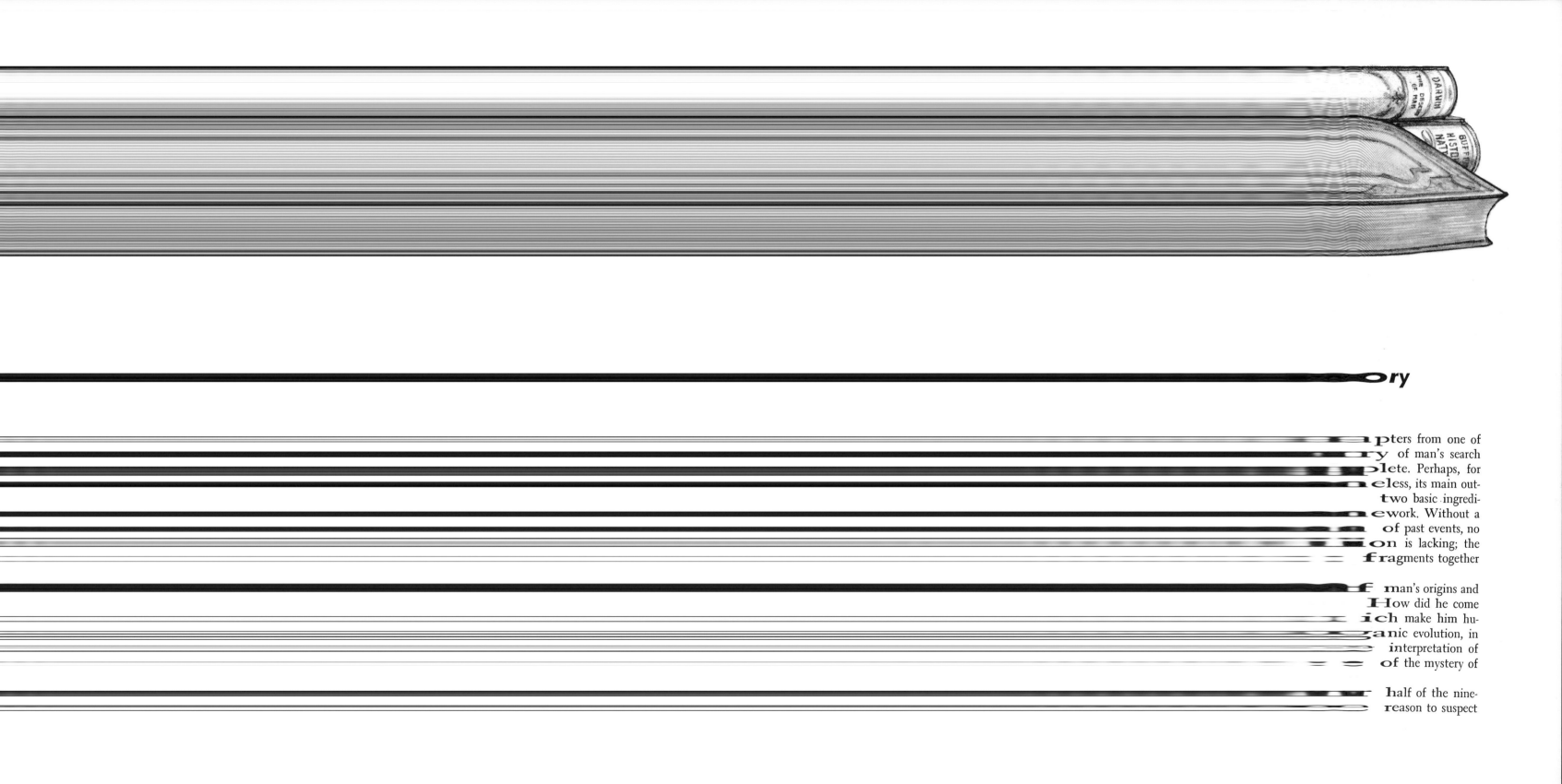

...ory

...pters from one of
...ry of man's search
...lete. Perhaps, for
...eless, its main out-
two basic ingredi-
ework. Without a
of past events, no
on is lacking; the
fragments together

...f man's origins and
How did he come
ich make him hu-
anic evolution, in
interpretation of
of the mystery of

half of the nine-
reason to suspect

that a mystery—one which coul

and development. The biblical

cieties with an authoritative

created the stars, the heaven, a

plant and animal life. As a last

His own image. Supporting the

1650 pronouncement by Arch

scholar, that all creation was

was obviously too brief for man

now is.

The biblical theory of creation

tion of its own authority. There

universe, and everything was in

rationally designed and ordered

principles which underlay the

human mind. If so, man woul

appreciation and understanding

Thus many were inspired by a

investigative activities so as to

same sort of faith inspired a diff

As evidence accumulated thro

literal interpretation of the boo

"SPECIES ARE

To rent the fabric of Christ

scientists. More typically they

within the guidelines establish

in fact, buttressed teachings

Carolus Linnaeus (Carl von L

the first edition of which was

doctrine of special creation.[2] In

as fixed, immutable. "The num

as that which existed at the st

Since species were brought

unchanging units, the essence

"type" (sometimes designated

tern").[4] The species type was

Linnaeus classified. Members

hibited characteristics in com

easily distinguishable. In other

ations. Such deviations were i

dental and irrelevant. For inst

I

A Mystery and a Theory

Our purpose is to acquaint you with pages and chapters from one of the the greatest mystery stories of all time, the story of man's search for his ancestors. The story is by no means complete. Perhaps, for reasons we will explore later, it never will be. Nevertheless, its main outlines are now well established. Every such story has two basic ingredients: a mystery and a theory, or interpretative framework. Without a mystery, there is obviously no need for reconstruction of past events, no need to search for clues. Without a theory, direction is lacking; the search for clues is random, and there is no way to tie fragments together into a meaningful whole.

The mystery with which we are concerned is that of man's origins and development. How did man arrive upon this earth? How did he come to exhibit the particular attributes and qualities which make him human? The general guiding theory, the theory of organic evolution, in this instance, not only provided direction and made interpretation of clues possible, but also brought to light the existence of the mystery of man's origins.

The mystery was not fully exposed until the latter half of the nineteenth century. Before that time there had been little reason to suspect

3

that a mystery—one which could be probed—surrounded man's origins and development. The biblical accounts provided men in Western societies with an authoritative explanation of such matters. God had created the stars, the heaven, and the earth, which He had filled with plant and animal life. As a last act of creation, He had made man in His own image. Supporting the authority of the biblical record was the 1650 pronouncement by Archbishop James Ussher, Irish prelate and scholar, that all creation was completed in 4004 B.C. Terrestrial time was obviously too brief for man to have ever been other than what he now is.

The biblical theory of creation gradually led, however, to the invalidation of its own authority. There was a place for everything in the biblical universe, and everything was in its place. The universe was perceived as rationally designed and ordered. Very probably then, it was reasoned, principles which underlay the masterly design could be grasped by the human mind. If so, man would be drawn closer to God by a better appreciation and understanding of the Creator's works and workings. Thus many were inspired by a faith in the order of nature to undertake investigative activities so as to better understand and glorify God. The same sort of faith inspired a different order of inquiry, scientific inquiry.[1] As evidence accumulated through the latter type of investigation, a literal interpretation of the book of Genesis became less tenable.

"SPECIES ARE THE WORK OF TIME"

To rent the fabric of Christian dogma was hardly the intent of early scientists. More typically they attempted to select and interpret facts within the guidelines established by the Church. The efforts of some, in fact, buttressed teachings of the Church. One such scientist was Carolus Linnaeus (Carl von Linne) of Sweden. His *Systema Naturae*, the first edition of which was published in 1735, gave substance to the doctrine of special creation.[2] In this work Linnaeus described the species as fixed, immutable. "The number of species," he wrote, "is the same as that which existed at the start of creation." [3]

Since species were brought into being by special creation and were unchanging units, the essence of a species was a divine idea, a pattern, a "type" (sometimes designated as an "archetype," or "primeval pattern").[4] The species type was readily discernible in most of the species Linnaeus classified. Members of each of these species populations exhibited characteristics in common that were more or less discrete and easily distinguishable. In other instances, the type was obscured by variations. Such deviations were ignored; they were considered to be accidental and irrelevant. For instance, what are now termed varieties or subspecies of plants were, to Linnaeus' way of thinking, members of a species temporarily modified by "whatever occasional cause." When this "occasional cause," or environmental factor, was removed, the plants would revert to the original type. The living world, in short, is static. Change, though it may occur, has no lasting effect.

Linnaeus imposed a false rigidity upon nature, as he himself came to suspect in his old age. A change in thinking seems to have resulted from his observations of plants that were quite different from the parental stock. The first such specimen brought to his attention Linnaeus labelled *Peloria*, "monstrosity." But the metamorphosed plant produced others like itself; it did not revert to the parental type. No doubt greatly troubled, Linnaeus concluded that the plant was a new species. In the final edition of *Systema Naturae* (1766), the famous dictum, *nullae species novae* ("there are no new species"), was omitted. Before his death the master proponent of the immutability of species reportedly expressed the view that "species are the work of time." [5]

Though Linnaeus was probably not aware of it, a few of his contemporaries shared, or were to share, the same view. One, Pierre Moreau de Maupertuis, was presenting biological essays before *Systema Naturae* was first published. His interest was in "the mystery of generation." The secrets of heredity were yet to be discovered, but Maupertuis' studies and conclusions anticipated the work of Mendel and others by more than a century.[6] One of his conclusions was that albinism, extra digits, and other hereditary variations are accidental products—results of what are now called mutations. The potential for such variations is always present; "chance or art brings them out." By "art," Maupertuis meant the creation of new species of animals through selective breeding. What man could do, nature could also do by altering the hereditary materials or action of the environment. In short, the diversity of life could have arisen from a single source. The many species and varieties were the results of mutations, geographical isolation, and migration.[7]

SPECIES HAVE A COMMON ORIGIN

The Comte de Buffon (Georges Louis Leclerc) also had a theory about diversity and change, a theory which even he could not fully accept. Where Linnaeus stressed differences among species, Buffon saw similarities. In the fourth volume of *Histoire Naturelle* (1753), he noted that when animals are compared, "there exists a certain primitive and general design, which we can trace for a long way." Even in the structures that make species distinct "there is a prodigious degree of resemblance, which irresistibly brings to our mind the idea of an original pattern after which all animals seem to have been conceived." For example, when man and horse are compared, "is not our wonder aroused rather by the resemblances than by the differences to be found between them?" [8]

As the "idea of an original pattern" implies, Buffon saw in the similarities "that all animals are descended from a single animal, from which have sprung in the course of time, as a result of progress or degeneration, all the other races of animals." [9] All species—including man—had a common origin. Differentiation was effected by progress or degeneration. The ass, for instance, had degenerated from the horse. But the changes must have been gradual, with a "large number of intermediate animals." Buffon could perceive no way in which the changes could have occurred, and there was an absence of intermediate species to connect the horse and the ass. For these and other reasons, theological and observational, he repudiated the theory of evolution he had constructed. [10]

Later in the century, a keen observer of nature, Erasmus Darwin, echoed Buffon in *The Botanic Garden* (1792): "As all the families both of plants and animals appear in a state of perpetual improvement or degeneracy, it becomes a subject of importance to detect the causes of these mutations." [11] In *Zoonomia* Darwin had more to say. He perceived a common thread in the diversity of life and possible reasons for the diversity:

> When we revolve in our minds the metamorphoses of animals, as from the tadpole to the frog; secondly, the changes produced by artificial cultivation, as in the breeds of horses, dogs, and sheep; thirdly, the changes produced by conditions of climate and of season, as in the sheep of warm climates being covered with hair instead of wool, and the hares and partridges of northern climates becoming white in winter: when, further, we observe the changes of structure produced by habit, as seen especially in men of different occupations; or the changes produced by artificial mutilation and prenatal influences, as in the crossing of species and production of monsters; fourth, when we observe the essential unity of plan in all warm-blooded animals,—we are led to conclude that they have been alike produced from a similar living filament. [12]

Since many of these changes occurred within a brief period of time, "would it be too bold to imagine, in the great length of time since the earth began to exist, perhaps millions of years before the commencement of the history of mankind, that all warm-blooded animals have arisen from one living filament?" [13]

The evolving from "one living filament" came about through interaction with the environment. In meeting their needs in a changing environment, animals unconsciously take on adaptive organs and fea-

6

tures. For example, the snout of the pig, the trunk of the elephant, the rough tongues of cattle, and the beaks of birds "seem to have been gradually produced during many generations by the perpetual endeavor of the creatures to supply the want of food, and to have been delivered to their posterity with constant improvement of them for the purposes acquired." [14]

Although *Zoonomia* attracted considerable attention, Erasmus Darwin's impact upon scientific thinking was apparently very slight. One reason, no doubt, was that university educators were hostile toward the idea of evolution. The fact that Darwin did much of his writing in verse may have been another factor; a poet was not too likely to be taken seriously when he ventured into scientific areas.

Erasmus Darwin had little immediate influence upon the development of a theory of evolution, but neither did he incur too much ire for his heretical ideas. A Frenchman with somewhat similar ideas fared less well. Before he died, the Chevalier de Lamarck (Jeanne Baptist Antoine de Monet) was to suffer personal and professional disrepute in his own country and abroad.

SLOW CHANGE OR SUDDEN CATASTROPHES

Like Buffon, Lamarck thought the classification of plants and animals established by Linnaeus was a bit arbitrary. In *Zoological Philosophy* (1809) he wrote: "The more products of nature we assemble the more obvious it becomes that almost all gaps between species tend to fill up and obliterate our dividing lines." [15] The close similarity of life forms suggested to Lamarck that organisms are in constant flux. But why? He decided that life was constantly emerging in simple forms. Through an unconscious striving to adjust to demands of the environment, many organisms attained greater complexity. The key to diversity, then, was environment. Great changes in environment created changes in wants, hence changes in behavior. "If new wants become constant or very lasting, they form new habits, the new habits involve the use of new parts, or a different use of old parts, which results finally in the production of new organs and the modification of old ones." The parts and modifications thus acquired were transmitted to future generations. However, "the constant lack of use of the same organ insensibly weakens it, deteriorates it, progressively diminishes its powers, and ends by causing it to disappear." [16]

The "transmutation" (evolution) of new forms was a very slow process. This was evidenced by the accumulation of fossils in the crust of the earth. The earth's crust, Lamarck reckoned, had taken millions of years to form.[17] But, "For Nature time is nothing. It is never a diffi-

7

culty, she always has it at her disposal. . . ." [18] The fossils, he declared, "are the genuine and actual predecessors of our present forms." [19]

Few understood or gave much credence to Lamarck's views on the antiquity of the earth. It is probable, however, that at least some features of his theory of evolution would have had more influence than they did had not Lamarck's ideas been in opposition to those of the brilliant and influential Baron Cuvier (Léopold Chrétien Frédéric Dagobert). If Lamarck's conceptions of slow change and evolution were correct, then Cuvier's theory of catastrophes was in error. Cuvier firmly believed he was right, so he criticized Lamarck's ideas. His attacks, sometimes personal, made Lamarck and his ideas objects of ridicule and scorn.

Cuvier's theory was persuasive, for it was couched within a framework of accepted beliefs and assumptions. The Flood which Moses reported was, Cuvier asserted, a geological fact. Five or six thousand years ago, this sudden catastrophe devastated the countries inhabited by man. The Flood ended when portions of the sea-floor were upraised to form present-day dry land.[20] Beneath the earth's surface there were layers or strata which marked prior catastrophes, acts of sudden destruction by God.[21]

As proof that the strata had been formed by sudden catastrophes, Cuvier pointed to fossils left by the last catastrophe: "In the northern regions it has left the carcases of some large quadrupeds which the ice had arrested, and which are preserved even to the present day with their skin, their hair, and their flesh." Had the cause of death not been sudden, they would have "been decomposed by putrefaction." The suddenness of prior "revolutions" (catastrophes) was evident in the "breaking to pieces and overturnings of the strata." [22]

Cuvier recognized a progression toward complexity in the fossil record, the more complex organisms being nearer the earth's surface. This hardly bespoke organic evolution, however. If evolution had taken place, there would also be fossil evidence of intermediate species. But there was no such evidence. Furthermore, present-day mammals and reptiles are too different from extinct mammals and reptiles to comprise identical species; the dead were of different species than the living.[23] A species, according to Cuvier's definition, was constituted of "all the beings belonging to one of these forms (perpetuated since the beginning of all things, that is the Creation)." [24] In short, the fact of special creation precluded the possibility of organic evolution.

But if all species had originated at the Creation, why were different species to be found in the succeeding strata? The answer Cuvier gave to this question was to haunt some branches of science to the present day.[25] The fossil record, he said in effect, was a consequence of successive catastrophes and migrations. Following the Creation, all the species—the living and those which were to become extinct—were distributed over the face of the earth. Some parts of the world were eventually visited by catastrophes that killed off the forms of life living there, making a number of species extinct quite early in geologic time. Thus did stratification of the earth's crust and the fossil record begin. In time, other species from areas that had not been touched by a cataclysm moved into former areas of destruction and became established there. And, in time, they suffered the fate of the earlier occupants; other species became extinct and part of the fossil record. Such events were repeated a number of times prior to the biblical Flood, when all parts of the world were affected. To Cuvier's way of thinking, redistributions of species—not evolution—accounted for the composition of the fossil record.

Ironically, Cuvier played a significant role in undermining the Christian tenets he ostensibly supported. As one of the founders of comparative anatomy, he could, from a few bones, reconstruct at least the chief outlines of great vertebrates of the past. His technique was to be used later by others in demonstrating the validity of evolution. Further, because of his considerable abilities and charm, he enhanced the prestige of science and created a popular interest in the world's past history.[26] By giving credence to antediluvian (pre-Flood) time, he added immeasurably to the age of the earth, as it was conceived by man. These substantial contributions were to help pave the way for a rejection of the authority of the biblical account of Creation.

PROCESSES OPERATE IN A LAWFUL MANNER

The orthodox thinkers, conscious of the threat some of Cuvier's ideas posed to established dogma, attempted to rise to the occasion. Valiant efforts were made to reconcile geological facts to biblical chronology. The fundamentalists were outraged, but the liberals were able to convince themselves that each of the six days of Creation was not "descriptive of that length of time in which this planet now performs its diurnal revolution." Rather, "day" was intended as a figurative term to designate "certain indefinite periods, in which particular parts of the great work of creation were accomplished. . . ." Taking this meaning into account, "The age of the world, according to the scriptural account, will then agree with that which is manifested by the phenomena of its stratification." [27]

Even greater efforts to mesh geology with theology were made when the works of a young amateur British geologist, Charles Lyell, appeared. Lyell had been grounded in "catastrophical or paroxysmal theory," but he noted that what he observed in nature was more compatible with views expressed by James Hutton in 1785: " 'In the economy of the world,' said the Scotch geologist [Hutton], 'I can find no traces of a beginning, no prospect of an end'; a declaration the more startling when coupled with the doctrine, that all past ages on the globe had been brought about by the slow agency of existing causes." [28] Geological formations and alterations, Hutton had explained, were due to natural processes that were on-going, such as the slow displacement of soils by rain and wind. The "Author of Nature," he said, could destroy what He had created, "but we may rest assured that this great catastrophe will not be brought about by the laws now existing, and that it is not indicated, by any thing which we perceive." [29] Hutton had merely made further application of an accepted scientific assumption: the processes of an orderly universe operate in a lawful manner.

Uniformitarianism—the doctrine that geological formations are fairly uniform consequences of slowly working natural processes—fitted neatly with some of Lamarck's views.[30] It is not surprising, then, that Lyell said of Lamarck's theories: "[They] delighted me more than any novel I ever read. . . . That the earth is quite as old as he supposes, has long been my creed. . . ." [31]

The "creed," supported by data, appeared in Lyell's *Principles of Geology*, the first edition of which appeared in three volumes between 1830 and 1833. An immediate popular and professional success, the work assured the eventual ascendancy of uniformitarianism. *Principles of Geology* also inadvertently—for Lyell was a man of deep religious convictions—heightened the developing conflict between science and religion. Not only did the work publicize pre-Flood antiquity, it also dispensed with a single creation. Lyell had compounded Cuvier's heresy. British clergy and laymen vigorously attempted to allay anxieties by showing, in one way or another, that science really agreed with the Scriptures.[32]

Lyell, despite his admiration for Lamarck, could not accept the French scientist's theory of the transmutation of species, in part because there were no fossils of intermediate species. Too, embalmed animals and evidences of plant life found in ancient Egyptian tombs were identical with present-day animals, seeds, and plants. Environment could not account for speciation, for "some of these animals have since that period been transported by man to almost every climate, and forced to accommodate their habits to the greatest variety of circumstances." [33]

In rejecting transmutation, or evolution, Lyell employed an argument used by anti-evolutionists to the present: If higher orders of plants and animals were "derived in a long series of generations from those of more simple conformation," another hypothesis is necessary in order to explain "why, after an indefinite lapse of ages, there were still so many beings of the simplest structure." Why, Lyell asked, "have the majority of existing creatures remained stationary throughout this long succession of epochs, while others have made such prodigious advances?" [34]

The "Author of Nature," Lyell believed, functioned more directly in the area of biology than He did in geology. Species were the result of many discrete special creations [35] (a view Cuvier rejected); "as often as certain forms of animals and plants disappeared, for reasons quite unintelligible to us, others took their place by virtue of a causation, which was quite beyond our comprehension." [36] At the creation of an animal or plant, however, we must suppose that "all the possible circumstances in which its descendants are destined to live are foreseen, and that an organization is conferred upon it which will enable the species to perpetuate itself and survive under all the varying circumstances to which it must be inevitably exposed." [37] On the whole, expressions of this sort were congruent with widely held beliefs in 1840 and even later.

A MISSING ELEMENT: MAN

With the vital exception of the origin of man himself, virtually all the elements necessary to the plot of our story had been introduced by the time the sixth edition of *Principles of Geology* appeared in June, 1840. The elements needed only to be drawn together in a comprehensible manner and given the right kind of publicity.

Lyell's works had communicated considerable understanding of the earth's strata and of slowly working geological processes. People were taking a closer look at the earth and its layers. Less well known, but later to assume considerable importance, were theories about the prior extent and actions of large glaciers. Louis Agassiz, a young Swiss who was to become a scientific leader in America, had proposed theories about an Ice Age; but his ideas were generally considered to be ridiculous by those who heard about them.[38]

Myths and superstitions about fossils had been largely swept away by 1840, though it was generally believed that many fossils were remnants of the Noachian Flood.[39] The ordering of fossils in the earth's strata, it was acknowledged, was from relatively simple to more complex forms of past life. Comparative anatomy made it possible to devise techniques for reconstructing at least the outlines of extinct species from fossilized bones. Paleontology in France and geology in Britain were common topics of discourse. Biological evolution was not.

Ignorance of biological evolution was due in part to ignorance about advances in the biological sciences. Just as morphology (the study of form and structure) confirmed the findings of paleontology concerning fossils, embryology and cytology (the study of cells) were beginning to confirm the kinship of all mammals. Human physiology was better understood; and the variability of the human body was beginning to be appreciated due to the work of Johann Friedrich Blumenbach, often referred to as the "father of physical anthropology." [40]

Widespread ignorance of evolution was due also to the manner in which scientists had dealt with the theories and ideas about evolution that had emerged from time to time. Such views had been generally ignored or ridiculed into near, or complete, oblivion. Too, common sense and religious beliefs made it impossible to visualize the series of changes over the long period of time ordinarily required for speciation. Generations of plants and animals remained essentially the same, even as far back as ancient Egypt; species seemed truly immutable.

Some of the theories, assumptions, and beliefs held in 1840 appear ludicrous in the light of present-day knowledge. But remarkable advances and upheavals in thought had already occurred within a relatively brief period of time. The world that Linnaeus had pigeonholed had become much more varied and fluid. Time was no longer so firmly fixed; it stretched from the Flood backwards into infinity. There was, in short, a greater latitude for investigating, synthesizing, theory-building.

Two constants remained unscathed by the maelstrom of change: the Flood and man. The fossil record supported what everyone knew—man was the final product of Creation, made to "have dominion over the fish of the sea, and over the fowl of the air, and over every living thing that moveth upon the earth." True, this exalted position had been questioned. Julien de Lamettrie wrote around 1750 that before they had language, men "were beasts among beasts." [41] Worse, the philosophers Immanuel Kant and Arthur Schopenhauer and others, like Buffon and Lamarck, had inferred or implied the transformation of apes into humans.[42] But such heretical views rarely reached public cognizance; if they did, they were soon repressed.

The Flood was the only major geological event which had occurred in the few thousand years since man's appearance. Both Lyell and Cuvier were in agreement with most of their countrymen that man had not been long on the antediluvian scene. But largely due to efforts of these two men, the conception of unlimited prehistoric time was accepted by several people, and some began to reinterpret "thunderstones" and hominid * fossils that were being uncovered in antediluvian deposits.

---

* Hominids are members of the family Hominidae, which includes both modern and extinct forms of man.

Thunderstones, or "ceraunites," as early scientists called them, were known during the Middle Ages. Though a few men in prior times had expressed doubt as to their origin, the general belief in 1840 was that the stones were shaped by natural forces, such as lightning. In the 1830's two Frenchmen questioned this belief. The first to do so, Casimir Picard, pointed out to a rather select group of men that the stones were found in the same geological stratum as bones of elephants, rhinoceroses, and hippopotamuses. The stones, he concluded, were weapons used by little-civilized men in hunting these animals. Picard's reports and evidence prompted a member of the select group, Jacques Boucher de Perthes, to also search prehistoric strata. What he found led him to argue before scientists and all of France that prehistoric man had made and used primitive stone tools. Boucher de Perthes argued to little avail; the belief that man always was as he now is, was impregnable. A few years later, however, Lyell, among others, was converted to the idea of prehistoric man by the weight of De Perthes' evidence.[43]

The antiquity of early hominid fossil finds was also discounted. Public opinion supported Cuvier's dictum: "Fossil man does not exist." All recognizably hominid skeletal materials were considered to be those of *Homo sapiens*, despite the fact that many such remains were found in association with remains of extinct mammals in Germany, France, England, and Belgium.[44] Such associations, it was generally believed, were spurious. The investigators had been careless or inept; there had been natural burials of humans in antediluvian deposits, or some un-fathomable accident had brought different kinds of fossils together.

And so, in 1840, and in the years immediately following, the Flood and man's position in the plan of Creation remained secure. But facts were accumulating, the world was changing, and ideas were being synthesized in new ways. The theory of evolution was on the verge of becoming public property, first in England, then throughout the Western world.

TWO BEST SELLERS

As one writer noted, "Evolution, when it came, struck an unprepared British audience as a profound moral shock." [45] It came, in 1844, via an anonymous book entitled *The Vestiges of the Natural Order of Creation*. The author was Robert Chambers, a journalist and amateur scientist. His book brought together many of the ideas and much of the information to which we have been referring and made evolution, or the "principle of development," comprehensible to the general public. Its thesis, flavor, and daring are suggested by the following quotation:

13

It has pleased Providence to arrange that one species should give birth to another, until the second highest gave birth to man, who is the very highest: be it so, it is our part to admire and submit. The very faintest notion of there being anything ridiculous or degrading in the theory [of development, or evolution]—how absurd does it appear, when we remember that every individual amongst us actually passes through the characters of the insect, the fish, and the reptile * (to speak nothing of others) before he is permitted to breathe the breath of life! But such notions are the mere emanations of false pride and ignorant prejudice. He who conceives them, little reflects that they, in reality, involve the principle of a contempt for the works and ways of God.[46]

As the last sentence suggests, *The Vestiges of the Natural Order of Creation* was not an anti-religious book. Chambers went to great lengths to assure his readers that the Scriptures were not being questioned. He attempted to enhance the dignity of God by relieving Him of the burden of creating each of the millions of different species, extinct and alive:

How can we suppose an immediate exertion of this creative power at one time to produce zoophytes, another time to add a few marine mollusks, another to bring in one or two conchifers, another to produce crustaceous fishes, again perfect fishes, and so on to the end? This would surely be to take a very mean view of the Creative Power. . . .[47]

Instead of creating endlessly, God created life once and then allowed nature to operate through the principle of development.†

Chambers' conception of the "Creative Power" did not appeal to the clergy or to the orthodox laity. Nor did his principle of development. *Vestiges* was roundly condemned as immoral and godless. Its scientific errors and absurdities were attacked by professional and amateur scientists. The ferocity and vigor of the attacks did nothing to diminish the book's popularity. It sold with the rapidity of a book banned in Boston, and evolution became public property for the first time. *Vestiges* won converts to the cause of evolution in England and elsewhere. A greater

---

* Chambers refers here to the principle that has come down to us as "ontogeny recapitulates phylogeny," that in the course of embryonic development, mammals pass through stages somewhat similar to those of lower organisms. Chambers had only superficial knowledge of the principle—in part because it was not yet fully developed—but he made it an important part of his argument. The hierarchy of living animals, for example, he interpreted as a recapitulation of the ascending order of fossils.—F. T. A.

† St. Augustine advanced a very similar idea about fourteen hundred years earlier. See Henry Fairfield Osborn, *From the Greeks to Darwin* (New York: The Macmillan Company, 1908), pp. 72–74.

number of people became inclined to consider evolution as a possibility should a better case for it be presented. In 1859 a better case was presented in *On the Origin of Species by Means of Natural Selection.* The author was Charles Darwin, grandson of Erasmus Darwin.

The Origin of Species became another best seller. The reaction to it was probably milder than even its author expected. Much of the rancor it might otherwise have received had been dissipated by the prior appearance of *Vestiges.* Also, Darwin had thoughtfully recruited two able advocates in the world of science—Thomas Huxley and Joseph Hooker—before *The Origin of Species* was printed. (Lyell had also been approached, but he seems never to have fully accepted the theory of evolution.) Of considerable importance, too, was the array of facts Darwin used to substantiate his theorizing. Huxley, in particular, used these facts to beat down the opposition, which in some instances was prompted by envy as much as by disbelief or religious convictions.[48] Indeed, it was facts which had converted Darwin to evolution. Before he began his around-the-world voyage on the *Beagle,* he had been firmly convinced of the immutability of species and of special creation. What he saw, informed as he was by Lyell's *Principles of Geology,* convinced him otherwise.

"MYSTERY OF MYSTERIES"

Facts accumulated during the voyage of the *Beagle,* Darwin wrote in the Introduction to *The Origin of Species,*[49] "seemed to throw some light on the origin of species—that mystery of mysteries." Subsequent years of data collecting and reflection led to certain conclusions which were, according to Darwin, in general like those another British scientist, Alfred Russell Wallace, had reached. Darwin noted that there were many facts—such as the ordering of fossils in the strata, "the mutual affinities of organic beings," "their embryological relations, their geographical distribution" —to suggest that "species had not been independently created, but had descended, like varieties, from other species." But was such a conclusion warranted? Not "until it could be shown how the innumerable species inhabiting this world have been modified, so as to acquire that perfection of structure and coadaptation which justly excites our admiration." Environment ("external conditions") could not wholly account for such modifications, nor could habit or volition of the organism itself.

What, then, did account for modifiability? The answer, Darwin suggested, was to be found in the struggle for existence. As Malthus had pointed out with regard to human reproduction, the "whole animal and vegetable kingdoms" reproduce too rapidly for all to survive. Consequently "there is a frequently recurring struggle for existence," and the organism that can "vary however slightly in any manner profitable to itself, under the complex and sometimes varying conditions of life will have a better chance of surviving, and thus be *naturally selected.* From the strong principle of inheritance, any selected variety will tend to propagate its new and modified form."

Natural selection, Darwin pointed out, "almost inevitably causes much extinction of the less improved forms of life" and results in what he called "Divergence of Character." The essence of this principle is that natural selection operates to eliminate excess numbers of identical or quite similar organisms in any given area. Factors which select against these organisms do not, however, select against more divergent forms. The more diversified the organisms of a given area are, the greater will be the number of individuals "capable of there supporting themselves." *

Darwin concluded the Introduction with these words:

> I am fully convinced that species are not immutable; but that those belonging to what are called the same genera are lineal descendants of some other and generally extinct species, in the same manner as the acknowledged varieties of any one species are the descendants of that species. Furthermore, I am convinced that Natural Selection has been the most important, but not the exclusive, means of modification.

The remainder of *The Origin of Species* is mainly an amplification and substantiation of the notion that variability is the key to evolution. The book is, in fact, one long argument for the validity of the theory of natural selection—not for the theory of evolution per se. (The term "evolution" does not appear in any of the earlier editions of *The Origin of Species*.[50]) In arguing his own theory, though, Darwin presented evidence and logic which for the first time made evolution plausible—even an established truth—to a significant number of scientists and laymen. As Julian S. Huxley has said, the principle of natural selection "made the brute fact of evolution scientifically comprehensible." † [51]

The search for man's origins had not yet begun. *The Origin of Species*

---

* Darwin makes it clear that natural selection does not *cause* variability. Rather, it acts to preserve "such variations as arise and are beneficial to the being under its conditions of life" (*The Origin of Species*, p. 99).

† Darwin's theory of natural selection, we shall see in the next chapter, was seriously challenged in the early decades of the present century. It emerged from the challenge modified, but greatly strengthened. Darwin equated natural selection with "survival of the fittest" in later editions of *The Origin of Species*. Today, it is recognized that the "fittest" are not necessarily those living things equipped to compete most effectively for food or other necessities. Indeed, there may be no competition at all in order for selection to take place. For instance, there has been no

contains but one sentence concerning man's origins. Through future researches, Darwin foresaw, "Much light will be thrown on the origin of man and his history." ("Much" does not appear in the first edition.) This single sentence and the total implication of the book made it clear that Darwin believed that man, like other species, had descended from a lower form. Some critics took Darwin to task for implying that man had descended from an ape. The criticism was not justified, as Darwin made clear in *The Descent of Man* (1871).

The Descent of Man [52] begins with with a description of common features and characteristics that man and lower animals share. "All the bones in his skeleton can be compared with corresponding bones in a monkey, bat, or seal. So it is with his muscles, nerves, blood-vessels and internal viscera. The brain . . . follows the same law. . . ." The human embryo "at a very early period can hardly be distinguished from that of other members of the vertebrate kingdom." Not only is man morphologically similar to monkeys and other mammals, he also experiences some of the same diseases and has similar healing and physiological processes. From these and other striking likenesses to other vertebrates, there is only one sensible conclusion that can be drawn: There is a "community of descent." Only "natural prejudice, and that arrogance which made our forefathers declare that they were descended from demi-gods" makes such a conclusion repulsive.

And so man was finally explicitly included in evolutionary theory. He, an animal descended from other animals, was part of the "mystery of mysteries." There were now questions to be answered: Since man was not a special creation, how had he originated? How and why did he diverge from his progenitors to become human? Where had he origi-

---

competition for oxygen in most animal populations; but there is no question that selection for respiratory efficiency has occurred in the past. Again, animal populations may be capable of satisfying their basic needs and yet become extinct through natural selection. Through selection, genes are sometimes acquired which have both favorable and unfavorable effects in the same individual. Such genes have resulted in high embryonic mortality, senescence, certain kinds of sterility, various hereditary diseases, and other unfavorable effects. See George C. Williams, *Adaptation and Natural Selection* (Princeton: Princeton University Press, 1966), pp. 26–27, 32–33.

The essence of selection is not that certain traits enable organisms to emerge victorious from some sort of struggle. Rather, the "fittest" are those able to transmit their biological heredity (their genotypes) to future generations at a higher average rate than others in the same environment. "Darwinian fitness," as Theodosius Dobzhansky has said in *Mankind Evolving* (New Haven: Yale University Press, 1962), "is measurable only in terms of reproductive proficiency" (p. 129). The organism that leaves more living offspring than its kin is more fit than they. As a rule, of course, it leaves more offspring because it is better adapted to its environment— it can compete more effectively for basic necessities if need be. We shall have more to say on this subject in Chapter 4.

17

nated? Who were his ancestors? Questions of this sort still occupy the efforts of many scientists.

Darwin had speculative answers to some of the questions that were raised. He made it clear that man did not spring from the apes. For that matter, "we must not fall into the error of supposing that the early progenitor of the whole Simian stock, including man, was identical with, or even closely resembled, any existing ape or monkey" (p. 155). While all monkeys and apes "proceeded from some one extremely ancient progenitor" which had resemblances to the Lemuridae, man was an "off-shoot from the Old World Simian stem." In terms of present-day classification, he is more like the Old World primates than the New World monkeys.* More particularly, he shares many similarities with Old World anthropoid apes; therefore, "we may infer that some ancient member of the anthropomorphous sub-group gave birth to man" (p. 154).

Like other animals, generations of early progenitors of man diversified and the diversifications were acted upon by natural selection. Similar variations followed "from co-descended organisms having a similar constitution, and having been acted on by like causes inducing similar modifications" (p. 152).

The place of man's origins, Darwin reasoned, was a "hot country," most probably Africa. "In each great region of the world the living mammals are closely related to the extinct species of the same region." Man's "nearest allies," the gorilla and chimpanzee, now live in Africa; therefore allied species now extinct also lived there. Further, the nakedness of man and the "frugiferous," or fruit, diet of present-day apes suggested a warm climate (pp. 155–156).

Darwin admitted that there was "a great break in the organic chain between man and his nearest allies, which cannot be bridged over by any extinct or living species." But he saw no reason for undue concern. The theory of evolution pointed the way; and the fossil record, he implied, would one day be much more complete. As Lyell had pointed out, "in all the vertebrate classes the discovery of fossil remains has been a very slow and fortuitous process." Besides, the regions "most likely to afford remains connecting man with some extinct ape-like creature" remained to be explored (pp. 156–157).

The theory was formulated at last, complete with explicit guidelines for searching for clues: Search in a hot country, probably Africa. Look for man's progenitors among early primates. Try to discover what forces had acted upon these progenitors, what adaptations were required of

* Differences between Old and New World primates are discussed in Chapter 5.

them. The guidelines of the theory were to be followed by untold numbers of professional, amateur, and quasi-scientists. Before inquiry began in earnest, however, the theory of evolution had to meet one of its most serious challenges. The challenge was serious because it came from perhaps the outstanding physicist of the nineteenth century, Lord Kelvin (Sir W. Thomson Kelvin).

CHALLENGE AND CONSEQUENCE [53]

A very long time had been required for simple forms to gradually evolve into complex organisms, for man to have been derived from some "lower form." Darwin was confident, however, that his friend Lyell and other geologists had established the antiquity of the earth beyond any reasonable doubt.

So far as the geologists knew, time before the Flood was limitless. They did not deal in precise figures. The physicists, who did, took the vagueness of the geologists as an indication of the weakness of their science. In 1865 Lord Kelvin presented a paper attacking the conception of unlimited geological time. Mathematical projections based on rates of the sun's heat loss, he said, demonstrated that the earth's crust could not have been stable for a long enough period to accommodate the theories of the geologists. At the most, the earth's age was 40 million years. Toward the end of the century, he was virtually certain that 20 million years was closer to the truth.

Lord Kelvin attacked not only the geologists but also the Darwinians. He was convinced of the "utter futility" of Darwin's "philosophy." He said the "doctrine that transmutation has taken place through 'descent with modification by natural selection'" was in grave error. Darwin was sufficiently disturbed by Kelvin's attack to make changes in *The Origin of Species*. Among other things, he abandoned uniformitarian evolution. Change, he decided, was not equally distributed throughout time, but was much more rapid at a very early period. Another interesting alteration in revised editions was the omission of the statement that probably a "far longer period than 300,000,000 years had elapsed since the latter part of the secondary period." Darwin was unwilling to match figures with Lord Kelvin.

Lord Kelvin's facts and deductions were indisputable within the framework of nineteenth-century physics. Most geologists reluctantly constricted their conceptions of geological time, leaving a new generation of evolutionists to work things out the best they could. Evolutionary scientists reasoned or sensed that if earth time was short, there must be some mechanism of rapid organic transformation. Near the end of the century a Dutch botanist, Hugo de Vries, proved that rapid transformation was possible. His experiments showed that new elementary species of plants could appear without intermediate steps and produce generations of their own kind. There was always a notable gap between the new species and those from which they came. The heights of new plants, for example, did not overlap heights among the original parental stock.[54] There were, in other words, no intermediate forms.

As the twentieth century got underway, one consequence of Lord Kelvin's challenge became more discernible. Knowledge that dramatic change—creation of a new species—can take place at one step seemed to eliminate a need for extensive studies of environmental effects. Change, when it came, apparently came from within the organism. Series of small changes were not acted upon by outside forces. For the time being, therefore, natural selection faded from the thoughts of many scientists. The focus of attention became the organism and its constituent parts. From such study came the data and theories which gave rise to a new science, modern genetics, which was to eventually give support to the theory of evolution. Some small credit for the inception of this new science, it would seem, should go to Lord Kelvin.

IS THERE A MYSTERY?

Colleagues tell us that a number of people throughout the United States are still ambivalent, if not hostile, toward evolution. In 1965 newspapers in a South Carolina city carried letters written by several citizens who opposed the teaching of evolution in the public schools. At that time three states—Arkansas, Mississippi, and Tennessee—carried statutes on their books which made it illegal to teach Darwin's theory in the public schools. One of these states, Mississippi, still had such a statute as late as 1968.

The anti-evolutionist argues from a set of premises which are outside the province of science. He cannot be convinced by the facts which convinced Darwin and others. If he is fair-minded, though, he will realize that his own theory or philosophy must satisfactorily explain the same phenomena which evolutionary theory takes into account, such as variability, change, geographic distribution of plants and animals, and the fossil record. The last, in particular, is likely to resist incorporation into a non-evolutionary scheme. For example, if man was the result of a special creation, made once and for all as he now is (and he is considerably diversified), how are the many less-than-human manlike fossils that have been discovered to be explained? Also, why do forms of life become less and less complex as we go deeper into the strata of the earth?

20

Cuvier, of course, answered the last question. He had no need to answer the first, for the hominid fossil evidence was not yet available. Another eminent nineteenth-century scientist did provide an answer which might satisfy many present-day anti-evolutionists; it satisfied not only many Americans of his day, but also many Europeans. The scientist was Louis Agassiz, Ice Age theorist, Harvard professor, and a man of considerable ability and influence. His theory, in essence, was an improvement upon Lyell's.

Agassiz contended that members of a species (one or more pairs) appeared at once in their present form, presumably created by God. The species then multiplied and spread out from its own particular center of origin as far as it could, the limiting factors being physical conditions (mountains, bodies of water, and so on) and resistance from other species. Should a species die out—destroyed by physical conditions, for instance—another species was created at once, again fully formed, to take its place. All of this occurred in accordance with a preordained plan, "carried out and working ever toward higher and higher conditions." [55] The plan proceeded toward an ultimate goal: "At each fresh creation God started with the forms of the age that had passed away, in order to improve his creatures progressively until they reached the final goal, man made in God's image." [56] That lower animals possessed similarities to man, either in embryological development or in adult features, was but a prophetic intimation of the "final goal."

Thus, Agassiz' argument, perhaps the best anti-evolutionist argument advanced, explains geographic distribution and the increasing complexity of the fossil record. Variability is the result of the introduction of new species,[57] though admittedly individuals of the same species are not exactly alike. Should a species depart too far from its typical form, it is destroyed, not changed into another species.[58] What Agassiz' theory does not satisfactorily explain is the mechanism for departure from the typical form, or the findings of De Vries. Many of De Vries' new species, even if produced by a preordained plan, did not evidence "working ever toward higher and higher conditions." Most mutants do not; their functioning is more often impaired because of change.

What we have said is not intended as a defense of evolution. No defense is necessary in our day. Most religious leaders agree that evolutionary theory does not exclude the possibility that God created all life and set the lawful processes of development into motion. To the scientist, a theory is a source of hypotheses and directions for inquiry. So long as the theory of evolution serves such purposes, it will be utilized. If a better theory is devised, evolution will become obsolete.

NOTES

1. See Alfred North Whitehead, *Science and the Modern World* (Cambridge, England: Cambridge University Press, 1953), pp. 15–16.

2. Loren Eiseley, *Darwin's Century: Evolution and the Men Who Discovered It* (Garden City, N.Y.: Doubleday & Company, Inc., 1958), p. 23.

3. As quoted in Herbert Wendt, *In Search of Adam* (New York: Collier Books, 1963), p. 65.

4. George Gaylord Simpson and William S. Beck, *Life: An Introduction to Biology*, 2nd ed. (New York: Harcourt, Brace & World, Inc., 1965), p. 491.

5. Bentley Glass, "Heredity and Variation in the Eighteenth Century Concept of the Species," in Bentley Glass, Owsei Temkin, and William L. Straus, Jr. (eds.), *Forerunners of Darwin: 1745–1849* (Baltimore: The Johns Hopkins Press, 1959), pp. 146–150.

6. See Bentley Glass, "Maupertuis, Pioneer of Genetics and Evolution," in Glass, Temkin, and Straus, *op. cit.*, pp. 59–77.

7. *Ibid.*, pp. 74–77.

8. As quoted in Arthur O. Lovejoy, "Buffon and the Problem of Species," in Glass, Temkin, and Straus, *op. cit.*, pp. 96–97.

9. *Ibid.*, p. 97.

10. *Ibid.*, pp. 98–99. For a concise summary of Buffon's ideas, see Eiseley, *op. cit.*, pp. 39–45.

11. As quoted in Eiseley, *op. cit.*, p. 47.

12. As quoted in J. Arthur Thomson, "Darwin's Predecessors," in A. C. Seward (ed.), *Darwin and Modern Science* (New York: G. P. Putnam's Sons, 1909), p. 7.

13. *Ibid.*, pp. 7–8.

14. As quoted in Henry Fairfield Osborn, *From the Greeks to Darwin* (New York: The Macmillan Company, 1908), p. 149.

15. As quoted in Wendt, *op. cit.*, p. 185.

16. Osborn, *op. cit.*, pp. 163–168.

17. Francis C. Haber, *The Age of the World: Moses to Darwin* (Baltimore: The Johns Hopkins Press, 1959), p. 178.

18. As quoted in Osborn, *op. cit.*, p. 187.

19. As quoted in Wendt, *op. cit.*, p. 187.

20. Sir Andrew Geikie, *The Founders of Geology*, 2nd ed. (New York: Dover Publications, Inc., 1962), p. 375.

21. Haber, *op. cit.*, p. 198.

22. Excerpt from Cuvier's "Essay on the Theory of the Earth," in Kirtley F. Mather and Shirley L. Mason (eds.), *A Source Book in Geology* (New York: McGraw-Hill Book Company, 1939), pp. 191–192.

23. Haber, *op. cit.*, p. 199; Arthur O. Lovejoy, "The Argument for Organic Evolution Before the *Origin of Species*, 1830–1858," in Glass, Temkin, and Straus, *op. cit.*, p. 391.

24. As quoted in Osborn, *op. cit.*, p. 195.

25. See, e.g., C. Loring Brace, "The Problem of the Neanderthals," in Peter B. Hammond (ed.), *Physical Anthropology and Archaeology: Selected Readings* (New York: The Macmillan Company, 1964), pp. 107–127, especially pp. 110–112.

26. Frank Dawson Adams, *The Birth and Development of the Geological Sciences* (New York: Dover Publications, Inc., 1954), p. 265.

27. James Parkinson, *Organic Remains of a Former World*, Vol. III (1811), as quoted in Haber, *op. cit.*, p. 200. Parkinson was one of the original members of the Geological Society of London.

28. Sir Charles Lyell, *Principles of Geology*, 9th ed. (New York: D. Appleton & Company, 1853), p. 52.

29. *Ibid.*, pp. 52–54. Lyell took this quotation from Playfair's biography of Hutton.

30. In a letter Charles Darwin wrote in 1844, he said: "Lamarck was the Hutton of geology" (as quoted in Gertrude Himmelfarb, *Darwin and the Darwinian Revolution* [Garden City, N.Y.: Doubleday & Company, Inc., 1959], p. 175).

31. As quoted in Haber, *op. cit.*, pp. 215–216.

32. For a summary of the geology based on the Scriptures before and after publication of *Principles of Geology*, see Milton Millhauser, *Just Before Darwin: Robert Chambers and Vestiges* (Middletown, Conn.: Wesleyan University Press, 1959), pp. 46–56.

33. Lyell, *op. cit.*, pp. 585–590.

34. *Ibid.*, p. 574.

35. Lovejoy, "The Argument for Organic Evolution . . . ," p. 369.

36. As quoted in Osborn, *op. cit.*, p. 227.

37. Lyell, *op. cit.*, p. 582.

38. Geikie, *op. cit.*, pp. 443–448.

39. For some of the earlier conceptions of fossils, see Lyell, *op. cit.*, pp. 24–27; Adams, *op. cit.*, Chap. 8; and Wendt, *op. cit.*, Chap. 1.

40. Millhauser, *op. cit.*, pp. 58–60; Wendt, *op. cit.*, pp. 203–204; C. L. Brace and M. F. Ashley-Montagu, *Man's Evolution: An Introduction to Physical Anthropology* (New York: The Macmillan Company, 1965), pp. 13–15.

41. Wendt, *op. cit.*, p. 76.

42. *Ibid.*, pp. 165–166; Himmelfarb, *op. cit.*, pp. 167–168; Lyell, *op. cit.*, pp. 575–576.

43. Andre Senet, *Man in Search of His Ancestors* (New York: McGraw-Hill Book Company, 1956), pp. 12–19; Wendt, *op. cit.*, pp. 237–240.

44. Senet, *op. cit.*, p. 20.

45. Millhauser, *op. cit.*, p. 81.

46. As quoted in Millhauser, *op. cit.*, p. 102.

47. As quoted in Millhauser, *op. cit.*, pp. 91–92.

48. See, for example, Gertrude Himmelfarb, *op. cit.*, Chaps. 13–14; Wendt, *op. cit.*, pp. 296–300; and William Irvine, *Apes, Angels, and Victorians* (New York: McGraw-Hill Book Company, 1955), Chaps. 1, 7, 8, 10 (*passim*).

49. Quotations and paraphrasing are from *On the Origin of Species by Means of Natural Selection, or the Preservation of Favored Races in the Struggle for Life*, 6th authorized ed. (New York: D. Appleton & Company, 1895).

50. Julian S. Huxley, "Darwin and the Idea of Evolution," in Huxley *et al.*, *A Book That Shook the World* (Pittsburgh: University of Pittsburgh Press, 1958), p. 1.

51. *Ibid.*, p. 2.

52. Quotations and paraphrasing are from *The Descent of Man and Selection in Relation to Sex*, 2nd ed. (New York: D. Appleton & Company, 1889).

53. Except as noted, factual materials in this section are drawn from Eiseley, *op. cit.*, Chap. 9.

54. Ruth Moore, *Man, Time, and Fossils*, 2nd ed. (New York: Alfred A. Knopf, Inc., 1963), pp. 140–142.

55. Joseph le Conte, *Evolution: Its Nature, Its Evidences, and Its Relation to Religious Thought*, 2nd ed. (New York: D. Appleton & Company, 1891), pp. 68–71.

56. As quoted in Wendt, *op. cit.*, p. 306.

57. Le Conte, *op. cit.*, p. 29.

58. *Ibid.*, pp. 71–72.

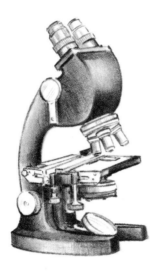

2

Mechanisms of Change

Mystery is born of, and sustained by, uncertainty. Its conception and nourishment stem from unanswered questions, from the failure of existing knowledge and beliefs to explain significant events or phenomena. There was no mystery concerning man's origins and uniqueness prior to *The Origin of Species*. Few people of the Western world had reason to doubt the scriptural explanation. Most firmly believed that man had been placed upon earth in his present form; God had so willed it. Darwin and his followers undermined this certitude, and a mystery was conceived.

Man did not suddenly emerge from the Creator's hands, the Darwinists argued. His beginnings were more humble; his creation, more protracted. Man, like all living things, had originated from biologically simple forebears. Along with many living animals, he had a long history of gradual modifications that transformed simple forms into increasingly complex organisms. The enormous body of evidence Darwin amassed convinced many that evolution had occurred. His factual material and theory of natural selection provided a strong case for the mutability of species. The Linnaean conception of fixed, static categories became less tenable. One important order of questions, however, remained unanswered: What causes biological variation? What mechanisms bring about the range of characteristics upon which natural selection acts? Darwin was aware that he did not fully understand variation. He knew that at least some variations are to some extent inherited, but neither he nor any other scientists of his day knew how biological heredity operates. Most believed that each parent contributes hereditary qualities to the offspring, who appears as a blend of the two parents. Darwin knew that a system of blending inheritance would mean eventual elimination of variation, unless there is some factor which creates new variation as fast as blending gets rid of it. But the only alternative to blending, so far as Darwin could tell, was the hereditary transmission of acquired characteristics—a Lamarckian idea which Darwin originally derided.[1]

Today, our understanding of heredity is more advanced, and we are able to identify mechanisms which produce variation within a species population. The section which immediately follows sketches the development of this understanding. The balance of the chapter provides a brief introduction to the mechanisms which produce variation.

PRELUDE TO UNDERSTANDING

Unknown to Darwin, some rather significant steps toward explaining biological variation were taken in his own lifetime. One such step was the temporary destruction of the general belief that life can originate spontaneously. For centuries it was widely believed that nonliving matter could give rise to lower organisms, such as maggots, fleas, and mosquitoes. Experiments conducted in 1668 by an Italian physician, Francesco Redi, demonstrated that maggots developed only in meat to which flies had free access. Experimenters who followed Redi confirmed his finding, and the belief that organisms arise from dead matter gradually died. The belief was revived somewhat, however, with the discovery of microbes shortly after Redi's time. At least some forms of life, it was reasoned, must originate spontaneously. How else could microbes get into gauze-covered jars of meat broth, milk, and wine? About the time *The Origin of Species* was creating a stir in England, Louis Pasteur set about answering that question. He found that if he killed the microorganisms with heat and protected the broth, milk, or wine from air, no new organisms appeared. If the sterilized substance was not protected, it soon swarmed with microorganisms again. Clearly, microscopic organisms were not generated by inorganic elements; they evidently traveled through the air.[2]

25

Pasteur's painstaking experiments demonstrated—for the time being —that life comes from life, not from dead or inert matter.* This finding coincided with a view expressed by Rudolf Virchow, the eminent German pathologist and political leader, a year before *The Origin of Species* appeared. The cells which make up an organism, he argued, come from preexisting cells. (Theodor Schwann, in 1839, first pointed out that all organisms are composed of cells.[3])

Virchow was right, but he did not know the details of cell division. These details first became known about 1880, when a German biologist, Walther Flemming, found that certain material in the cell nucleus absorbs red dye. The nucleus would then stand out against a clear background and could be easily observed through a microscope. The material (*chromatin*, from the Greek word for "color"), Flemming could see, collects into pairs of threadlike bodies, or *chromosomes* ("colored bodies"), during cell division. Because these bodies play such an important role in cell division, the process was called *mitosis* ("thread"). Just before the cell divides, the chromosome pairs are pulled apart; one of each pair ends up in each of the new cells.[4] (See page 28.)

Studies of heredity were undertaken during Darwin's lifetime, but it was not realized until after his death that there is an association between heredity and material in the cell. In an 1883 publication, Wilhelm Roux described activities of the cell nucleus during cell division and drew two inferences therefrom: heredity is particulate, and the hereditary particles are in the chromatin. A few years later, in 1892, August Weismann refined these inferences. The chromosomes, and only the chromosomes, he asserted, bear the hereditary particles. He also held that the number of heredity carriers in the sex cells is halved prior to reproduction. This number is restored when the egg is fertilized—when the nuclei of the egg and sperm are fused into a *zygote*.[5]

Rediscovery of Mendel

Careful experiments backed Roux's inferences, but the experiments, by Gregor Mendel, an Austrian monk, were known to very few scientists prior to 1900. In that year, Hugo de Vries, then others, called attention to Mendel's classic paper of 1866.

---

* Contrary to a belief which persisted for several years, Pasteur did not prove that life cannot originate spontaneously. What he demonstrated was that, under present-day conditions, the spontaneous rise of living organisms is highly improbable. Many scientists now believe that under far different conditions—when the earth was young —life did originate from nonliving matter. See, for example, Asimov's discussion, "The Origin of Life," in *The Intelligent Man's Guide to the Biological Sciences* (New York: Pocket Books, 1964) or Irving Adler, *How Life Began* (New York: New American Library, 1957).

Mendel had found, as Roux had reasoned, that hereditary materials are discrete, particulate. Physical characteristics are not an amalgam, a blending together, of parental heredities. Instead, individual characteristics of either parent may find expression in the progeny. Thus descendants of generations of tall plants, when cross-pollinated with descendants of generations of short plants, produced all tall plants, not medium-sized plants. The hybrid plants, when allowed to pollinate themselves, yielded both tall and short offspring—further evidence that hereditary factors are discrete.

The fact that all first-generation (and most second-generation) progeny were tall indicated to Mendel that hereditary factors can be dominant (tallness) or recessive (shortness). The fact that the tall hybrids produced some short plants demonstrated that the number of hereditary factors can exceed the characteristics which find expression. Mendel discovered something else which may have surprised him. Beginning with the second-generation progeny, each generation of plants had the same approximate average ratio of tall plants to short plants (3:1). Although Mendel could not predict which individual plants would be tall or short, he found he could estimate fairly accurately how many in the total population would be tall and how many would be short.

In more complex experiments, Mendel found that two characteristics will sort out and recombine independently of each other. Plants normally raised from round, yellow seeds were crossed with plants which normally produced wrinkled, green seeds. The first-generation plants had round, yellow seeds. A crossing of these plants yielded a generation which produced round-yellow, round-green, wrinkled-yellow, and wrinkled-green seeds. Most were round and yellow; roundness and yellowness are dominant factors. As in his earlier experiments, Mendel found that the frequencies of traits in the second-generation offspring allowed him to predict the ratio with which traits in subsequent generations would appear. Again, too, he found that he was unable to anticipate the occurrence of traits in specific seeds. The population, not the individual, is the unit of prediction. This finding was to have significance in the founding of what is now known as *population genetics*.[6]

To explain some of his findings Mendel had to assume that hereditary factors occur in pairs. Tall plants that have short offspring must carry a factor for tallness *and* a factor for shortness. Similarly, hybrid seeds must carry dominant and recessive factors for color and shape. Mendel's assumption struck a responsive chord in an American scientist, Walter S. Sutton. Chromosomes also occur in pairs. Was there any connection between these pairs and the pairs of which Mendel wrote? Sutton reasoned that there was. His argument, presented in a 1903 paper, firmly linked cells and heredity. The field of cytogenetics was born.

Figure 1.   **MITOSIS.**

  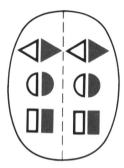

Cell nucleus with three   Each chromosome is replicated.   Pairs line up opposite
pairs of chromosomes.   one another.

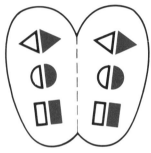  

The cell divides   . . . two identical daughter cells, each
into . . .   with three pairs of chromosomes.

Sutton's argument, in brief, was that there are too many similarities between chromosomes or chromosomal behavior and Mendel's hereditary factors for the two to be unrelated. Hereditary factors, for instance, retain their individuality from generation to generation; chromosomes retain their "morphological individuality" despite numerous cell divisions. Like hereditary factors, chromosomes segregate (in the sex cell during *meiosis*, the special cell division to which Weismann had referred) and recombine (in the zygote). Since the organism develops from the cell, in which there is a union of single chromosomes from the male and the female, it follows that the hereditary factors—or *genes*, as they were later named—are on or part of the chromosomes.[7]

The term *gene* ("to give birth to") originated with a Dane, Wilhelm Johannsen. He coined two other terms that gained acceptance: *genotype*, the genetic makeup of an organism; and *phenotype*, the observable features of the organism.[8] Mendel's experiments demonstrated that organisms may be phenotypically similar, yet genotypically dissimilar. Some of the tall hybrid plants, for example, carried only the dominant genes for tallness; others carried genes for both tallness and shortness.

Johannsen's experiments with self-pollinating plants proved that organisms can be genotypically similar and phenotypically different. Observable characteristics of the plants could be made to vary, he found, by manipulating their environments. However, characteristics acquired in this manner did not show up in subsequent generations. The genotype, in other words, was not modified by changes in the environment.

Johannsen's findings taken together with findings by Hugo de Vries signalled the death of Darwin's particular interpretation of natural selection. New species do not emerge as a consequence of environmental changes alone, Johannsen's experiments demonstrated. New species do appear, De Vries had discovered, as a consequence of mutations. The two sets of findings set in motion a line of reasoning that may have gone something like this: The range of variation is fixed by the genotype. Therefore, for evolution to occur, the genotype must be altered in some manner. Since changes in environment do not cause genotypic changes, while mutations do, evolution must result solely from mutations. If mutations are in themselves the whole evolutionary process, then Darwin's theory of natural selection is obviously in error.

Figure 2.   MEIOSIS.

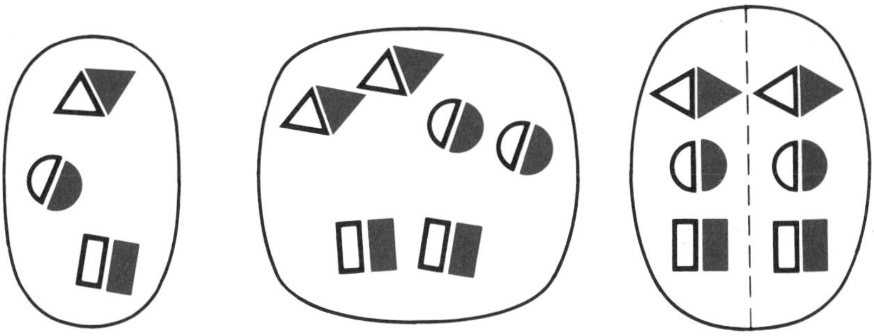

Cell nucleus with three pairs of chromosomes.

Each chromosome is replicated.

Pairs line up opposite one another.

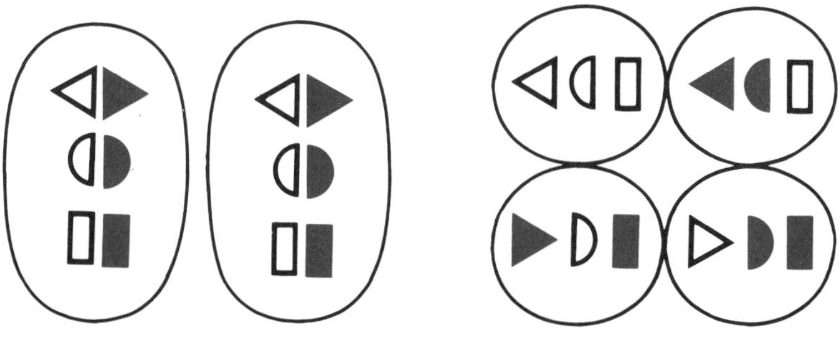

The cell divides into two identical cells, as in mitosis, but . . .

. . . each cell further divides into two cells, each with half the original number of chromosomes.

29

And so Darwin's theory was rejected. For a number of years most genetical biologists refused to consider the possibility that natural selection might play a role in evolution. Most nongenetical biologists, on the other hand, remained convinced of the importance of Darwinian selection.[9]

Mendelism Expanded

Mendelism—called "genetics" by William Bateson, one of its most enthusiastic proponents—was soon applied to a variety of theoretical and practical problems.[10] One of the problems had to do with human heredity. Could Mendel's findings help explain patterns of human inheritance? Among the first to seek an answer was Wilhelm Weinberg, a German physician. The techniques he employed in his quest helped lay the cornerstone of population genetics.

Weinberg had already established, prior to his acquaintance with Mendel, that "twinning" is apt to be a hereditary trait. He discovered that multiple births (twins, triplets, etc.) occurred with greater frequency among women whose mothers or sisters had twins than among other women of two German cities. After learning of Mendel's work, Weinberg apparently asked himself whether twinning is a dominant, recessive, or equivalent trait. Expected frequencies for these three possibilities were compared with observed frequencies. Weinberg conceded: "The situation found in the inheritance of twinning best finds its explanation in the assumption that the trait for twinning is inherited according to the Mendelian rule and is recessive."

Weinberg's calculations went beyond those of Mendel. He took into consideration a factor Mendel had deliberately avoided, randomness in mating. Mendel had allowed no pollen from foreign plants to fertilize the experimental plants; they were closely inbred. But among people, Weinberg noted, there is a random mating (*panmixis*) with regard to any specific genetic trait. For example, a man does not consciously or unconsciously select his wife because she does or does not carry the hereditary trait for twinning.

"How," Weinberg wondered, "does the numerical influence of Mendelian inheritance behave under the influence of panmixis?" The search for an answer began with a hypothesis: There are "initially m males and females who are pure representatives of type A, and likewise n individuals who are pure representatives of type B present." If these people mate randomly, the genetic composition of their offspring can be calculated as follows:

30

$$(mAA + nBB)^2 = \frac{m^2}{(m+n)^2} AA + \frac{2mn}{(m+n)^2} AB + \frac{n^2}{(m+n)^2} BB$$

or if $m + n = 1$

$$m^2AA + 2mnAB + n^2BB.$$

Panmixis among this second-generation would produce the same relative frequencies. Weinberg found the answer to his question in the symbolism of the binomial theorem.* [11]

* For the benefit of the reader who does not understand how Weinberg arrived at his answer, a brief explanation follows: Consider the combinations of heads and tails that two people, John and Henry, can obtain if each flips a coin. Each could turn up heads (HH) or tails (TT). Again, John's coin may be heads and Henry's tails (HT), or Henry may have heads and John tails (TH). One combination— HH, HT, TH, or TT—is as likely to occur as the other, but a heads-tails combination is twice as likely to occur as two heads (or two tails). The combinational probabilities, then, are .25 (HH) + .50 (HT, TH) + .25 (TT). These are the same figures which are obtained by expanding the binomial $(.5 + .5)^2$.

The figures within the parentheses represent the probabilities involved in a single event, the toss of one coin. Because there are two sides to a coin and one side is as likely to turn up as the other (assuming the coin is honest), the probability that heads will turn up is .5; the probability that tails will turn up is also .5. Therefore, $.5 + .5 = 1$. (Note that the total of probabilities for an event add up to 1. Any event that occurs is 1, and the probable outcomes of that event add up to 1.)

Multiplication of $(.5 + .5)$ by $(.5 + .5)$ is indicated because the two coins are alike so far as probable outcomes are concerned, and what happens to one coin has no effect upon the other. The fact that John flips a head in no way determines what Henry flips; the events are independent. A rule of probability theory states that the probability that two or more independent events will occur together is the product of the probability of one event times the probability of the other. The probability that John will flip heads (tails) is .5; the probability that Henry will flip heads (tails) is .5; the probability that both will flip heads, $.5 \times .5 = .25$. Another rule says that when an independent event may occur in more than one way, its probability is the sum of the probabilities for each way the event can take place. Thus, the probability for obtaining a head-tail combination is .25 (HT) + .25 (TH) = .50.

If we go back to Weinberg's formula and substitute .5 for m and .5 for n, we have $(.5AA + .5BB) = .25AA + .50AB + .25BB$. That is, 25 per cent of the first-generation offspring are likely to carry only dominant genes; 50 per cent, both dominant and recessive genes; and 25 per cent, only recessive genes.

There are nine possible matings among the first-generation offspring: between those who are homozygous with respect to the dominant gene (AA × AA), between dominant and recessive homozygotes (AA × BB), between heterozygotes (AB × AB), and so on. By multiplying the expanded side of the equation by itself, it will be seen that the proportion of phenotypes among the second-generation offspring is identical to that among the first-generation offspring. And so it will be for the third, the fourth, and each subsequent generation.

Genes or alleles (different expressions, or alternative forms, of the same gene) are probably seldom if ever combined in the equal proportions of our illustration. Some genes or alleles are extremely rare in some or all populations (such as the gene for albinism), while others—both dominant and recessive—appear in high frequency in every related population. It is therefore possible—and not at all unusual—for a vast majority of a given population to be homozygous with respect to either a dominant or a recessive gene or allele. It is also possible for most members to be heterozygous with respect to one or more genes.

Weinberg presented his findings and formula in 1908. In the same year, G. H. Hardy, a mathematician at Cambridge University, arrived at the same solution to gene frequencies within a population. Thus was born the Hardy-Weinberg Law, the cornerstone of population genetics. The law mathematically illustrated the conservation of hereditary traits. It demonstrated why a dominant trait could not so increase in frequency as to replace the recessive trait. There is a tendency for the "gene pool," the combined genotypes of a population, to reach an equilibrium; gene frequencies tend to remain stable generation after generation.

One implication of the Hardy-Weinberg Law was quite clear. Evolution cannot take place unless genetic equilibrium is upset or forestalled. How had the equilibrium been disturbed? One answer came from De Vries' studies of plants: mutations. Mutations also occurred in other organisms, it was discovered, but with less dramatic effects. There are no sudden appearances of new species in animals as in plants, and observable mutations occur more slowly in animals. Experimental testing of mutational theory was therefore not particularly fruitful during the early years of the present century.

The groundwork for productive mutation experiments with animals was laid, around 1910, by Thomas Hunt Morgan and his associates at Columbia University. For several years they subjected the small fruit fly (*Drosophila melanogaster*) to intensive investigation. Knowledge about genes was vastly increased. Among other things it was discovered that genes occupy specific places, or loci, on the chromosome; and these positions are sometimes altered during meiosis. During this division, parts of two single chromosomes sometimes become tangled; and *crossover*, the exchange of bits of chromosomes, is effected.[12] It was found, too, that mutations are transmitted in the manner of any other single Mendelian trait, such as height or color. Further, some traits changed by mutations are sex-linked, as are some traits not affected by mutations. Their inheritance is determined by genes on the sex chromosomes.* [13]

Research on mutations was revolutionized in 1927. In that year one of Morgan's former students, H. J. Muller, found that mutations can be induced by the application of X-rays. Mutations which occur naturally could thus be speeded up. Later, other so-called mutagenic agents were discovered.[14]

---

* The male carries an X-chromosome and a Y-chromosome (among others); the female, two X-chromosomes. Sex of the offspring is determined by the particular male chromosome that fertilizes the egg cell. The offspring is female if there is an XX combination in the zygote, and male if there is an XY combination.

A Blind Spot Eliminated

By about 1930 the major spadework for a basic understanding of heredity and variation had been accomplished. By then, too, geneticists recognized that "it is not inheritance *and* variation which bring about evolution, but the inheritance *of* variation." [15] But all variations, even when inherited, do not persist from generation to generation. This fact was no doubt noted, but most genetical biologists failed to see the evolutionary significance of it. They were temporarily blinded. As Professor George Gaylord Simpson recollects,

> Around 1900, and for a generation or so thereafter, experimental biologists were concerned mainly with what is now considered classical or Mendelian genetics. The gene was to biology then what DNA * has been more recently: an exciting breakthrough, or the banner on a bandwagon. Mutations were recognized, and we learned how to follow the mutant form of a gene (its alleles) or of chromosomes through their effects on plants and animals bred in the laboratory. Although it was not then known just what mutations are—and still is not completely known—it became clear that they affect development and produce individuals with new hereditary variations. Mutations were thus correctly recognized as the basic materials for evolutionary change.
>
> Such discoveries generate enthusiasm, and enthusiasts are all too likely to become temporarily blinded. . . . Some of the genetical enthusiasts decided that mutations are not only materials for evolution but are, in themselves, the whole process. They supposed that mutation produced new kinds of organisms, which become new species either forthwith or by accumulation of further materials. Adaptation occurred when a mutation just happened to coincide with a possible way of life.[16]

The survival of a relatively few organisms in certain laboratory and field experiments illustrated Simpson's last point. These organisms survived noxious gases and chemicals, while most did not, because they had experienced mutations that coincided with the "way of life" imposed by the experimenters. Another phenomenon, however, was less readily explained by mutational theory alone. Animals transplanted to new environments had been known to evolve into new subspecies. Mutations could account for the biological changes—but why were members of the original species no longer around? According to the Hardy-Weinberg Law, dominant genes could not supplant recessive genes.

---

* DNA, or deoxyribonucleic acid, is the primary constituent of chromosomes and is regarded by biologists as the basis of gene activity.—F. T. A.

How, then, could mutated genes displace their non-mutated counterparts? Within a generation after a mutation, there should be a fixed ratio between the normal and mutant forms. Therefore the transplanted populations should have included members of the original species. Why didn't they?

Many nongenetical biologists had an answer for these questions: Natural selection had acted upon the animals in a manner which eliminated those traits which distinguished the original species. The subspecies members were better fitted to survive in the new environment than the initial transplanted stock. But, as we have seen, natural selection was a dead issue so far as most genetical biologists were concerned.

Natural selection became a live issue again during the 1930's and 1940's with the publication of what Simpson terms "a series of fundamental books . . . by geneticists, biometricists, systematists, paleontologists, and other organismic biologists." [17] The Preface of one of the first of these books, written by Ronald A. Fisher and appearing in 1930, began with the observation: "Natural Selection is not Evolution," despite the fact that "the theory of Natural Selection has been employed as a convenient abbreviation for the theory of Evolution by means of Natural Selection." [18] As the truth of this observation was realized, the "enthusiasts' " blind spot was eliminated. The result was a synthesis, the genetical theory of natural selection, "a logical unification of Mendelism and Darwinism." [19]

Such were the events which led to an understanding of heredity, variation, and the mechanisms of organic change. We turn now to a more direct examination of such mechanisms.

ORGANIC CHANGE

"As far back as we can trace the real history of man, we can discover none of the changes that Darwin suggests." This statement was contained in a letter printed in a 1965 newspaper. Like others before him, the letter-writer found the theory of evolution difficult to accept because no large-scale organic changes have been reported within the past two or three thousand years. Such doubts are understandable. Since few people live to be eighty years of age and older, a century seems a very long time to most of us; and the period occupied by "real history" seems vast. It is extremely difficult to think in terms of millions and tens of millions of years, which we must do if we are to understand human evolution.

Evolution does not mean the sudden appearance of an entirely new form of life. It means, as Darwin wrote, "descent with modifications."

A gross organic change is actually the cumulation of slight changes—some more abrupt than others—over many generations. Humans have been instrumental in bringing about such changes in domestic animals and plants through controlled breeding and cross-pollination. The wide variety of dogs alive today is a clear example. Over a hundred breeds of dogs are now recognized in dog shows; several breeds show but slight resemblance to the stock from which they were originally developed.[20]

Man's success in bringing forth new breeds (varieties, races, sub-species) of animals indicates that biological change is not uncommon among at least some kinds of organisms. Selective breeding to develop new strains of chickens, pigs, or horses would be impossible if the off-spring were exact replicas of their parents. Each of us is aware, too, that human children display physical characteristics that distinguish them from their parents. Clearly, organic change in many life forms is associated with sexual reproduction.

Change as a Consequence of Sexual Reproduction

Reproduction begins, and is sometimes completed, when a new cell comes into being. A single-celled organism perpetuates itself through division. Materials in the cell nucleus are replicated, then the cell splits in two. The resulting daughter cells are identical (or nearly so) to the parent cell. Organisms that reproduce sexually experience the same kind of cell division (mitosis) when new cells are added in growth or old cells are replaced. However, mitosis does not begin until after the zygote is formed by the union of a male gamete (sperm) and a female gamete (egg).

Both gametes and body cells contain chromosomes in their nuclei. Hundreds of genes positioned on each chromosome control the complexity and organization of the cells. Body cells have paired chromosomes, but in the gamete they are not paired. Chromosomes in a sex cell separate and find their way into two gametes during the special division known as meiosis. Which half of a pair goes into which gamete is apparently a matter of chance.

Fusion of the sperm and egg into a zygote is a re-pairing of chromosomes. The zygote thus has the same number of chromosome pairs as do the body cells, and it divides in the same manner as they. The typical human body cell, for example, contains twenty-three pairs of chromosomes; the human gamete, twenty-three single chromosomes. The twenty-three single chromosomes from each parent combine in the zygote to form twenty-three pairs.

Since half of the genetic materials necessary for reproduction is furnished by each parent, it is evident that no offspring can be an exact replica of either parent. A moment's reflection will also show that no two individuals of a sexual species can be exactly alike (not even mono-zygotic, or "identical," twins, say some).[21] Each gamete contains but a sampling of the genetic materials of a parent, and two gametes rarely if ever contain identical samples. Since sampling goes on in two parents, the odds against identical materials coming together are high. Should these odds be overcome, there are still many different ways in which the materials can combine—even without benefit of crossover, which not infrequently adds to the variety of combinations. In short, the number of the permutational and combinational possibilities of genes and chromosomes is astronomical.

The genotype of each member of a sexual, biparental population is unique. Consequently, the phenotype of each individual is also some-what different from all others for genetic reasons alone. Some phenotypic differences may, of course, be attributable to differential interaction with the environment. Variations in diet, for example, may account for variations in height and weight among genetically similar individuals. On the other hand, a diet that adds to one individual's weight may not affect another's weight because of slightly different genotypes.

The direct evolutionary effects of genotypic-phenotypic variations are difficult to estimate. In small populations—and every population was small at some time—unusual combinations are more likely to occur (see below), which may have influenced the evolution of some species. More important, apparently, is the indirect role variation has played. Because individuals of a breeding population vary, all do not experience selective factors in the same way. Forces which destroy or benefit most members may not destroy or benefit others, as we shall have occasion to note throughout this book.

The permutational and combinational possibilities of genes and chromosomes, we said, can be practically infinite. Our everyday observa-tions, however, indicate that young cats, dogs, and children are pretty much like their parents. They are not exactly like them, true. But we have only occasional difficulty in identifying at least one of the parents of the offspring we see daily. It would seem, then, that only a relatively small proportion of all the genetic possibilities are realized. Why is that?

Hardy and Weinberg found one answer. The "hereditary conservation of genes is a populational characteristic and . . . if all other factors remain constant the frequency of particular genes and genotypes will be constant in a population generation after generation." [22] Since genes are "by far the most stable of all organic structures," [23] there is a ten-dency toward genetic equilibrium. Once equilibrium is attained, evolu-tion is impossible. An actual experiment will make this last point clear.

An equal number (fifty) of roosters and hens with black plumage were brought together with an identical number of roosters and hens that had splashed-white plumage. Half of the offspring of the combined flock had blue plumage, the other half was equally divided as to black and splashed-white. The next generation had the same proportions: 25 per cent black, 50 per cent blue, and 25 per cent splashed-white.[24]

The results were what might be expected according to Weinberg's formula. Genetic equilibrium was reached within a single generation, as the Hardy-Weinberg Law predicts. It was reached, in part, because mating was random—coloration did not enter into the selection of a mate. A second condition implicit in the law was also fulfilled: the population was self-contained so far as mating was concerned. No chickens from outside the experimental flock bred with members of the population.

Evolution within the flock, as matters stand, is virtually impossible. Genes (or alleles, different expressions of the same gene) will continue to appear in much the same frequency generation after generation. The ratio of one gene (or allele) to another will remain more or less fixed. Thus an established range of variation will persist indefinitely—unless the genetic equilibrium is upset.

How can the equilibrium be upset? Failure to fulfill either of the two conditions mentioned is one means. Should the black chickens suddenly develop an aversion to mating with splashed-white chickens, the ratio of genes responsible for coloration would be drastically altered. Modification of the gene pool would also follow an invasion of red roosters that successfully mated with the hens.

Neither of the conditions met in the experiment is always fulfilled in the wild state. Mating goes on between different local and subspecies populations, and variations in color or other traits sometimes result in differential mating opportunities for members of either sex. It is very probable, therefore, that these factors had some influence upon human evolution, particularly in combination with selective factors. If cross-breeding took place quite often or the basis for mate selection changed frequently, the consequences for evolution may have been considerable.

A third factor could also modify the gene pool of the chicken population: mutations. Mutations, we have noted, can upset genetic equilibrium and extend the range of heritable variation.

Change Through Mutations

A mutation is a relatively permanent change in hereditary materials. As currently used, the term refers to change in the number, arrangement, or architecture of chromosomes;[25] change in the number of arrangement of genes; [26] or change in the chemical structure of one or more genes.[27] For our purposes, a mutation is a genetic change which is potentially heritable if mating is effected; but it is not necessarily inherited. An animal may inherit a mutant gene from its parents and, at the same time, carry a mutant gene that was not part of the parental genotypes.

Mutations occur spontaneously in most, if not all, forms of life, from microorganisms to man. The frequency with which they occur varies as to particular genes or chromosomes, over time, and from species to species. Some mutations, however, take place with enough regularity for rates to be estimated or calculated.[28] Causative factors are not fully understood; but it is known that mutations can be induced by radiation sources (X rays, ultraviolet light, gamma rays, cosmic rays, and so on),[29] by temperature extremes * and certain chemicals,[30] and by the actions of viruses.[31]

The effects of a mutation may be imperceptible in the phenotype, or detectable only with the aid of special techniques. Again, the effects may be quite dramatic—death, deformity, striking morphological or physiological change. How the phenotype is affected depends, in part, upon the particular gene that is transformed and what the change does to its interaction with other genes. Some phenotypic characteristics are the products of interaction among a number of genes, but one gene may affect several different aspects of the phenotype.[32]

Most of the mutations which are known are supposedly harmful, but the number of unknown mutations probably exceeds the number of those that have been recognized. Mutations which do not interfere with procreation, directly or indirectly (primarily by causing an animal to be rejected as a mate), may accumulate from generation to generation. The accumulation of deleterious or potentially deleterious mutants every generation is sometimes referred to as a *genetic load*. A genetic load may be quite large if the mutant genes are recessive or, when dominant, not particularly detrimental. When carriers of recessive genes are mated, however, the resulting homozygosity of mutant alleles may produce early deaths, disabilities, or sterility among the offspring. Among humans, the children of cousins, uncle and niece, and other not particularly close relatives suffer greater mortality at birth and thereafter than do children of unrelated spouses.[33]

If the accumulating mutant genes are not particularly deleterious, actually or potentially, they may become as frequent as normal genes. They may eventually supplant the normal alleles.[34] Whether or not

---

* According to Victor A. McKusick, the wearing of trousers raises scrotal temperatures considerably—enough, perhaps, to be a factor in mutations. See *Human Genetics* (Englewood Cliffs, N. J.: Prentice-Hall, Inc., 1964), p. 117.

they do depends largely upon factors external to the carriers of mutated materials. Size of population is one factor.

In a large population—where the Hardy-Weinberg Law is most likely to hold—the destiny of a mutant gene is like that of any other low-frequency allele. That is, provided it does not suffer random loss, the mutant will turn up occasionally in individual genotypes.* Like other genes, it will tend to appear in fixed ratio. It may, like any other gene, undergo mutation (sometimes "back-mutation," a reverting back to an approximation of its former condition).[35]

Random loss or fixation of a mutated gene is possible in any breeding population. The theoretical probability that either will occur increases as the size of the population decreases.[36] Given the same ratio of the original form of a gene to its mutated allele, random loss of a few of the latter might mean elimination of the allele from the gene pool of a small, isolated population. In a very large population, the same number of losses is likely to have little or no effect upon the composition of the gene pool. If the allele is not lost through chance occurrences, the probabilities of an increase in its frequency are greater in the small population than in the large one. This follows from the fact that mating between carriers of the allele and subsequent production of offspring homozygous with respect to the allele is more likely. (Consider, for instance, the chances of five male carriers mating with five female carriers in a population of one hundred and in a population of 10 million—all factors other than population size being equal.)

In short, gene frequencies are more likely to fluctuate widely from the norm in a small, isolated population than in a large, open population. A low-frequency mutated gene may within a few generations become a high-frequency allele—or it may be displaced altogether—through chance occurrences.† This random fluctuation of frequencies through chance occurrences is known as *genetic drift* (also *drift, random drift, Sewall Wright effect*).

The evolutionary significance of genetic drift is difficult, if not impossible, to determine. In theory, there is no reason why such a phenom-

---

* Examples of random loss include failure of the carrier of a rare gene, mutant or normal, to mate, and failure of the gene to show up in the gamete that helps form the zygote.

† Chances involved here are somewhat analogous to those involved in coin-tossing. There is a fifty-fifty chance (theoretical probability: .50) that heads will turn up each time a coin is tossed. But the first few tosses may turn up all heads or all tails (occurrences: 1.00 and 0.00). The more often the coin is tossed, however, the more closely the theoretical probability will be approached. In other words, the smaller the number of coin-tosses (or different expressions of a gene), the more likely the frequency of heads (or a particular allele) will vary from the norm or theoretical probability.

enon should not have played an important role, but there are no techniques for counting gene frequencies of fossil populations. No scientist, to our knowledge, questions that there were and are random fluctuations of gene frequencies. Some, however, such as Ernst Mayr, believe that "drift" has been used to explain too many puzzling evolutionary changes. To Mayr's way of thinking, all or virtually all, cases listed in the literature as "evolutionary change due to genetic drift" can be interpreted in terms of another factor which affects the fate of the mutant gene. That factor is selection.[37]

Selection and Change

Organic change, it is clear, is hardly an unusual phenomenon. It occurs with each birth in a bisexual population. In both bisexual and unisexual species, genotypes are altered by mutations. Genes are shuffled from time to time through nonrandom mating, breeding between different populations, and chance factors. Despite change, phenotypes obviously vary only within certain limits. Heritable traits cluster around an average or norm in the larger populations. Variation is greater in some species than in others, and some traits vary more widely than do other traits. Whatever the variation, though, most members in an established population show but slight departure from the norm. The existence of phenotypic norms is, of course, a reflection of some measure of genetic equilibrium.

How is genetic equilibrium possible if organic change is so common? How can equilibrium be even approximated if mutations and unusual genetic combinations occur with any regularity? Evidently all genotypes are not equally successful. Some are lost through chance; many are eliminated by selective factors.

In a sense, selection begins at conception. Certain genetic combinations do not permit normal development of the embryo from the zygote. Other combinations are unable to survive in the uterine environment. If birth is effected, mutant or rare nonmutant genes sometimes fail to become part of the gene pool because they result in premature death of the carrier. Again, the deviant may maturate, yet be unable to reproduce for one reason or other. It may, for example, fail to inherit—or inherit in distorted form—a distinctive feature which normally elicits sexual response in a potential mate, such as the red breast of the male robin.

Adults may select mates because the latter have a particular trait or more of some attribute than others of the same sex. Sexual selection among humans and nonhumans may be on the basis of such characteristics as color, vocal ability, and stature. People sometimes engage in social selection, too. That is, a husband or wife is chosen because he or she possesses a socially valued attribute, such as wealth or upper-class status.

So far as evolution is concerned, the most important kind of selective process appears to be natural selection. The living (biotic) and physical environment with which members of a population interact affects the genotypic-phenotypic variations differentially. Members with some traits or variations of traits succumb more readily to predation, disease, climate, or other environmental hazards than do others. The result is an unequal distribution of phenotypes in any local population. Most members are pretty much alike with regard to certain traits, such as size, coloration, and muscular development. There is, in other words, a phenotypic norm. The majority of the members, for example, may weigh approximately 24 ounces. A lesser number weigh about 22 and 26 ounces, even fewer weigh 20 and 28 ounces, and so on, until an upper and lower limit is reached. Those individuals that deviate most from the norm are least numerous.

The existence of phenotypic norms suggests that individuals that most closely approximate the norm of their population are the "fittest" of their group, the best adapted to the population environment. The "fittest," we noted in the first chapter, are those members able to transmit their genotypes to the next generation more successfully than any others in their environment. They have a biological makeup that allows them to contribute proportionately more to the gene pool than their kin. This they may do because they enjoy better health, escape predation more readily, have a longer life span, or enjoy some other advantage over other organisms that draw upon the same environmental resources. However, the primary function or purpose of natural selection is not the betterment of the individual. Natural selection operates to promote the effective reproduction of a population. In so doing, it may indirectly promote the welfare of certain members of the population. Individuals are not selected so that they may live better or longer; they live better or longer because by so doing there is a greater likelihood that the population will be perpetuated into the future.*

* Much of what we have said obviously does not apply to human populations today. Rarely, if ever, do all members of a human population reproduce as effectively as they could, biologically speaking. In our own society, for instance, very few females begin having children as soon as they are physiologically capable of doing so. Few bear children for as long as they are potentially fertile. Again, many apparently healthy men and women contribute nothing to the population gene pool for one reason or another; they are not married, they are members of an association that demands celibacy, they do not want children, and so on. Reproduction is encouraged, discouraged, and forbidden by laws, customs, and beliefs. Culture as well as biology determines "fitness."

Natural selection is yet another factor that can upset genetic equilibrium. This stems from the fact that selective pressures vary in time and space. Organisms ideally suited to environmental conditions at one period in time or in one particular geographic location may perish or suffer reduced reproductive success at another time or in another place. Consequently, migration to a new environment or marked change in an existing environment often alters genotypic-phenotypic norms. Former deviants become normal; formerly normal types become less numerous, perhaps extinct. It is known, for example, that only the small (deviant) members of a burrowing species survived a long, hard freeze in Europe a few years ago. The animals were unable to come to the surface for food, and the normal-sized members starved to death. The once numerically inferior small animals are now numerically superior.[38]

It is known, too, that normal bacteria, viruses, and other microorganisms can be killed with certain chemicals or gases while their mutants cannot. Many a farmer knows but too well that a few insects have a disconcerting propensity for surviving the most potent insecticides and starting new populations. Variations due to mutations are evidently a critical factor in allowing organisms to adapt to some drastically altered environmental circumstances.

In the past, as in the present, perhaps only those organisms modified by mutations managed to survive some of the drastic environmental changes scattered throughout geologic time. There is no doubt that these and lesser changes upset genetic equilibria. When new equilibria were approximated again, the organisms that contributed most heavily to the heredity of subsequent generations were genotypically-phenotypically different from their predecessors. Any event or circumstance which alters the interaction between organisms and environment may have evolutionary consequences. "Descent with modification" occurred not only because some organisms succumbed to selective pressures, but also because some were better equipped than others to exploit available opportunities, usual or unusual. Again, an accidental or deliberate choice between alternatives may have had far-reaching effects. For some reason or other, a few early prosimians elected to make the trees their habitat; others chose the ground. The latter made little evolutionary history; among the tree-dwellers were the ancestors of man.

NOTES

1. C. H. Waddington, "Theories of Evolution," in S. A. Barnett (ed.), *A Century of Darwin* (London: William Heinemann, Ltd., 1958), pp. 5–6.

2. Cf. Isaac Asimov, *The Intelligent Man's Guide to the Biological Sciences* (New York: Pocket Books, 1964), pp. 151–152.

3. George Gaylord Simpson and William S. Beck, *Life: An Introduction to Biology*, 2nd ed. (New York: Harcourt, Brace & World, Inc., 1965), pp. 64–68.

4. Isaac Asimov, *The Genetic Code* (New York: The New American Library, Inc., 1962), p. 19.

5. Conway Zirkle, "The Knowledge of Heredity before 1900," in L. C. Dunn (ed.), *Genetics in the 20th Century* (New York: The Macmillan Company, 1951), pp. 54–55.

6. Most of Mendel's original paper, translated, is reprinted in James A. Peters (ed.), *Classic Papers in Genetics* (Englewood Cliffs, N. J.: Prentice-Hall, Inc., 1959).

7. Walter S. Sutton, "The Chromosomes in Heredity," in Peters, *op. cit.*, pp. 27–41; Simpson and Beck, *op. cit.*, pp. 173–176.

8. H. J. Muller, "The Development of the Gene Theory," in Dunn, *op. cit.*, p. 86.

9. George Gaylord Simpson, "Biological Sciences," in Robert M. Hutchins and Mortimer J. Adler (eds.), *The Great Ideas Today, 1965* (Chicago: William Benton, Publisher, 1965), p. 309.

10. W. E. Castle, "The Beginnings of Mendelism in America," in Dunn, *op. cit.*, p. 60.

11. Wilhelm Weinberg, "On the Demonstration of Heredity in Man," in Samuel H. Boyer, IV (ed.), *Papers on Human Genetics* (Englewood Cliffs, N. J.: Prentice-Hall, Inc., 1963), pp. 4–15; © 1963. By permission of Prentice-Hall, Inc., Englewood Cliffs, New Jersey.

12. A. H. Sturtevant, "The Relation of Genes and Chromosomes," in Dunn, *op. cit.*, pp. 102–103.

13. Theodosius Dobzhansky, *Genetics and the Origin of Species*, 3rd ed. (New York: Columbia University Press, 1951), p. 27; Simpson and Beck, *op. cit.*, pp. 175–185.

14. Simpson and Beck, *op. cit.*, p. 214.

15. H. J. Muller, "Variation Due to Change in the Individual Gene," in Peters, *op. cit.*, p. 107.

16. Simpson, *op. cit.*, pp. 308–309.

17. *Ibid.*, p. 310.

18. Ronald A. Fisher, *The Genetical Theory of Natural Selection*, 2nd rev. ed. (New York: Dover Publications, Inc., 1958), p. vii.

19. George C. Williams, *Adaptation and Natural Selection* (Princeton: Princeton University Press, 1966), p. 20.

20. Ruth Moore and the Editors of *Life*, *Evolution* (New York: Time Inc., 1962), pp. 86–87.

21. Ernst Mayr, *Animal Species and Evolution* (Cambridge: Harvard University Press, 1963), pp. 138, 148; George Gaylord Simpson, *The Major Features of Evolution* (New York: Columbia University Press, 1953), p. 60.

22. Jay M. Savage, *Evolution* (New York: Holt, Rinehart & Winston, Inc., 1963), p. 27.

23. Dobzhansky, *op. cit.*, p. 19.

24. Savage, *op. cit.*, pp. 27–28.

25. Edward O. Dodson, *Evolution: Process and Product* (New York: Reinhold Publishing Corp., 1960), Chap. 14: Savage, *op. cit.*, p. 43.

26. Savage, *op. cit.*, p. 44.

27. R. P. Levine, *Genetics* (New York: Holt, Rinehart & Winston, Inc., 1962), pp. 128–135.

28. *Ibid.*, pp. 124–125; Theodosius Dobzhansky, *Evolution, Genetics, and Man* (New York: John Wiley & Sons, Inc., 1955), pp. 55–63; Bertram S. Kraus, *The Basis of Human Evolution* (New York: Harper & Row, Publishers, 1964), pp. 99–101; 104–105; Victor A. McKusick, *Human Genetics* (Englewood Cliffs, N. J.: Prentice-Hall, Inc., 1964), pp. 112–116.

29. Kraus, *op. cit.*, p. 99.

30. Dobzhansky, *Evolution, Genetics, and Man*, pp. 41–45.

31. Maurice Whittinghill, *Human Genetics and Its Foundations* (New York: Reinhold Publishing Corp., 1965), p. 362.

32. Mayr, *op. cit.*, pp. 264–265.

33. Theodosius Dobzhansky, *Mankind Evolving* (New Haven: Yale University Press, 1962), pp. 146–150.

34. Theodosius Dobzhansky, "The Genetic Nature of Differences Among Men," in Stow Person (ed.), *Evolutionary Thought in America* (New Haven: Yale University Press, 1950), pp. 125–126.

35. George Gaylord Simpson, "The Study of Evolution," in Anne Roe and George Gaylord Simpson (eds.), *Behavior and Evolution* (New Haven: Yale University Press, 1958), p. 17.

36. Simpson, *The Major Features of Evolution*, pp. 120–121.

37. Mayr, *op. cit.*, pp. 204–214.

38. *Ibid.*, p. 187.

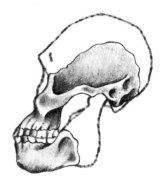

3

Fossils and Time:
Problems and Techniques

With the understanding of organic change, the mystery conceived in Darwin's day achieved full flower. The question of man's origins expanded to include questions concerning the peculiar direction of human development. If man descended from primitive primates, as Darwin believed, why did he not turn out to be another species of apes? Why did he, of all creatures, become bipedal, talkative, and culture bearing? What sort of forces were responsible for making him human? The mystery became, in short, where did man come from, and why did he become the unique being that he is?

This was a much more complex mystery than the early followers of Darwin envisioned—if they envisioned a mystery at all. To some, apparently, there was less a mystery to be probed than a problem to be solved. The problem was to locate the "connecting link" that bridged the gap between man and his subhuman ancestry. Few seem to have visualized any difficulties in identifying this semi-human, should its remains be found.

Perhaps Eugene Dubois, one of the first men to validate Darwin's ideas about human evolution (see Chapter 13), thought along these lines. If he did, he was disillusioned when he submitted fossils he found in Java to the scrutiny of European scientists. Several scientists agreed with Dubois that the fossils were from a transitional form, an animal that was neither ape nor man. Many others rejected this "ape-man" interpretation. Some identified the animal as an extinct ape; another group insisted that the remains were from a modern man. Like many others before and since, Dubois found that the hardest of facts are subject to varying interpretations.

Fossils are still subject to varying interpretations, as we shall see in later chapters. Some of the problems associated with interpretation may also be gleaned from materials presented in this chapter. The stress here, however, is upon techniques rather than problems. The first section illustrates how organic fossils can be identified and used as evidence. The second section shows how and why the temporal dimension figures into interpretations of evidence from the past.

INTERPRETING FOSSILS

Cuvier, the staunch proponent of catastrophism, was reportedly awakened one night by a student dressed as the Devil. "I have come to devour you," said the student. Cuvier took one look at the horns on the "Devil's" head and the shoes shaped like cloven hoofs. "Devour me? I doubt whether you can. You've got horns and hoofs. According to the Law of Correlation you only eat plants." With that Cuvier turned over and went back to sleep.[1]

The Law of Correlation Cuvier formulated is based on the idea that there is a lawful relation between form and function that extends throughout the organism. A carnivore will have not only teeth for ripping and reducing meat to a size that can be swallowed, it will also have claws and anklebones. A mammal that develops teeth for cutting and chewing vegetation will develop horns and hoofs. The development of one organ or part of the body is thus accompanied by the predictable development of other organs and body parts.* [2]

Experience has demonstrated that Cuvier was right in principle, but sometimes amiss with regard to details. There is, indeed, an intimate relationship between form and function, as we shall have frequent occasion to note. There are also exceptions to the manner in which Cuvier postulated this relationship. According to his scheme, an animal with claws is a flesh eater; but a fossil animal has been found that had

---

* In Cuvier's words, "Every organized being forms a *whole*, a unique and closed system, whose parts mutually correspond and contribute to the same ultimate action by reciprocal reaction. None of these parts can change unless the others also change, and, consequently, every one of them taken separately indicates and implies all the others." See George Gaylord Simpson, *Principles of Animal Taxonomy* (New York: Columbia University Press, 1961), p. 43.

claws and skull characteristics which leave no doubt it consumed vegetation.[3]

Cuvier's understanding of relationships between form and function and his knowledge of vertebrate anatomy enabled him to reconstruct fossil animals with considerable accuracy. He had a reputation for being able to reconstruct an entire skeleton from a single bone, an ability no modern paleontologist claims to have. It is very probable that the French scientist's skills were exaggerated by his admirers. Certainly not all of his reconstructions were from single bones, as the following example shows.

A Cuvier Reconstruction

By chance, some small fossil bones came into Cuvier's hands. He was told that more could be found in the gypsum quarries of the Paris region. A systematic exploration of the region turned up about a hundred bones and teeth. Upon inspection, Cuvier discovered that the fossils were not from one type of animal, but from two. What sort of animals were they? The parts offered clues, but they did not reveal the identity of the specimens. Before positive identification could be made, the animals would have to be reconstructed.

The teeth provided one indication that there were two kinds of animals; some teeth told what sort of animals they were. The canines ("dog" or "eye" teeth) were of different lengths, but the molars (grinding teeth) were quite similar. They were thick-set and massive, and they had been worn down at the top. The shape and wear indicated that the molars had been used in chewing vegetation. Both animals were herbivores. Fairly complete limbs showed that one herbivore had two toes; the other, three toes. Which toes belonged to which animal? Cuvier found the answer by painstakingly fitting skull fragments together.

Enough skull fragments had been found to reveal that one of the animals had a head somewhat like that of a modern camel. Nasal bones in the other head suggested a short trunk, like that of the tapir. Could the other body parts have been part of an ancient camel and an ancestral tapir? They certainly could have been. Living camels have two toes; living tapirs have three. Canines in modern tapirs always project above the dental surface more than do camel canines.

Thus did Cuvier reconstruct, in their general lines, the skeletons of two herbivores that became extinct about 50 million years ago. Shortly after he completed this task, a complete skeleton of the tapir ancestor was discovered. Except for some minute details, it was like the tapir Cuvier fitted together.[4]

From the Known to the Unknown

The approach Cuvier employed is still the basic approach used in the interpretation of fossils. From his knowledge of living organisms, the paleontologist is able to identify fossil forms. By analogy, he can also draw reasonable inferences concerning aspects of an organism's behavior and its ecological characteristics (that is, relations to its environment). The more the scientist knows about the habits, habitats, and relations of modern forms, the more inferences he can make about life in the past. Unfortunately, information about living animals is often lacking.[5]

To illustrate, let us suppose that a fossil animal has been identified as an herbivore. What are some of the inferences we can make? The size and kind of animal give some indication as to the kind and relative abundance of its food supply (under normal conditions). This, in turn, tells something about climate, terrain, and altitude (assuming plant life in the past required the same combination of environmental circumstances as living plants). An environment that would support herbivores and vegetation would also support other kinds of organisms—predators, scavengers, insects, microorganisms, and so on; so some of the possible relations with other organisms are known.

Moving from the known to the unknown is seldom as simple or as certain as we make it appear. In the absence of supporting data, what we have termed "inferences" are actually hypotheses. Generally, such data are available, having been accumulated over the years. Fossils have been plotted as to frequency of occurrence and as to location. They have been correlated with one another and with strata that make up the earth's crust. Fossils and the deposits in which they were found have been subjected to chemical, mineral, and microscopic analyses. Not only have the organisms themselves been minutely studied, but also any evidence of their presence which was preserved—excrement (coprolite), tracks, burrows, or teeth marks. Probably the most common application of the known to the unknown is in the interpretation of parts of animals.

Hard Parts and Soft Parts

Hard parts (shells, bones, teeth) are usually the only parts of an animal that fossilize. Only under unusual circumstances, such as desiccation in a protected place or freezing, are soft parts like muscles and organs preserved. More often than not, parts of a skeleton or skull are missing, partially destroyed, or distorted. Reference to the anatomy of a comparable living animal can usually correct such deficiencies. If necessary, approximations of soft parts can also be made in a similar manner. Some soft parts leave marks and impressions (depressions, elevations, ridges, grooves) upon hard parts which facilitate interpretation. Impressions on the inside of the skull, for instance, can supply information about the brain it once housed.[6] Marks left by the attachment of muscles to bones may reveal behavioral possibilities, since different muscles and different degrees of muscle power are required for various activities.

Surface features cannot always be inferred from hard parts alone. Were ancient horses colored and marked as they are today, or were they striped like zebras? There is no way of knowing. Did ancestral camels have humps? Cuvier's restoration showed none. But for cave paintings and frozen fossils, it might once have been assumed that mammoths, like living elephants, had little or no hair.

Teeth—even a single tooth in some instances—can supply important information. Not only representatives of broad categories, such as classes (mammals, reptiles, and so on), but even certain species can be identified by the shape, number, arrangement, and variety of teeth. Mammalian species are sometimes distinguished by such minor dental details as the manner in which enamel is distributed, or not distributed, around the base of a tooth, the number and arrangement of mounds of enamel (cusps) on the crowns, and the manner in which crests are formed.[7] Mammalian teeth are unique in that they are differentiated into incisors, canines, premolars, and molars. The number of these different kinds of teeth varies in time and from one mammal grouping to another. Primates, for example, usually have fewer incisors (cutting teeth) than other mammals; and today's higher primates have fewer premolars than their primitive ancestors.

A mammal's teeth not only identify it, but also tell something of its eating habits. Well-developed canines and shearing back teeth (molars and premolars) indicate a preference for meat. Predatory behavior is implied by large, sharp canines and relatively light jaws and back teeth. Grazing mammals have heavy, ridged grinding teeth and incisors adapted to cropping. A varied diet is suggested by low-crowned teeth and a fairly large number of non-shearing cusps (as in pigs and humans).[8]

Modern animals employ teeth for purposes not directly related to the digestive process—such as combat, defense, holding, carrying, digging, and gnawing. There is no reason to doubt that teeth performed similar functions in the past. This is especially true of specialized teeth, such as the prominent incisors of gnawing animals, like beavers. Certain combinations of teeth found today may have functioned in the past as they now do. Among the primates, for example, long canines are found in combination with non-shearing back teeth; the canines, according to some writers, are used primarily for defense.

49

Features of the skull often provide information about behavioral possibilities. Size and shape of the skull and impressions left by the brain serve as indices of general intelligence and the emphasis given to sensory equipment (for example, sense of smell and sense of sight). The presence of close-set eye sockets indicates that the animal had overlapping vision. A long mammalian snout implies heavy reliance upon the sense of smell. Location of air passages on top of the head, as in the modern alligator, suggests that the animal spent a lot of time in water. The position of the foramen magnum, the large hole in the skull through which the spinal cord passes, usually varies with the habitual posture of animals, thereby providing an idea as to how an animal may have locomoted.

Some parts may serve to confirm what other body parts suggest. The earliest dinosaurs had strong birdlike hind limbs and smale forelimbs. A reasonable inference is that they locomoted somewhat as do long-legged ground birds of today and used the forelimbs for grasping. The position and shape of bone sockets and hip bones and a long tail that would have served as a counterbalance suggest the same thing. The dinosaurs had sharp teeth and claws, which could have been used in holding and tearing food into digestible pieces.[9]

The foregoing is illustrative of what can be learned from fossil parts. A fossil animal can usually be identified—sometimes on the basis of a single bone or tooth—and ideas can be gleaned concerning its behavior and ecological circumstances by comparing the dead with the living. Interpretation is possible because animals of the past bear similarities to present-day animals. Suppose, however, that an animal had a feature different from any found today. How could it be interpreted? An example will show the procedure in such a case.

A small number of prehistoric reptiles possessed enormous, flat jaw teeth unlike those of any other reptiles. What were the teeth used for? The shape of the reptile's girdle, long paddle-like extremities, and other features were similar to known reptilian relatives adapted to marine life. What kind of food could a marine reptile eat that would require large, flat jaw teeth? In addition to these teeth, the reptile had heavy projecting pegs for front teeth. Other animals root or dig for food with heavy, projecting front teeth. What kind of food would be buried in a marine habitat? The size and markings of the jawbone which held the teeth implied that the creature had powerful jaw muscles. This suggested that the food was tough or had a hard covering. What could it be? The answer that was reasoned was mollusks. The unusual teeth were specialized for crushing mollusk shells.[10]

Interpretation of the unusual, then, is also a matter of working from the known to the unknown. What is known need not pertain to organisms closely related to the fossil animal. It may be a comparable function, such as digging with projecting teeth, or similarities in environment or habitat, or likenesses in shape, content, or anything else.

Whether a fossil represents the usual or the unusual, all available information may be employed in its interpretation. This point needs to be made because of the nature of fossil evidence, a matter to which we shall presently turn. Too, some similarities among organisms are not genetically derived. A case in point is the Tasmanian wolf. Despite its name, it is not related (except very distantly) to the true wolf. The two are very similar in appearance and habits because they are products of what is termed *convergence*. That is, they owe their organic likenesses to similar adaptations to similar environmental conditions, not to a common ancestry.[11] (The Tasmanian wolf, incidentally, is a marsupial —a mammal that carries the newborn in a pouch.) Another source of similarity among living animals that are not genetically related is *mimicry*. One animal takes on one or more characteristics of another as a means of adaptation.[12] There are harmless snakes, for example, that have gradually acquired the coloration of the highly poisonous coral snake, thereby discouraging predatory attacks.[13] Since surface features are usually involved in mimicry, its existence in a fossil is difficult to detect unless other information is available.

Knowledge about fossils and living organisms is constantly expanding. New techniques give promise of fuller and more accurate interpretations of extinct organisms. Studies in comparative biochemistry, for instance, may soon make it possible to identify past forms of life from "chemical fossils." This possibility rests on a recent discovery that organic molecules persist unchanged or little altered from their original structure even though the organism of which they were a part has long since vanished. In the not too distant future, it is likely that classes, genera, and perhaps species can be identified by the molecules they left.[14] At the present time, many questions concerning the past cannot be answered with certainty. Some answers must be tentative because the fossil record is far from complete.

Fossil Incompleteness [15]

Large numbers of fossils have already been found and many more will be discovered in the future. Whatever the number, the total remains will represent but an exceedingly small sample of all things that have ever lived. Worse, the sample is biased. One source of bias has been the almost complete destruction of soft parts. This is not necessarily a serious problem in the case of animals with hard parts; but many organisms, particularly early forms, had no hard parts.

It is quite apparent that even animals with hard parts failed to become part of the fossil record. Herein lies another source of bias. The vast majority of organisms are destroyed or made unrecognizable by decay, scavengers, chemical action, frost, and other forces. Those that were preserved were, for the most part, buried shortly after death in sediments free of destroying elements such as bacteria and chemicals. The habits and habitats of many animals precluded such burial.

All fossils have not had equal chances of discovery—another biasing factor. Natural forces, such as erosion, floods, and uplifts in the earth's surface, have made some fossils more accessible than others. Mining, tunneling, road-building, and other human activities have also un-covered—and destroyed—many fossils. Terrain, climatic conditions, specialized interests—these and other considerations have entered into more deliberate efforts to find fossils.

The fossil record, despite its inadequacies, is complete enough for many purposes. Today's scientists believe that they have the tools and materials necessary for answering most of the major questions about evolution. Many minor questions can be answered by drawing upon the information and insights of various disciplines and by reasoning. Sampling, even biased sampling, has the obvious advantage of permitting a more thorough analysis of units. A comprehensive study of an entire species population, dead or alive, is usually impossible, but a few members of several populations can be studied intensively.

The scientist who works with fossils today knows that his basic data are not necessarily representative of extinct populations. He is, therefore, less dogmatic about "facts" than were a number of his predecessors. His conclusions tend to be hedged with qualifications—not only because of the nature of fossil evidence, but also because of problems associated with the dating of fossils.

DATING THE PAST

Late in 1912 the *Manchester Guardian* announced the discovery of one of the most significant fossil finds that had ever been made. In a gravel pit at Piltdown, England, the newspaper reported, there had been found almost certain proof of man's apelike ancestry. The specimen's combined features were such as Darwin himself had implied in *The Descent of Man*. The braincase, reconstructed from nine unusually thick pieces of cranium, was undoubtedly human. The mandible (lower jaw) found in association with the skull fragments was more the size and shape of an ape's jaw. Marks on the jaw left by muscles were characteristics ordinarily found only on an ape mandible. One item not mentioned in the *Guardian*, since it was found only after intensive

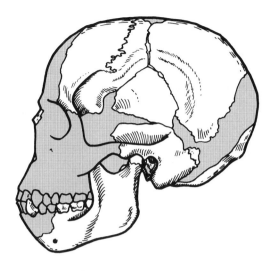

Figure 3. *Eanthropus dawsoni*. Unshaded areas represent cranial bones and teeth found in gravel pit at Piltdown, England.

searching, was a loose tooth, a canine. This tooth had a length intermediate to that of the canines of man and apes.

The human skull, the apelike jaw, and teeth that were human or semi-human all belonged to the same animal. Such was confirmed by two facts: all the parts had been found within a few feet of one another, and the fossils were similar in color. The coloration indicated that *Eoanthropus dawsoni* (*Eo*, "dawn"; *anthropus*, "man"; *dawsoni*, in honor of the discoverer, a man named Dawson) was ancient. The bones and teeth had obviously been slowly stained by chemicals in the ground. The stratum in which the bones had rested also attested to the antiquity of Piltdown man; it was, according to Dawson, a layer laid down during the "Early Ice Age" (Lower Pleistocene, in more modern terminology).

The Early Ice Age, it was believed, dated back some 500,000 years—long before *Homo sapiens* appeared. *Eoanthropus'* pre-*sapiens* existence was further confirmed by items found near the remains. These included flint implements fashioned in a manner similar to known prehistoric tools and weapons and some more primitive than any known artifacts. An elephant bone had evidently been shaped to form a club. Fossil remains of mammals, some long extinct in Britain, appeared with and below the other items.

The established facts—that the skull and jaw belonged together and that the creature predated modern man—made one conclusion inevitable: *Eoanthropus* was ancestral to *Homo sapiens*. The status of *Eoanthropus* remained secure—but not unquestioned—for over forty years. During all of these years there were men who found it difficult to accept the specimen as an authentic ancestor to man. Some who doubted eventually accepted the arguments of those who believed; some yielded their doubts when a second, less complete, Piltdown specimen was uncovered. Others, however, remained skeptical, and their numbers increased as evidence from other parts of the world accumulated. From the standpoint of skeletal structure, Piltdown man did not fit into the total picture of human evolution that was unfolding. Late in the 1940's, geologists supplied the skeptics with additional ammunition. *Eoanthropus*, the geologists decided, was not as ancient as had been thought.

In 1949 Dr. Kenneth Oakley reported that he had measured the amount of fluorine in the bones. The fluorine content showed that none of the skull fragments from either of the Piltdown sites could be older than 50,000 years at most. This meant that Piltdown man could not possibly be a human ancestor, for more human-like forms existed even prior to that time. If *Eoanthropus* was not a human ancestor, what was it? To some, it was a divergent line of human evolution that went nowhere. Some believed it might be another fossil specimen of Late Ice Age *Homo sapiens*. To yet others, the remains represented two fossil creatures, a man and an ape. Piltdown man was a problem.

In the early part of the 1950's the doubts of one skeptic, Dr. J. S. Weiner, turned into suspicions. He had reason to be suspicious. For one thing, no one had been able to find the second site. Dawson, who discovered this site as well as the first, died in 1916 without leaving a single clue as to its location. Furthermore, the fossil evidence was not completely convincing. The knobs (condyles) of the mandible that fit into the skull were broken off, and the only anatomical feature which connected the skull with the jaw were the teeth. The teeth, to Weiner's way of thinking, were not what they should have been. Flat, worn molars and a canine unduly worn for the age of the specimen suggested but one thing: the teeth had been deliberately ground down.

Dr. Weiner carried his doubts to the authorities at the British Museum, where the specimen was kept. An intensive reexamination and analysis of the whole array of evidence began. The bones and stones were viewed through microscopes, compared with materials found in like strata of other areas, and subjected to a variety of laboratory tests. Weiner's suspicions were confirmed. The teeth had been altered, as had other evidence. The stains, for example, were artificially induced; they were not the result of an aging process. What is more, items originally thought to be of the same age were not. Some were of more recent origin than others. Piltdown man was a forgery!

Two types of chemical tests revealed that there were discrepancies in the ages of the Piltdown man fossils. One type, which had been worked out in the 1940's, was based on the loss of organic content. Bones preserved under similar conditions, it had been found, lose the nitrogen of their protein at a relatively slow, fairly constant rate. All the *Eoanthropus* remains, then, should have had equal proportions of nitrogen. They did not. The canine dentine had a higher nitrogen content than the molars, indicating that the former was more recent than the latter. Skull fragments from both Piltdown sites proved to be more ancient than the jaw.[16]

The other chemical test was a refinement upon Oakley's earlier fluorine analysis. The longer a bone is in a deposit which has fluorine—and many deposits do—the more fluorine it absorbs. Therefore, bones introduced into a deposit at the same time—as the jaw, canine, and skull presumably were—should have equal percentages of fluorine. This was not the case. The fluorine content was highest in the skull fragments.[17]

Other tests and close physical inspection substantiated the finding that the mandible and skull could not be from the same animal. More recently, radiocarbon (carbon-14) tests showed that the skull was not even of Early Ice Age origin. At most, it was 720 years old.[18]

Why did the Piltdown forgery go undetected for so long? A contributing factor, no doubt, was that the discovery of a creature similar to *Eoanthropus* was anticipated. Perhaps national pride or envy overcame scientific skepticism to some extent. Significant fossils were being turned up elsewhere, but not in England, the home of Darwinism. Important as these factors may have been, the successful perpetration of the forgery depended upon the clever manipulation of time clues. Final dissolution of the Piltdown-man problem came when the time clues were proven to be false. The forgery was fully bared by means of new or refined techniques for dating fossil materials.

The entire incident, from inception to disproof, highlights a very important problem in the interpretation of fossils, the problem of assigning proper dates to evidence. The incident also illustrates the two classes of dating, relative and absolute (or chronometric).

Relative Dating

An accurate reconstruction of the past, historical or evolutional, necessitates a temporal ordering of events. Ideally, a sequence is established in terms of specific temporal units. For example, event A took place in 34 B.C., event B in 1260 A.D.; organism A lived 192 million years ago, and organism B died 26 million years before the present. Attainment of the ideal is not always possible in reconstructing the story of man. Fortunately, it is not always necessary. The main outlines and many of the details of human evolution can be determined by knowing relative ages —organism A lived prior to organism B; organism B was contemporaneous with organism C, and so on.

Relative dating is possible because men have discerned an orderly procession of certain events of the past. One of the most important, so far as the interpretation of fossils and prehistory is concerned, was the stratification of the earth's crust. Natural forces—such as floods, volcanic action, winds, melting glaciers—and man, with his buildings and garbage, superimposed one layer upon another. Since lower strata were laid down earlier than upper strata, objects embedded in the former are usually of greater antiquity than those found in strata nearer the surface. We say "usually," for strata have sometimes been disturbed by nature and by man.

Layers of the earth's crust are unique in their composition, content, and properties, as well as relative positions. In natural formations, strata vary as to mineral content, density, evidences of erosion, electric and radioactive properties, and assemblages of flora and fauna.[19] The last type of variation is, itself, a criterion of age. Some life forms, species, and structural modifications appeared earlier in time than did others; some combinations of life preceded other combinations.[20] In manmade formations, strata characteristically vary with regard to the kind, manufacture, and design of artifacts. Evidences of dietary differences among successive occupants of a site may also differentiate one stratum from another.

The fact that strata are unique makes possible a practice known as *correlation*. The age of a stratum (or objects in it) can be determined by matching its characteristics with characteristics of strata that have already been dated. Correlation is particularly useful—though it has its hazards [21]—in piecing together sequential records. Forces which deposited (and sometimes removed) layers did not affect all areas uniformly. Consequently, areas have strata which represent different segments of geologic history. By matching strata from different areas, sequences of geologic and evolutional events can be put together.* [22]

Strata vary in their makeup as a consequence of the succession of events and processes which altered the earth's surface. Different forms of life evolved, and many became successful or extinct at different points in time. Inorganic matter was changed by such forces as heat, weathering, and chemical action. Floods, climatic swings, upheavals,

* To illustrate, suppose that area A has strata 1, 2, 4; area B, strata 3, 4, 5; and area C, strata 5, 6, 7. By matching the identical stratum in A and B, stratum 4, a stratum missing in area A (stratum 3) is filled in and the sequence is extended. When stratum 5 is matched in areas B and C, the sequence is extended by two more strata. Actual examples can be found in books cited in this subsection.

volcanic activities, and other natural events resulted in differing distributions of both organic and inorganic matter throughout geologic time.

Individual strata and sequences of strata vary to the extent that geologists have been able to divide geologic time into units. The beginning of the fossil record serves as a division between the longest periods of time, the Cryptozoic ("hidden life") and the Phanerozoic ("evident life") eons. During the former eon which occupied about five-sixths of geologic time, life was either absent or of such a nature as to leave no uesful fossil record. The Phanerozoic Eon is subdivided into three eras. This division is based upon changes in the kinds of organisms that were dominant at different times. The Paleozoic ("ancient life") Era was characterized chiefly by invertebrates and primitive plants. Reptiles were the dominant form of life during most of the Mesozoic ("medieval life") Era. Birds and mammals became dominant during the Cenozoic ("recent life") Era.[23] Periods, epochs, and other subdivisions of an era are based on indications of change wrought by natural events, such as the deposition of clay upon a sandstone formation during a flood or the supplanting of arctic fauna by animals adapted to a warm climate.

Successful perpetration of the Piltdown hoax depended, to some extent, upon the employment of stratigraphic clues. Had scientists not been convinced that *Eoanthropus* was several hundred thousand years old, the fraud might have been discovered much sooner. The major time clues, so far as many analysts were concerned, were the faunal remains. Below the *Eoanthropus* skull, at the base of the gravel deposit, was a femur of an extinct elephant. This particular species, it was known, dated back to a time period that preceded the last Ice Age. Fragments found in association with the skull were also from "warm" fauna (a hippopotamus, for example).

Artifacts were used by the perpetrator of the hoax to substantiate the relative age of the Piltdown man (or woman, according to some). The raw materials from which the implements were fashioned—bone and flint—provided one index of antiquity. The use of flint, and presumably bone, preceded the use of metals by several centuries. It was evident, too, that techniques employed in the manufacture of the flint implements were less advanced than those reflected in prehistoric implements that had been found on the Continent. There was, in short, some basis for concluding that the Piltdown artifacts were made and employed by an ancient ape-man.

Artifacts, like strata and fossils, underwent sequential changes. It is possible, therefore, to assign relative dates to man-made objects—and perhaps the strata from which they come—on the basis of varying characteristics. In addition to raw materials and techniques employed in the manufacture of objects, artifacts have varied as to usage, variety, complexity, and styles. Stone hand axes, for example, were in use long before pottery vessels or stone hoes and scythes. A single all-purpose stone implement was eventually replaced by several specialized stone tools and weapons.

Sequences, once established, aid in the interpretation of material in disturbed strata. Conversely, they may indicate that strata have been disturbed. For instance, there has been some confusion as to the chronology of certain hominid types. Sometimes the basis for confusion was the presence of *sapiens'* characteristics in fossils found in a stratum below the remains of less advanced hominids. Thus, modern man was thought to have evolved prior to these hominids—until it was reasoned that prehistoric man had buried his dead.

When there are doubts as to the relative ages of fossils brought together by natural or human disturbances, chemical tests such as were used in the analysis of Piltdown man may be employed. The chemical composition of one bone is compared with that of others in the same deposit. As a rule, a measurement of mineral matter which becomes part of the fossil, notably fluorine, is more feasible than a measurement of changes in organic matter, such as loss of nitrogen.[24]

Microscopic studies currently serve somewhat the same purpose as chemical tests. In time, electron and polarizing microscopes may be of aid in establishing relative ages of specimens exposed to similar environmental conditions (in the deposits). Microscopic dating is possible because fossilization is processional—one modification follows another in order. The process begins with the disappearance of all organic structures (marrow and bone cells) and ends with a chemical metamorphosis of inorganic substances. It is possible, therefore, to compare two or more bones in the same deposit and determine whether one is older than another.[25]

Absolute or Chronometric Dating

An absolute date is a more or less specific date or time range, such as 1968 or 1850 to 1900. Absolute dating is usually accomplished in either of two ways: The specimen or minerals in the deposit from which the specimen comes are measured directly, or the age of one deposit is inferred from the known age of a like deposit.[26]

Most of the techniques employed in dating man and his predecessors establish ages by measuring the rate at which a radioactive element disintegrates. The best known is the carbon-14 test. W. F. Libby, who discovered this technique, found that all living organisms maintain a constant ratio of radioactive carbon-14 * to carbon-12, a stable form of carbon. Plants absorb the radioactive carbon during the normal metabolic processes, and animals eat either plants or plant-eating animals. When an organism dies, absorption of the radioactive carbon ceases. That which is present disintegrates at a constant rate. Ages are calculated from the ratios of radioactive to stable forms of carbon. Quality, kind, and sometimes quantity of specimens determine how far back ages can be calculated. At present, the upper limits are around 50,000 to 60,000 years.

Half of the radioactive carbon is dissipated in between 5,000 and 6,000 years (a figure often cited is 5568 ± 30 years). Other radioactive elements used for dating have slower rates of disintegration. The *half-life* of uranium-238, for instance, is approximately 4.51 billion years. In application, this means that uranium-238 is not suited for dating materials as recent as 2 or 3 million years.

Potassium-40 that was buried in such a manner as to trap argon-40, a decay product, promises to be the most useful of the elements in establishing ages of man's more human-like predecessors. The half-life of potassium-40, 1.3 billion years, allows the dating of strata laid down 2 or 3 million years ago, thereby supplementing uranium-238. There is still a dating hiatus in the range 60,000 to 2 million years ago.[27] However, argon extraction procedures have been refined, and two geologists report that they have been able to obtain high precision ages for formations that occurred during this hiatus.[28]

These and other absolute dating techniques have not solved all the problems of chronology. One reason is that usable radioactive materials are relatively scarce. Some decay too quickly or too slowly to have any utility in understanding human evolution. More often, there is an absence or immeasurable quantity of radioactive isotopes in fossils, deposits, and formations. One of the limitations of carbon-14, for instance, is that it does not always deposit in the bones of animals in sufficient quantity to activate sensitive laboratory instruments.[29]

When radioactive elements are present in measurable quantities, there is no assurance that the dates derived are always accurate. Elements are not uniformly distributed, and widely different dates are sometimes obtained from samples taken at the same stratum level. Several samples are usually analyzed and a mean (average) age is computed. This practice, when it can be followed, reduces error—but it does not guarantee accuracy. For one thing, the sampling may not be adequate. In addi-

---

* 14 is the *mass number* of this particular form, or isotope, of the element carbon. The mass number of an isotope is the sum of protons plus neutrons in its nucleus. Carbon always has six protons (hence, an *atomic number* of 6), but the number of neutrons varies from six to eight (C-12, C-13, and C-14).

tion, most or all elements in the mineral occurrence may have been altered by contamination or weathering. There is a further possibility that half-life figures are not correctly computed. They have been changed several times in the past and are today not at all identical in the Soviet Union and the United States.[30]

Errors are, of course, taken into consideration when they are known or suspected. Rarely is any specific age-determination accepted until all available information is brought to bear. The fossil record is a particularly valuable reference, since the sequential development of life forms is known. In fact, according to one writer, fossil correlations "seem to be safer guides in most cases" in making specific age-determinations than analyses of radioactive materials.[31]

There are many questions about time yet to be answered, but the unanswered questions of today are not necessarily the unanswered questions of tomorrow. It is very likely that new chronometers will be discovered and existing ones refined in the near future. Radioactive chronometers, it might be noted, are a twentieth-century phenomenon; most have been developed since World War II.

Fossils are necessary, but hardly sufficient, evidence to solve the mystery of man's origins and becoming. Bare bones may reflect the results of activities and relationships, but they do not directly reveal what these activities and relationships actually were. As we saw earlier in this chapter, clues of this sort are derived from the study of living animals. In Part II we shall see that living organisms can also provide an understanding of evolutionary consequences that stem from the interaction of organism and environment. This understanding will make the fossil record, which is surveyed in Part III, more meaningful.

NOTES

1. Herbert Wendt, *In Search of Adam* (New York: Collier Books, 1955), pp. 174–175.
2. *Ibid.*, pp. 170–171.
3. George Gaylord Simpson, *Principles of Animal Taxonomy* (New York: Columbia University Press, 1961), p. 44.
4. This example is adapted from Andre Senet, *Man in Search of His Ancestors* (New York: McGraw-Hill Book Company, Inc., 1955), pp. 187–189.
5. James R. Beerbower, *Search for the Past: An Introduction to Paleontology* (Englewood Cliffs, N. J.: Prentice-Hall, Inc., 1960), p. 34.
6. George Gaylord Simpson, *Life of the Past* (New Haven: Yale University Press, 1953), pp. 39–40.
7. Everett C. Olson, "Morphology, Paleontology, and Evolution," in Sol Tax

(ed.), *Evolution After Darwin*, I (Chicago: University of Chicago Press, 1960), 539.

8. Simpson, *Life of the Past*, pp. 45–46.

9. Edwin H. Colbert, "Morphology and Behavior," in Anne Roe and George Gaylord Simpson (eds.), *Behavior and Evolution* (New Haven: Yale University Press, 1958), pp. 28–29.

10. Adapted from Alfred S. Romer, *Vertebrate Paleontology*, 2nd ed. (Chicago: University of Chicago Press, 1945), pp. 193–199.

11. Bertram S. Kraus, *The Basis of Human Evolution* (New York: Harper and Row, Publishers, 1964), pp. 146–147.

12. Simpson, *Principles of Animal Taxonomy*, p. 79.

13. Ernst Mayr, *Animal Species and Evolution* (Cambridge: Harvard University Press, 1963), p. 196.

14. Geoffrey Eglinton and Melvin Calvin, "Chemical Fossils," *Scientific American*, 216 (January 1967), 32–43. For further examples and discussion see Simpson, *Principles of Animal Taxonomy*; Beerbower, *op. cit.*; John Imbrie and Normal Newell (eds.), *Approaches to Paleoecology* (New York: John Wiley & Sons, Inc., 1964); Don Brothwell and Eric Higgs (eds.), *Science in Archaeology* (New York: Basic Books, Inc., Publishers, 1963).

15. The materials in this subsection are drawn mainly from George Gaylord Simpson, "The History of Life," in Tax, *op. cit.*, pp. 117–180.

16. J. S. Weiner, K. P. Oakley, and W. E. Le Gros Clark, "The Solution of the Piltdown Problem," in Robert F. Heizer (ed.), *Man's Discovery of His Past: Literary Landmarks in Archaeology* (Englewood Cliffs, N. J.: Prentice-Hall, Inc., 1962), pp. 33–34.

17. Except for information derived from the article cited in the previous note, facts concerning Piltdown man are drawn from J. S. Weiner, *The Piltdown Forgery* (London: Oxford University Press, 1955).

18. Kraus, *op. cit.*, p. 62.

19. W. C. Krumbein and L. L. Sloss, *Stratigraphy and Sedimentation*, 2nd ed. (San Francisco: W. H. Freeman & Company, Publishers, 1963), pp. 28–36.

20. Carl O. Dunbar, *Historical Geology*, 2nd ed. (New York: John Wiley & Sons, Inc., 1960), p. 9.

21. See, e.g., articles by A. O. Woodford and Luna B. Leopold, and by Walter B. Langbein in Claude C. Albritton, Jr. (ed.), *The Fabric of Geology* (Reading, Mass.: Addison-Wesley Publishing Company, Inc., 1963).

22. Dunbar, *op. cit.*, pp. 9–12; Beerbower, *op. cit.*, pp. 187–199.

23. Carl O. Dunbar, *The Earth* (Cleveland: The World Publishing Company, 1966), pp. 17–21.

24. John Buettner-Janusch, *Origins of Man* (New York: John Wiley & Sons, Inc., 1966), pp. 23–24.

25. Antonio Ascenzi, "Microscopy and Prehistoric Bone," in Brothwell and Higgs, *Science in Archaeology*, pp. 330–342.

26. Kenneth P. Oakley, *Frameworks for Dating Fossil Man* (Chicago: Aldine Publishing Company, 1964), p. 7.

27. Facts about absolute dating are drawn from Dunbar, *Historical Geology*, pp. 20–25; and Kraus, *op. cit.*, pp. 58–60.

28. J. F. Evernden and G. H. Curtin, "Potassium-Argon Dating of Late Cenozoic Rocks in East Africa and Italy," *Current Anthropology*, 6 (1965), 343–385.

29. Frank C. Hibben, *Digging Up America* (New York: Hill & Wang, Inc., 1960), p. 30.

30. A. O. Woodford, *Historical Geology* (San Francisco: W. H. Freeman & Company, Publishers, 1965), pp. 205–206.

31. *Ibid.*, p. 218.

II

CLUES FROM THE PRESENT

4

Relations, Change, and Adaptation

A variety of changes affected the England of Darwin's day. Among them was an increase in the tempo of urbanization and industrialization. New machinery turned out finished goods more rapidly and more economically than did other means of production, but the machinery was heavy and expensive, so workers had to come to where the machines were situated. The workplace of thousands shifted from the home to the factory, from the farm to the village or town. As factory towns and villages sprang up, a rather unusual phenomenon was noted. Red clover in the fields around the settlements began to grow more luxuriantly than did clover in nearby rural areas. This was unusual because the villagers did nothing to encourage such growth. They neither cultivated nor fertilized the fields. Nor did any change in climate or rainfall bene-fit only the village clover. The sole distinguishing factor was the density of human populations. Red clover thrived better in the vicinity of a human aggregation. What was there about a clustering of people that would result in an abundance of clover?

Darwin's studies provided two important clues. He discovered that bumblebees, because of their long tongues, are the only insects that can effectively pollinate the deep red clover flowers. And earthworms, Darwin had found, greatly enrich the soil. It was reasonable to assume, there-fore, that an increase in bumblebees or earthworms would further the growth of clover. What might cause an increase in bumblebees or earth-worms? Did human settlements encourage their migration in some way? Or was there something about human settlements which increased births or decreased deaths among these animals?

The first possibility seemed unlikely. Bumblebees or earthworms may have immigrated from nearby fields, but their numbers could not have been significant. A large-scale movement would have been reflected by adverse effects in the nearby fields. There were no such effects. Too, there had been no special reason for mass migration; initially the fields were much alike.

Were bumblebees or earthworms reproducing abnormally, or were they living longer? The presence of dormice and moles in the fields suggested an investigation of the latter alternative. Dormice feed upon bumblebee combs and larvae, and moles prey upon earthworms. If either of these animal populations was experiencing unusual mortality, the number of premature deaths among bumblebees or earthworms would obviously be reduced. Was there anything about a human aggre-gation that was lethal to dormice or moles? There was—cats. Cats prey upon these predators. When people came to the factory towns and vil-lages, they brought cats with them. A concentration of humans meant a goodly number of cats.

And so it was. The cats, it was found, decimated dormice and mole populations. There were then more bumblebees to pollinate the clover and more earthworms to enrich the soil. Humans, because of their fondness for cats, had indirectly contributed to the abundance of clover. As Darwin observed, "Plants and animals remote in the scale of nature are bound together by a web of complex relations."

The foregoing elaboration upon one of Darwin's examples illustrates not only that living things are "bound together," but that they are re-lated in different ways. Further, the manner in which one organism is related to another may vitally affect its chances for survival. How an organism is related to other forms of life obviously depends upon its biological makeup and the sort of adaptation this makeup permits. Thus, the relationship between bumblebees and clover was quite different from that between bumblebees and dormice. Each animal was adapted to obtaining and digesting different kinds of food.

Our example also illustrates that change can affect chances for survival. In this instance, a change in the biotic environment altered, in one way or another, the life chances of every plant and animal in the fields. Life chances would have been altered, too, had there been a notable change in the physical environment, such as a marked decline in rainfall.

One bit of information which the example does not provide is the ultimate fate of the dormice and moles. Perhaps they were totally eliminated. Again, a few may have been able to adjust to the presence of the cats. Survival may have been furthered by a new kind of adaptation—by changing the time at which food was sought, for example, or by migration, or by burrowing deeper into the earth.

Relations, change, and adaptation have influenced the destiny of all living things, including man. It is with these three factors that we are principally concerned in this chapter. Although evolving man receives no direct mention, he is ever in the background. Nonhuman or prehuman, our ancestors managed to adapt to changing biotic and natural environments. We, their descendants, are living proof that they did. And our biological makeup and behaviors reflect the relationships in which they were involved and the adaptations they made.

WEB OF RELATIONS

Why are organisms "bound together"? Our example shows us that the reasons may be varied. In the case of the bumblebees and clover, two different forms of life were related by an important function each performed for the other. The bumblebees pollinated the red clover, and the clover furnished bumblebees with nourishment. This kind of reciprocal relationship, *mutualism*, also linked the clover and earthworms. The former provided organic material the latter could ingest, and the earthworms enriched the soil for the plants.

The most common type of relationship in the fields—*predation*—directly benefitted but one party to the association, the predator.* In some instances, the predator was also the prey—a link in a *food chain*. The clover nourished the bumblebees, the bumblebees were a source of food for the dormice, and the dormice were eaten by the cats. Two other

* Indirectly, predation may benefit the entire community by controlling the numbers of those animals that subsist upon vegetation. In the absence of predators, rabbits, deer, and other animals have been known to exhaust edible vegetation in certain areas.

binding relationships possibly existed in the fields that are not illustrated in the example: *parasitism* and *commensalism*. The cats, let us say, hosted fleas; and the clover plants provided protection from the sun— and nothing else—for another organism. In both instances, only one of the parties to the relationship benefitted. The fleas benefitted at the expense of the cats, an example of parasitism. The shaded organism neither aided nor harmed the plants, illustrating commensalism.

Whatever the type of relationship, it is evident that every animal owes its existence to at least one other form of life. To survive, an animal must have continuous or regular association with the form or forms upon which it it depends. The dependent animal is often depended upon, so that a series of interlocking and overlapping relations develop within a given area. Thus, an animal that feeds upon plant life may host parasites, excrete wastes from which nutriments are extracted, be eaten by one or more kinds of predators, or be consumed wholly or in part after death by various scavengers. Any of these animals may, in turn, be links in other food chains and parties in mutualistic and commensal relationships.

A population that is held together in more or less continuous association within a limited geographic area (such as a field or pond) constitutes what ecologists call a *community* (*biotic community*). A characteristic of community life is a division of labor. The various members perform different "jobs" or functions that contribute to the continuity and stability of the total community. As in our example, some organisms function to make life possible for other members of the community. Others, like the dormice and moles, help preserve an equilibrium among community elements by checking population growth. By reason of its function, or "job," each form of life occupies a unique position with relation to other forms and with relation to the physical environment. Such a position is referred to as a *niche* (*ecological niche, econiche*).

The specialized structure of the bumblebees (notably the long tongues and wings) indicates that the niche an animal occupies depends upon its biological makeup. The moles occupied their particular niche because they had equipment for digging and digesting earthworms. The clover and the dormice had yet other structures and filled yet other positions in the fields.

FITNESS FOR SURVIVAL

Why does an animal have the biological makeup—the arrangement and specialization of cells—that it has? That is, why is one kind of animal physically different from another? One word that answers questions of this sort is "heredity." Members of one species differ from members of any other species because their genetic heritage is different. However, if we go backwards in time, we find that species of today once had common ancestries. The answer to our question, then, must be "heredity plus. . . ." Plus what? Our discussion thus far implies "heredity plus environment."

Among other things, a living animal must have energy. Energy is constantly expended in the manufacture and maintenance of cells, in digestion, respiration, and other internal processes, or in movements of the body or its parts. Since animals cannot obtain energy from the sun, as do plants, they must convert organic matter—plants and other animals—into energy. Species survival obviously requires that some members have the ability to obtain food regularly. Other vital needs, such as a need for drinking water or a place to nest, must also be satisfied until offspring are produced.

In addition to satisfying vital needs, survival entails a successful coping with environmental imperatives. Members of the species must avoid death or unusual debility from such factors as predation, disease, and changes in the physical environment until mating has been accomplished. In short, they must be adapted to their biotic and physical environments. They must have a fitness for survival.

Fitness for survival often entails adaptation to an environmental imperative not mentioned thus far, competition. Competition within a species is likely, since members usually utilize the same need-satisfiers. It can also occur between species. In either case, the adaptation may be migration to another habitat, finding an adequate substitute for the need-satisfier, or elimination of competitors through killing or intimidation.

Another kind of adaptation has been suggested by V. C. Wynne-Edwards—the control of numbers. According to Wynne-Edwards, some species have evolved elementary forms of social organization which function to maintain a fairly constant ratio between numbers and required food supplies. Once this ratio is achieved, innate mechanisms go into operation. Fertility of adult females is reduced, individuals migrate, or there is cannibalism of the young. Amount of space is also regulated by innate mechanisms in some instances. Rats and flour beetles, among others, begin to limit their numbers by a decrease in female fertility and cannibalism before all available space is occupied even when the food supply is held constant. Balance between numbers and both food and space is sometimes achieved through *territoriality*, staking out areas from which competitors are excluded.[1]

In short, fitness for survival means having physical traits or behavior appropriate to the total environment. What an organism *can* do is a function of biological makeup. What it *must* do is a function of its particular needs and the combination of factors external to the organism. The simple adult sponge cannot move about, but it can survive nonetheless. Food is brought by sea currents, and there is no need to avoid voracious predators. A predatory mammal, on the other hand, must not only move about; it must have biological equipment for locating, killing, and digesting its prey. The prey can survive as a species only if some members have traits or abilities that permit evasion, defense, or rapid reproduction.

The adaptive potential of an animal may or may not be fully realized, depending in large measure upon environmental circumstances. Again, environmental demands may call for responses which the animal is incapable of making. One animal, for instance, may find that it can eat a variety of foods in an area where no particular kind is plentiful. Another animal with the same capacities may become habituated to one type of food that is abundant and eat no other. A third animal's digestive equipment may be so highly specialized that it can extract nourishment from only one kind of food; once this food is exhausted, it starves to death in the midst of nutritional plenty.

The discussion thus far suggests that the biological makeup of an animal is strongly influenced by its environment. The environment places a premium upon certain characteristics, physical and behavioral, and animals lacking such characteristics perish or migrate. One biological type is selected; another is eliminated. Thus, the structure and capabilities of an animal reflect its own and its ancestors' adaptation to environmental circumstances. Since environments vary as to opportunities and imperatives, could not varied environments be an important factor in the diversity of life forms? We will explore this possibility.

DIVERSITY AND CHANGE

If environment is a molding force, as we have implied, genetically separate forms should exhibit physical or behavioral similarities if exposed to similar environments. One instance was presented earlier, that of the Tasmanian wolf and the true wolf. There are many other examples of convergent evolution to support our hypothesis. For example, the whale, a mammal, looks and behaves like many deep-water fish. Burrowing mammals in the grasslands of North America, South America, Asia, Africa, and Australia have several characteristics in common, as do other grassland mammals in these geographic areas.[2]

A different test of our hypothesis would be to compare genetically similar animals that have been subjected to different environmental conditions. If the hypothesis is valid, they should exhibit noticeably different characteristics. One variation that is found among the whole range of nonhuman animal life is coloration, an adaptation to varying backgrounds.[3] That is, varieties (subspecies, races) of a species often-times have different coloring and markings that reflect differences in habitat. A specific case is the western rattlesnake. Variations in color and markings of this animal seem to be correlated with differences in the color and composition of the soil.[4]

Given enough time, more than surface features can be affected by differences in environment. After generations of living in caves, fish have lost their fins and eyes. Other cave-dwellers have acquired longer organs of touch or a sharper sense of smell than their relatives in the outside world.[5] Over the course of time, members of the order Chiroptera (bats) have come to vary considerably in body size, dentition, head shape, structure of the tongue, and other physical characteristics. Much of this variation is associated with differences in diet which, in turn, reflect differences in environment. For example, species of fruit bats found in tropical Africa have expansible lips for holding fruit and pointed fruit teeth for piercing the rinds. Bats in Cuba and the Bahamas have pointed heads and long tongues with brush-like tips, features which allow them to extract pollen and nectar from flowers. The common vampire bat (*Desmodus rotundus*), which inhabits both arid and humid regions in Central and South America, is equipped with incisor teeth so sharp that it can inflict painless bites. Its usual food is the blood of sleeping horses, burros, cattle, and occasionally men.[6]

It seems safe to conclude, then, that environments do play an important role in the shaping of biological makeups. Because environments differ, the makeups differ, even among closely related animals. Genetic materials determine in large measure what the structure and functioning of an organism are to be, but environmental factors decide their ultimate fate. Natural selection favors the continuance of some makeups—in greater and lesser numbers—and eliminates others completely.

Another conclusion appears to be warranted: Environmental change is essential to biological evolution. If environments remained static, life forms would be able to change but little. Major changes through new combinations of genetic materials or through mutations could not occur, for the extreme variants would be selected against. In order for the extreme variant to survive, the situation external to it must be altered. A simple illustration will make this point clear.

Over a century ago, numbers of a species of light-colored moth could be found near English settlements. When not in flight, they rested on tree trunks. The trunks, which were covered with lichen, provided an excellent background. The moths' light, spotted coloring blended with the coloring of the lichen. It was difficult for predatory birds to see them. Meanwhile a black variety of this species fared less well. When they rested on the tree trunks, they were readily visible to the birds. The variety, a mutant form, was therefore an oddity.

As the years passed, the black moths became less of an oddity. Their numbers increased, while the number of "normal" light-colored moths declined. The latter became an oddity. This reversal was due to a change in environment. Soot from factories and homes gradually destroyed the lichen and blackened the tree trunks. The coloration of the mutant moths, therefore, provided excellent camouflage; the light-colored insects stood out in stark relief against the black background. Had the environment not changed, natural selection would have continued to favor the original form. It did change, however, and the mutant variety was favored.

If the theory of evolution is valid, it is clear that major environmental changes were necessary for the present diversity of life forms to have evolved. According to the theory, the earliest forms of animal life were simple, fairly uniform organisms. Gradually they became more complex, more diversified. This in itself was change, of course—change in biotic environments. But what made the change in biotic environments possible? Geologic evidence indicates that drastic changes in physical environments preceded the appearance of some of the more complex organisms.

FOSSILS AND EARLY ICE AGES

The oldest known fossils are of a simple, bacteria-like organism that lived approximately 3 billion years ago. A billion years later, organisms were but slightly more complex. From then—about 2 billion years ago—until roughly 720 million years before the present, the fossil record is devoid of animal life. About 720 million years ago there were animals that burrowed like worms and primitive, clamlike brachiopods.[7]

Fossils from the Cambrian Period, which began about 570 million years ago, reflect greater diversity and complexity. By the end of the Cambrian (500 million years ago), representatives of almost every major animal phylum had made their appearance. A major exception was the phylum of chordates, which includes the vertebrates. In other words, there were no fishes, reptiles, birds, or mammals; but marine invertebrates were well established.[8]

Before the appearance of the diversified life of the Cambrian Period, major changes were experienced in much, if not all, of the world. Many pre-Cambrian changes left no imprint upon the geologic record. But two glaciations did. Exactly when these glacial periods began and ended has not been firmly fixed. The first possibly took place before the appearance of the varied forms of 720 million years ago. The second glacial period, the "Infra-Cambrian," ended just prior to the beginning of the Cambrian Period. More is known about the Infra-Cambrian than about the first glacial period, but it is reasonable to assume that the earlier period had somewhat similar effects upon living things.

During the course of the Infra-Cambrian glaciation and the subsequent interglacial period, the face of the earth was changed considerably. Much of the sea was frozen or cooled. As moisture was converted to snow and ice, dry land appeared where shallow waters had once stood or moved. The sheer weight of ice sheets caused depressions in some parts of the earth's surface and elevations in others. Rocks and soils were displaced and moved by icebergs and melting masses of ice.

These processes took place over millions, or tens of millions, of years. During this long period organisms were subjected to many stressful and lethal experiences. Lowered temperatures eliminated many directly or indirectly (for example, by reducing or killing food supplies). Freezing, desiccation, entrapment beneath ice, and burial eliminated many others. Individuals and entire populations were forcibly transported from one location to another by movements of ice, water, and earth.

Not all organisms that survived the glaciations and their aftermaths experienced the same perils. A few may have not been affected at all. Most, it would seem, had to make some unusual adjustments. This they were able to do because of genetic alterations which gave them a potential for adaptation to changed conditions. The changed conditions included not only dangers but also opportunities. Habitats and niches, vacated and newly created, were available. New food chains were forged, and new communities were formed. Organisms able to occupy new habitats were often able to satisfy vital needs and meet environmental demands quite readily. When this happened, populations increased. Concomitantly, variability increased, for there were more possible genetic combinations. Some variants were able to adapt to different ecological niches or to new habitats, and further variability became possible.

We do not know for certain that what we have sketched actually happened. It seems plausible—but processes do not fossilize. Fortunately, there is living evidence that new habitats do contribute to diversity. The evidence is to be found on a group of islands some six hundred miles off the coast of Equador, the Galapagos Islands.

DARWIN'S FINCHES: AN ADAPTIVE RADIATION

Geologically speaking, the Galapagos Islands are relatively young. As land masses, the fourteen islands are younger in origin than some of the life found on them. After they arose from the sea, they were gradually populated by plants and animals brought by movements of the sea and the wind. Each form of life made possible the existence of some other form, and communities and niches developed that could support a variety of living things.

The Galapagos archipelago was one of the places visited by young Darwin when he served as a naturalist aboard the *Beagle*. There he saw many plants and animals that were new to him. Similar kinds of life took on differing structures and functions on the various islands, which were separated by strong currents. Separated from the mainland and, often, from other islands, successful migrants had evolved into new and varied species.

Among the animals Darwin observed were the finches which have since been named in his honor. Mainland finches subsisted upon seeds, as did many of those on the islands. Many others, Darwin noted, had other sources of food. Genetic changes had altered the beaks so that some could eat insects and some were adapted to eating plants. The structure and behavior of variants had, in some instances, been further modified. Several insect-eaters, for example, could catch both flying and crawling insects. The members of one species were essentially woodpeckers, finding their prey beneath the bark of trees.* [9]

By the time of Darwin's visit, more than a dozen species of finches had evolved from the original stock. The new habitat with its unoccupied niches had permitted *adaptive radiation*, a rapid increase in number and variety of a form. Radiation had not occurred among mainland finches, for they lacked the same environmental opportunities.

CONCLUSIONS

To perpetuate its kind, an animal must satisfy its vital needs while meeting environmental demands. This entails the exploitation of life-sustaining opportunities offered by the natural environment and by other organisms to which the animal is related. It also involves successful coping with biotic and natural hazards until reproduction is effected. Such an animal has fitness for survival. It is adapted to its environment.

The adaptive potential of an animal is limited by its inherited biological makeup—modified, perhaps, by genetic alterations. Opportunities and selective forces vary from place to place and change throughout time. Features and behaviors that are adaptive to one set of environmen-

---

* These "woodpeckers" lack the long tongue which is an adaptation of the tree woodpeckers, but they compensate with an interesting kind of behavior. After chiseling a crevice in the bark with its beak, one of these birds will break off a cactus spine and use it to probe in the crevice for the insect.

tal circumstances may be inadequate or maladaptive elsewhere or at a different time. We find, therefore, that phenotypes and genotypes differ in space and in time.

Evolution, then, has been a consequence of change in both environments and genotypes. New genetic combinations or mutations alter the adaptive potential of an animal. More often than not, this animal is less fit for its environment than others of its kind. However, if selective forces and opportunities have changed, its potential for adaptation may be greatly enhanced. The genetic variant sometimes survives conditions lethal to other members of its species. When variants achieved superior adaptation or were the sole survivors of change, the genetic heritage of subsequent generations became different from that of earlier generations. A new species evolved or began to evolve.

Selective forces and environmental opportunities may be lessened or increased for specific types of living things by alterations in the biotic or natural environment. Voluntary or forced movement to a new habitat or community can have the same effect. In either case, evolutionary change may occur. Such change is especially likely when the environment contains empty or poorly filled niches. These niches may allow some variants—and variants of variants—to survive and increase in number, to undergo adaptive radiation.

We now have some idea as to why man's biological makeup and behaviors are different from those of any other animal. The foregoing suggests that our ancestors experienced unusual environmental circumstances and that they were able to adapt to the demands and opportunities of their environment differently from other animals. What were these circumstances and adaptations? Our closest living kin, the nonhuman primates, provide us with clues for answering this question. These animals are the subject of the next two chapters.

NOTES

1. V. C. Wynne-Edwards, *Animal Dispersion in Relation to Social Behavior* (London: Oliver and Boyd, 1962).

2. Illustrations of grassland animals can be found in Peter Farb and the Editors of *Life, Ecology* (New York: Time Inc., 1963), pp. 136–137.

3. See Hugh B. Cott, *Adaptive Coloration in Animals* (London: Methuen & Co., Ltd., 1957).

4. Jay M. Savage, *Evolution* (New York: Holt, Rinehart & Winston, Inc., 1963), p. 81.

5. See Farb and the Editors of *Life, op. cit.*, pp. 132–133.

6. Ernest P. Walker *et al.*, *Mammals of the World*, I (Baltimore: Johns Hopkins Press, 1964), 182–392.

7. *Time*, 86 (November 12, 1965), 100.

8. W. Brian Harland and Martin J. S. Rudwick, "The Great Infra-Cambrian Ice Age," *Scientific American*, 211 (August, 1964), p. 35. Facts about the Infra-Cambrian are drawn from this article, pp. 28–36.

9. For illustrations, see Ruth Moore and the Editors of *Life, Evolution* (New York: Time Inc., 1962), pp. 30–31.

5

Living Primates

What biological makeups enabled our ancestors to survive? What behaviors did they employ? How, in other words, did our antecedents adapt to their environments? Questions of this sort can be answered only by working from the known to the unknown, the approach discussed in Chapter 3. The known in this case consists of other members of the order to which man is assigned, the order Primates.*

To better understand man, living and fossil, increasing attention is being devoted to nonhuman primates. A new specialty, primatology, has developed. Monkeys and apes are being observed in the wilds and in artificially created habitats. Captured and domesticated animals are studied in zoos, homes, and psychological and physiological laboratories. From study and experimentation has come a sizeable body of knowledge about man's nearest living relatives, knowledge that throws considerable light upon human evolution.

The diversity of living primates greatly enhances—and sometimes complicates—our understanding of fossil forms. Fortunately, this diversity includes descendants of the most primitive primate forms. While

---

* It is customary to capitalize "Primates" when referring to the order. No capital is used when reference is made to primates in general or to groupings of primates.

these primates, the prosimians, are not identical with the earliest known primates, they are similar to them in a number of respects. Present-day prosimians, along with living monkeys and apes, provide clues as to how our nonhuman ancestors may have adapted to their environments at different stages of evolution.

In Part III we shall have quite a bit to say about major categories of the order Primates. It is desirable, therefore, to have a nodding acquaintance with primates in general and with living representatives of taxa within the order. This is provided in the present chapter. In the next chapter, the focus will be upon behavior.

A WORD ABOUT CLASSIFICATION

The classificatory scheme used by modern taxonomists is an expansion of the Linnaean hierarchy. The scheme is hierarchical in that it consists of a sequence of levels, and each lower level encompasses a less varied assemblage of animals than the level above. The levels, with the exception of the lowest, are subdivided. Linnaeus' hierarchy consisted of six levels; Cuvier added a seventh. This hierarchy is given below (the placement of man is given in parentheses):

Kingdom	(Animalia)
Phylum	(Chordata)
Class	(Mammalia)
Order	(Primates)
Family	(Hominidae)
Genus	(*Homo*)
Species	(*sapiens*)

Present-day classifications may include as many as twenty-one levels. The additional levels are mainly "super," "infra," and "sub" levels; such as superphylum, infraorder, and subspecies.

The major criterion for ranking is propinquity of descent.[1] The ancestry of a species, for example, is less diverse than the ancestry of a genus, the next higher level.* The genus population is closer geneti-

---

* An animal species is generally considered as a closed breeding system, a population whose members recognize each other as potential mates and seek each other for the purpose of reproduction. Breeding results in viable offspring that, at sexual maturity, are biologically capable of reproducing viable offspring. Because each species is a closed breeding system, members of one species can usually be distinguished from those of another. Recognition of fossil species is often complicated by variation and evolutionary changes.

cally than other populations that make up a family, and so on. All animals are related, but kinship becomes increasingly distant as the hierarchy is ascended.

A population assigned to a classificatory unit is a *taxon* (plural, *taxa*). All vertebrates are assigned to the phylum Chordata, a taxon. As indicated above, a taxon at one level includes populations of taxa at lower levels. Thus, the Chordata include all animals classified as mammals; the class Mammalia includes all members of the order Primates.

GENERAL CHARACTERISTICS OF THE PRIMATES

Animals now classified as members of the order Primates vary considerably both physically and behaviorally. At the same time, there is no single, peculiarly Primate character which is shared by all members.[2] Unlike members of other mammal groupings, the Primates lack conspicuous specializations which readily identify them as members of the same order. Their dentition, for instance, is not specialized for eating flesh, as are the teeth of the Carnivora; or for non-masticatory functions, as are the chisel-like incisors of the Rodentia. Some primates have snouts, but most do not. Some are diurnal in their habits, while a few are nocturnal. Primates live exclusively in the trees, partially in the trees, and wholly on the ground.

How, then, can we define the order Primates? A negative feature, Wilfred E. Le Gros Clark suggests, is the *lack* of specialization. During their evolution, Primates retained primitive features which were lost or modified in other mammals.[3] The limbs of most terrestrial mammals, for example, underwent modifications that gave greater stability during locomotion. Limb bones became less free to rotate, and digits were reduced in number.[4] Primate limbs, on the other hand, continued to be flexible; pentadactylism (having five fingers and five toes) was retained. The clavicle (collar-bone) remained intact in the Primates; it tended to shrink or disappear in some other groups of mammals.[5] Except in a few instances, the Primate dentition remained capable of masticating a fairly wide range of foodstuffs.

After the Primates evolved from a generalized mammalian stock, apparently, the digits gained greater flexibility. Nowadays they are used not only for grasping but oftentimes for manipulating objects. All or most of the digits usually have flattened nails and sensitive pads. The brain, particularly the cerebral cortex, has become larger in Primates than in other land mammals of comparable size. The sense of sight has become dominant over the other senses. Most—not all—primates have relatively large eyes, set in bony orbits, that are capable of conjugate vision (both eyes focus on the same point, thus assuring clear, sharp vision). Compared with other mammals of similar size, members of the order Primates maturate slowly and have long life spans. Relatively few give birth to more than one offspring per pregnancy. Typically both young and adults live in social aggregates of some kind, such as a family or band.

SUBDIVISIONS OF THE ORDER [6]

Living Primates are classified as members of one of two suborders: the Anthropoidea ("manlike") and the Prosimii ("pre-monkeys"). As their name implies, the latter exhibit the greater number of primitive characteristics. (A chart showing the classification of living Primates appears on the end papers in the front of the book.)

Prosimii

The living prosimians are the smallest and simplest of the Primates. Even so, they are quite varied as to structure, behavior, and habitat. The suborder is therefore divided into four infraorders: Tupaiiformes, Tarsiiformes, Lorisiformes, and Lemuriformes. Further subdivisions need not concern us. They will be noted as mention is made of representatives of various infraorders.

As a suborder, living prosimians reflect gradations of evolutionary development between a basic mammalian stock and higher primates. It is this evolutionary continuity we wish to stress. To do so we need but look at the tree shrew (Tupaiiformes), the true lemur (Lemuriformes), and the tarsier (Tarsiiformes).*

Tree Shrew (Family: Tupaiidae; Genus: *Tupaia*; Species: *glis*) Because the tree shrew exhibits characteristics of both the Insectivora and the Primates, it has proven difficult to classify. The problem—which is by no means unique to the tree shrew, as we shall see—derives from the fact that the Linnaean classificatory system is static, while evolution is dynamic. The system, which is the best we have, does not allow for changes which occur as one species evolves into another. Since the tree shrew does not fit neatly into any cateogry, it has been variously classified as a member of the Insectivora, the Primates, and the Menotyphla, an order intermediate to Insectivora and Primates.

---

* The infraorder we do not discuss, the Lorisiformes, consists of two subfamilies, Lorisinae and Galaginae. The former, which includes the slow-climbing pottos, that look like small teddy bears, and the slender loris (no tail, a long body, and stiltlike extremities), are believed to be insectivorous. In captivity, however, they eat almost anything offered them. The Galaginae, or "bush babies," have long bushy tails, range from the size of large mice to small rabbits, and are fast hoppers and jumpers. All members of this infraorder are arboreal and nocturnal.

Tree Shrew

Tarsier

Lemur

Figure 4. Living prosimians.

The nonprimate appearance of the tree shrew is reflected in its generic name, *Tupaia*, which is derived from a Malay word for squirrel. Unlike more advanced primates, the tree shrew has a long bushy tail and a narrow snout with tactile bristles and a moist muzzle. The eyes are located on either side of the long snout, making binocular vision impossible. A further affinity with insectivores is implied by the presence of a throat gland like that found only in insectivores. On the other hand, several muscles or characteristics of muscles which the tree shrew displays are peculiar to other Prosimii. The structure of the middle ear and features of the brain suggest that the tree shrew is a primate. Other features, such as the makeup of the placental and fetal membranes, imply a status intermediate to Insectivora and Primates.

Although the tree shrew's long snout suggests a keen sense of smell, it has a proportionately smaller amount of olfactory apparatus than does a primitive insectivore. Less of the brain is used as an olfactory center, and more is devoted to sight. Compared with insectivores, the tree shrew's brain is fairly large and complex. The dentition is primitive (that is, a type which appeared early in evolution), but primate-like. All digits end in sharp claws. The thumb (pollex) and big toe (hallux) are not fully opposable—they cannot be pressed against the other digits for grasping purposes—but there is a tendency for them to function independently of the other digits.

Most tree shrews live on or near the ground (although they were once thought to be primarily arboreal). Their diet consists primarily of insects. Captive tree shrews eat almost anything, generally holding food in both "hands." These tiny creatures (they weigh only a few ounces) apparently live in small family groups. The gestation period is about four weeks. Two births per pregnancy are typical, and weaning occurs within a few weeks. Like other mammals, the female seemingly experiences estrus (period of sexual "heat").

Lemur (Superfamily: Lemuroidea; Family: Lemuridae; Subfamily: Lemurinae; Genus: *Lemur*) Features of the tree shrew suggest a link between two mammalian orders. Characteristics of the lemur imply an evolutionary link between lower mammals and monkeys (German naturalists refer to them as *Halbaffen*, or "half apes"). Like the tree shrew, the lemur has a long bushy tail and a snout with a moist muzzle and sensory whiskers. The lemur's eyes, however, are above its snout; and the eyes are close together. Conjugate vision appears to be well advanced, for lemurs can move with great facility through the trees. Color vision seems to be present, too.

Lemurs are from 12 to 20 inches long (head and body), or about twice the length of the tree shrew. Their adult dentition is typically prosimian: four incisors, two canines, six premolars, and six molars in each jaw.* The digits are quite flexible, and all but one have flattened nails. The single clawed digit is sometimes referred to as a "toilet digit" because it is employed in grooming. Like monkeys, the lemur uses the forward extremities for grasping and manipulating objects. Kinship with monkeys is further suggested by similarities in the size and structure of the brain, mutual grooming activities (removing foreign matter from the coats), and group living. Some lemurs, like some monkeys, inhabit rocky promontories.

The exact range of the lemur's diet does not seem to be known. Vegetable matter is apparently the main source of food, but insects may also be eaten. Mating is seasonal, perhaps only once a year. Gestation lasts about nineteen weeks, and the usual number of offspring is one. For the first two months of life, the infant appears to be relatively helpless, clinging to the mother's belly as she moves about. Weaning takes place at about six months. The life span of the animal that lives in the wilds is not known, but captive lemurs have lived more than twenty-five years.

Tarsier (Family: Tarsidae; Genus: *Tarsius*) Tarsiers, living (one genus) and extinct, are more like monkeys than are the lemurs. Tarsiers have, in fact, sometimes been classified as Anthropoidea. Like higher primates, they have noses instead of moist muzzles; and the upper lip is free and mobile. The foramen magnum is farther forward in the base of the skull than in other prosimians; an upright posture is possible when the tarsier hops. The brain, particularly the visual center, is more highly developed than in the lemur. The digits are mobile, with special pads at the tips that allow the tarsier to cling to flat smooth surfaces. Nails on digits are flat, but two digits of the feet have clawlike nails that are used in grooming. Dentition is not typically prosimian; there are, for example, fewer incisors in the mandible. Unlike other prosimians, the tarsier's eyes are set in complete bony sockets. The eyeballs cannot move in their sockets, but the head can be turned almost 180 degrees in either direction. The long tail lacks the hairy covering of other prosimian tails.

The tarsier derives its name from the unusually long tarsal bones of the foot; they are about the same length as the long bone in the arm. Its eyes are literally larger than its stomach. The enormous eyes enable the tarsier to see insects in dim light (it is nocturnal), and the modified

* The number of different teeth are usually presented in formulae. The adult lemur formula is $\frac{2.1.3.3}{2.1.3.3}$. Figures above the line represent teeth in the upper jaw, beginning with the midline of the face. Figures below the line represent teeth in the lower jaw. The formula thus reads: 2 incisors, 1 canine, 3 premolars, and 3 molars in each half of the jaw. Teeth in both jaws are usually noted because the number may vary from one jaw to the other. The tree shrew formula, for instance, is $\frac{2.1.3.3}{3.1.3.3}$.

foot provides leverage for leaps to catch the insects. This small animal, which is about the size of a very young kitten, can jump four feet or more vertically. .

Because of their nocturnal habits, the tarsiers are difficult to study. They apparently live in pairs, rather than in larger social groups, and eat lizards as well as insects. Mutual grooming has been observed. Mating possibly occurs more than once a year. The females have placentas resembling those of humans and have menstrual cycles, as do higher primate females in general. The length of neither the gestation period nor the period of infant dependency is known, but maturation appears to be rapid. The single youngster per pregnancy is, at birth, well furred, open-eyed, and capable of short hops and some climbing. When the mother moves from place to place, the infant clings tightly to her abdominal fur. For creatures their size, tarsiers are fairly long-lived. One captive female was almost twelve years of age at death.

When all characteristics are considered, the Tarsiiformes appear to be intermediate to the other Prosimii and the Anthropoidea. They are neither fully prosimian nor completely anthropoid. Indeed, some scientists have viewed them as primitive representatives of the prosimian lineage from which the Anthropoidea diverged.

Anthropoidea

As a rule, members of the suborder Anthropoidea have large, complex brains, nails on all the flexible digits, visual acuity, conjugate and color vision, and not too highly developed senses of smell and hearing. Many

A   B

Figure 5. (A) New World or platyrrhine monkey (genus: *Cebus*) and (B) Old World or catarrhine monkey (genus: *Macaca*).

anthropoids have opposable thumbs. Tactile sensations from the finger-tips are integrated in the brain with visual sensations from the eyes. Anthropoids tend to live longer, have longer periods of gestation and infant dependency, and rely more upon complex social learning than do other mammals. Typically, there is but one birth per pregnancy.

The suborder Anthropoidea is usually divided into three superfamilies: Ceboidea, the New World monkeys of Central and South America; Cercopithecoidea, the Old World monkeys of Africa and Asia; and Hominoidea, apes and man. We shall distinguish the first two super-families and then discuss the apes.

Monkeys The Ceboidea or New World monkeys provide an interest-ing example of adaptive radiation and parallel evolution. In a tropical paradise practically free of competition, they evolved into an amazingly varied and colorful variety of arboreal forms. The prosimian stock from which they evolved is believed to be different from that which gave rise to Old World monkeys. There are a number of similarities between the two superfamilies, but many primatologists point out that the sim-ilarities are more apparent than real.

New World monkeys and Old World anthropoids (apes and mon-keys) are broadly distinguished by the manner in which their nostrils are aligned. The former have nostrils widely separated by a broad sep-tum; the nostrils diverge outward, or flare. For this reason, the Ceboidea are often called platyrrhines or Platyrrhini ("broad-nosed"). Man and the Old World anthropoids have parallel nostrils and are sometimes re-ferred to as catarrhines or Catarrhini ("down-nosed").

Another general feature which distinguishes the Ceboidea is denti-tion. Their basic adult dental formula is lemuroid: $\frac{2.1.3.3}{2.1.3.3}$. The other anthropoids, including man, have fewer premolars (dental formula: $\frac{2.1.2.3}{2.1.2.3}$).

Of the two families of Ceboidea, the Callithricidae, or marmosets, are the most primitive. They are unusually small for monkeys—some are about five inches in length, exclusive of a long tail, and weigh slightly more than two pounds. They are the only known higher primates to habitually give birth to two or three infants at a time. Marmosets lack the visual acuity of other monkeys but have a keen sense of smell. The marmoset also has "claws" (modified nails shaped like claws) on all digits and lacks a fully opposable thumb or big toe. It has only two molars on either side of each jaw. Females exhibit some indication of a menstrual cycle. Gestation takes from 130 to 150 days, and the young are sexually mature at an age of 12 to 15 months.

The other family, the Cebidae, have nails on all fingers and toes, but the thumb is either non-opposable or virtually absent. Some cebids are approximately the size of squirrels. Most range in length from about 22 to 36 inches, exclusive of tails, and weigh as much as 20 pounds. Details of brain structure differ, but the cebids parallel the Old World monkeys in brain development and in intelligence. Three genera of Cebidae have long prehensile tails, a feature absent in Old World monkeys. Such a tail serves as a "third hand" for grasping objects or hanging from limbs. It has been suggested that the swampy ground in many parts of the South American tropical forests encouraged this adaptation.

All Old World monkeys supposedly belong to the family Cercopithecidae, which is comprised of two subfamilies, the Cercopithecinae and the Colobinae. The Cercopithecinae include terrestrial and semi-terrestrial monkeys, such as baboons and macaques. The Colobinae are predominantly arboreal and have complex stomachs specialized for digesting leaves and other vegetation. Other Old World monkeys are omnivorous.

All of the Cercopithecoidea have ischial callosities, thickened areas on the rump which permit comfortable sitting in trees. Several have cheek pouches for storing food. Both these features are absent among New World monkeys. Cercopithecoidea range in size from about one to four feet, exclusive of tails. The heaviest, mandrils, often weigh over a hundred pounds. Females experience menstrual bleeding, have definite 27 to 52-day menstrual cycles, and usually give birth to one infant at a time. The young of the larger genera may nurse two years or more.

What the omnivorous cercopithecoids eat often depends upon what the habitat has to offer. Monkeys in the wild have been known to consume such foods as leaves, shoots, tubers, roots, nuts, seeds, berries, fruits, cultivated crops, spiders, insects, eggs, birds, crabs, reptiles, and mammals. With rare exceptions, Old World monkeys live in groups. Many spend their lives in fairly large groups—troops or bands. On the whole, they are vocal animals, communicating and defending territories with hoots and cries, or simply chattering.

Apes (Family: Pongidae) The superfamily Hominoidea includes all living and extinct forms of apes, the family Pongidae, and all living and extinct forms of man, the family Hominidae. *Homo sapiens* is the only living representative of the Hominidae. There are three living genera of Pongidae: the *Hylobates* (gibbons and siamangs, or great gibbons); *Pongo*, a single species of orangutans; and *Pan*, single species of chimpanzees and gorillas.* The chimpanzees and gorillas are African apes;

* There is no universal agreement as to the classification of the Primates. In some schemes the siamangs are considered as a separate genus, *Symphalangus*. The *Hylobates* and *Symphalangus* may be regarded as a separate family, the Hylobatidae. Some writers also classify the gorilla as a separate genus, *Gorilla*, comprised of two species, *gorilla* and *berengei*.

gibbons and orangutans are restricted to southeast Asia. Orangutans, chimpanzees, and gorillas are frequently referred to as "great apes."

The smallest of the apes, the *Hylobates*, resemble the Old World monkeys in body size and size of teeth. Like the Old World monkeys and unlike most other apes in the wild, they have ischial callosities. The gibbons range from about 18 to 25 inches in length and weigh between 11 and 15 pounds. Siamangs are from 5 to 10 inches longer and from 6 to 13 pounds heavier than the gibbons. The upper extremities of the *Hylobates* are unusually long (the arm span of the siamang is about 6 feet), the digits are long and slender, and the thumbs are short and set far back in the palms. These features and small body size enable the gibbons and siamangs to swing hand over hand through the trees—to *brachiate*—with extraordinary agility. They also run along tree branches or on the ground, employing the hind limbs for locomotion and the long upper extremities as balancing poles. Both gibbons and siamangs are omnivorous. The former seemingly live in family groups of two to six individuals; the latter, in small troops of four to ten or more. The gestation period is about seven months, and the single infant is born with little or no fur. Physical maturity is reached in from six to ten years.

The orangutan (Malay for "wild-man-of-the-woods"), many believe, is more closely related to the gibbons than to other great apes. Orangutans and gibbons have unusually long arms, and the ratio of arm length to leg length is very large in both. Both are arboreal and brachiators. There are, however, some notable differences. Visible sexual dimorphism (differences in male and female) is minimal in the gibbons; it is pronounced among orangutans. The male orangutan is, on the average, twice as heavy as the female. He averages about 165 pounds and may reach 200 pounds, while the female averages around 81 pounds. Jaws and teeth, particularly the canines, are proportionally larger in the male. Along with the large jaws are heavy temporal muscles (used for chewing) and a sagittal crest on top of the skull to give these muscles room for attachment. The male's face is hairless, very often, except for long sideburns. This feature, along with a high forehead, gives him an unusually human appearance above the nose.

Orangutans seemingly live in small family groups, though they have been found singly. They subsist primarily upon fruit; but their diet may also include leaves, seeds, bark, eggs, young birds, and shellfish. The gestation period is eight to nine months. The young are apparently nursed for long periods (one in captivity was nursed for six years). Full growth is attained within ten to twelve years, and they may live for thirty to forty years in the wild. Orangutans give evidence of being as intelligent as chimpanzees, but they are introverted by nature and generally die prematurely when captured.

A full-sized (there is a pigmy form) male chimpanzee is at least 6 inches taller than the average orangutan and about 50 pounds lighter. The male chimpanzee ranges from 60 to 67 inches; the female is approximately one foot shorter and weighs about 88 pounds. All in all, sexual dimorphism is less pronounced among chimpanzees than among orangutans. The male chimpanzee has no sagittal crest, and his teeth and jaws are similar to those of the female.

Chimpanzees have been studied more thoroughly than the other great apes. This has been due, in part, to their generally extroverted, noisy, and inquisitive nature. Interestingly, chimpanzees, like humans, have different shades of skin color. Their skins vary from a grayish pink that is almost white, to black; there are also shades of yellow. The amount of hair on the head and body is also variable. Some chimps are bald. As among humans, the hair turns gray with age.

Chimpanzees ordinarily live together in small groups of about three to seven (larger groups have been observed), each of which is headed by an adult male. Their diet consists mainly of fruit and vegetable materials, often supplemented with meat. They will catch and kill small animals, including monkeys; and they have been known to attack and kill fairly large mammals. The gestation period averages about 230 days. Infant dependency lasts about two years, and full growth is reached around the twelfth year. The life span of the chimpanzee in the wild is thought to be forty or more years.

The largest of the Primates, the male gorilla, ranges from about 5 to 6 feet in height. Some have been known to reach 6 feet 6 inches. Noncaptive males are estimated to average 400 pounds; the female weighs about half as much. The male gorilla has a large sagittal crest, huge brow ridges, enormous teeth, and a prominent nuchal crest (ridge across the back of the skull to which neck muscles are attached). The female's skull can hardly be distinguished from that of a male chimpanzee.

Like the chimpanzee, the primate it most closely resembles, the gorilla sleeps and sometimes feeds in trees. It walks across ground on all fours, as does the chimp, using the knuckles of the hands for support. (Monkeys and the orangutan use the flat of their hands for support.) Like the orangutan, the gorilla is unusually quiet as compared with other higher primates. It is mild-mannered—"stoic," according to some observers.

The gorilla's diet appears to be confined to fruit and vegetable materials. So far as is known, it does not kill or eat other animals. The young suckles as long as eighteen months, or even longer; it is apparently dependent for a much longer period. The gorilla young develops about twice as rapidly as a human child. Gorillas have been studied less intensively than several other primates, but they are presumably as intelligent as chimpanzees.

MAN'S CLOSEST KIN

Most—not all—authorities agree that our closest living relatives are the apes. The great apes, they believe, share more homologies (resemblances due to inheritance from a common ancestry) with us than do the monkeys. Evidence in support of this point of view comes from a variety of sources, including comparative anatomy, biochemistry, studies of blood, and serology. We shall look briefly at but some of this evidence.

Anatomically, a number of features distinguish adult Hominoidea from adult monkeys. For one thing, monkeys, like other quadrupedal mammals, have narrow, oval rib cages. The rib cage of an adult hominoid is broad and flat; its vertebrae are more toward the center of the thoracic (chest) cavity. This means that the vertebral column of man and the apes is more toward the center of gravity in an upright posture than is a monkey's spine. The sternum (bone that extends down the midline of the chest) is broader and flatter in the hominoids.[7]

In the monkey the scapulae (shoulder blades) lie to the side of the thorax, lateral to the rib cage. This location contributes to effective use of the forelimbs in quadrupedal locomotion. The scapulae in man and apes are situated to the rear of the rib cage; the shoulder joints are in one plane with the spine.[8] Such an arrangement, in combination with other anatomical features, makes the mechanics of brachiation (hand over hand progression) less difficult for adult Hominoidea than for adult monkeys.

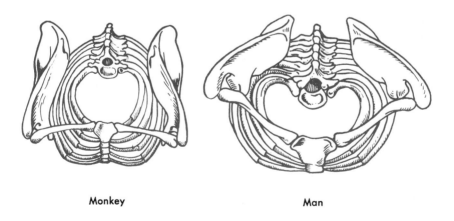

Monkey   Man

Figure 6. Shoulder girdle and thorax of adult macaque and man, looking down from the base of the skull. (Not drawn to scale.)

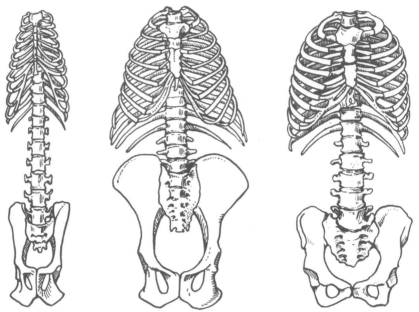

Figure 7. Trunk skeletons of a monkey (*Macaca mulatta*), chimpanzee, and man (Not drawn to scale.)

Monkeys and other mammals that typically employ all four extremities in locomotion normally have greater flexibility of the spine in the lumbar (waist) region than do the hominoids. The former average more lumbar vertebrae than the latter and have a comparatively long waist. Man and the apes, on the other hand, average more sacral (pelvic) vertebrae. As a consequence of this differential distribution of vertebrae, the hominoid pelvis and thorax are closer together than is the case with other primates. The number of cervical (neck) vertebrae does not vary, but they are proportionately longer in man and apes than in most other primates (exceptions: spider monkeys and tarsiers). Since the Hominoidea have no external tails, they have fewer caudal vertebrae than monkeys.[9]

The extremities, particularly the forelimbs, are quite similar in apes and man. Relative to trunk height, the hominoid arm is longer than any Old World monkey arm; the hands are also relatively longer.[10] The entire arm, including the wrist, is said to have greater flexibility than the monkey arm.[11]

Few ape skulls have a cranial capacity which even approaches the lower range of the present-day human skull.* Due to differences in

* Published estimates of brain sizes vary. The smallest human brain appears to have a volume of between 800 and 900 cc.; the largest, about 2,000 cc. The gorilla's cranial capacity ranges from about 420 to 750 cc.

body size alone, the size of a great ape's brain is in excess of that of any monkey. Size, however, may not be the only difference. The brain of the great apes, with its complex convolutions, is more manlike than is that of the monkey.[12] Some scientists have noted that the number of "excess" or "adaptive" cortical neurons—cells over and above those which can be accounted for by body size—in a monkey's brain is less than half the number found in a chimpanzee's brain. Man, in turn, has at least twice as many "excess" neurons as any of the great apes.[13]

Genetic affinities between apes and man have been affirmed by a number of laboratory tests. It has been found, for instance, that patterns of serum proteins distinguish apes and man from the monkeys.[14] Man resembles the apes, especially the chimpanzee, in ABO blood groups, MN blood groups, and with regard to gamma globulin.[15] The African apes (chimp and gorilla) and man are quite similar with regard to chromosomes [16] and hemoglobin.[17]

In stressing similarities between apes and man, we should not lose sight of the fact that monkeys, particularly Old World monkeys, are also like man in many ways. They resemble man so closely, in fact, that they are used in experiments and tests which might be harmful to humans, notably in medical research (including space medicine).[18] Old World monkeys are usually susceptible to some of the same viruses as man, while New World monkeys are not.[19] They experience some of the same physical ailments and infections, such as arthritis, sinus infections, dental diseases, and cancer. Man, monkeys, and apes also share common parasites, such as pinworms, lice, and probably hookworms—part of man's inheritance from his prehuman ancestors, according to one parasitologist.[20]

There is other evidence, some of which we shall have occasion to mention later. It, too, strongly suggests that our genetic ties are with the apes, more probably with the African apes. Along with the similarities, there are of course important differences.

DIFFERENCES BETWEEN MAN AND APES

Man's physical uniquenesses are found mainly in two areas of the body, above the neck and below the waist. Many of these differences are associated in some way with upright posture and bipedal locomotion.

Apes, monkeys, and even some prosimians occasionally stand and move about on their hind limbs. Only man does so habitually, for a number of anatomical reasons. For one thing, the foramen magnum is, in postnatal life, farther forward in the human skull. Thus the head is balanced upon the vertebral column when the upper part of the body is erect. No large neck muscles are needed to hold the head up or direct

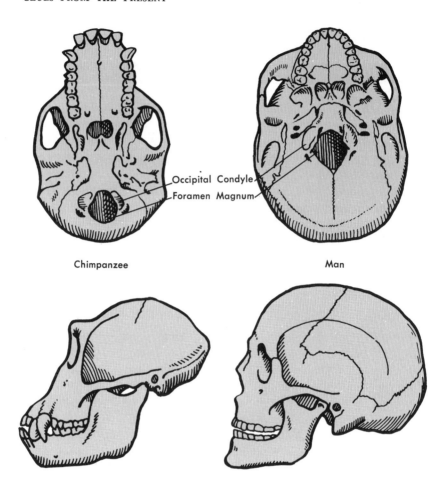

Figure 8. Skulls of chimpanzee and man, basal and side views. (Not drawn to scale.)

the gaze horizontally. Consequently, man lacks the prominent cervical (neck) spines and the high ridge on the rear of the skull, both of which serve as attachments for heavy neck muscles in apes.[21]

The vertebral column of the quadrupedal ape is basically an arch in its appearance. In man, the column is modified with curvatures that give it somewhat of an S-shape when viewed from the side. These curves enable the entire vertebral column to better withstand the weight of the head and viscera and to better maintain balance in an upright position.[22]

An ape's hips are broader and shorter than the hips of a monkey. The human pelvis, especially the upper part (ilium), is even broader and shorter; the upper edge is also more tilted. These differences allow more room for the attachment of muscles that support the trunk in an erect posture and more surface for the attachment of the large leg muscle, the gluteus maximus. Muscles are also brought into a different alignment with the hip joint.[23]

Associated with exclusive use of the hind limbs for locomotion are slight differences in bones and muscles in the lower extremities. Man's leg bones are relatively longer than an ape's, and his foot is specialized for walking. The foot has a heel, an arch, and a relatively large big toe that is aligned with the other toes. In acquiring these supporting features, evolving man presumably lost the flexibility of digits which characterizes the more handlike foot of the ape.[24]

Human hands, freed from any necessity to support the body, are well suited for holding objects and for delicate manipulations. The digits are supposedly more flexible than those of other primates. Proportional lengths of the digits are also better adapted for grasping purposes; the thumb is longer than that of many monkeys, and the fingers are shorter than those of the brachiating apes.[25] Man's hands apparently serve

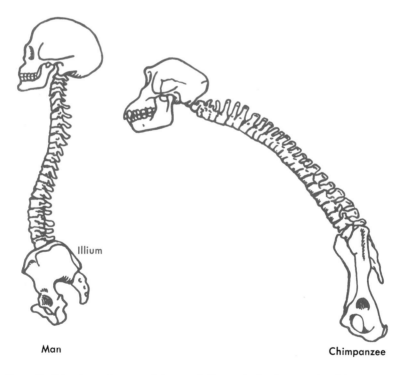

Man

Illium

Chimpanzee

Figure 9. Side views of ape and human skull, vertebral column, and pelvis.

functions similar to the large teeth in apes, such as defense, peeling, and carrying.

Human teeth are smaller than ape teeth. Consequently, the human jaws are not as heavy or as protruding. The teeth are also arranged differently toward the front of the mouth. The human palate and dental arcade are rounded and evenly curved, while the ape's teeth are arranged in an almost rectangular, or U, form. (See Figure 8.) Lighter jaws require less musculature for mastication; less bone surface is required for the attachment of muscles. We find, therefore, that man has nothing which approximates the sagittal crest of the gorilla. The supraorbital torus (heavy ridge above the eyes), which is prominent in the African apes, is absent or comparatively slight in man.

The heavy chewing apparatus of the ape makes for a relatively large face. Its cranium, on the other hand, is relatively small. The reverse is true of modern man's head, which has comparatively more bone structure devoted to the brain case. The human forehead is more vertical, less slanting; and the rear of the skull is more rounded. There is more space in the human skull for brain. This brain is, of course, more complex than that of any ape.

Other differences will be touched upon in later chapters. Those mentioned above will, however, distinguish man from any other animal. With his large brain, upright posture, bipedalism, versatile hands, and generalized primate characteristics, man has been able to successfully adapt to a myriad of environments.

NOTES

1. George Gaylord Simpson, *Principles of Animal Taxonomy* (New York: Columbia University Press, 1961), p. 53.
2. W. E. Le Gros Clark, *History of the Primates*, 5th ed. (Chicago: University of Chicago Press, 1965), p. 28.
3. *Ibid.*
4. Bernard G. Campbell, *Human Evolution* (Chicago: Aldine Publishing Company, 1966), pp. 108–109.
5. Le Gros Clark, *op. cit.*, p. 29.
6. Materials for this section are drawn from the following sources: Ernest P. Walker *et al.*, *Mammals of the World*, I (Baltimore: The Johns Hopkins Press, 1964), 393–478; Carleton S. Coon, *The Origin of Races* (New York: Alfred A. Knopf, Inc., 1963), pp. 119–148; and John Buettner-Janusch, *Origins of Man* (New York: John Wiley & Sons, Inc., 1966), pp. 181–292.
7. Adolph H. Schultz, "Age Changes, Sex Differences, and Variability As Factors in the Classification of Primates," in Sherwood L. Washburn (ed.), *Classification and Human Evolution* (Chicago: Aldine Publishing Company, 1963), pp. 104–106.

8. Adolph H. Schultz, "The Specializations of Man and His Place Among the Catarrhine Primates," *Cold Spring Harbor Symposia On Quantitative Biology*, XV (Cold Spring Harbor, N. Y.: The Biological Laboratory, 1950), 41.

9. Adolph H. Schultz, "Characters Common to Higher Primates and Characters Specific for Man," *The Quarterly Review of Biology*, II (1936), 279–280; "Age Changes, Sex Differences, and Variability . . . ," pp. 102–105.

10. Schultz, "The Specializations of Man . . . ," p. 43.

11. S. L. Washburn and Virginia Avis, "Evolution of Human Behavior," in Anne Roe and George Gaylord Simpson (eds.), *Behavior and Evolution* (New Haven: Yale University Press, 1958), p. 425.

12. W. E. Le Gros Clark, *The Antecedents of Man* (Chicago: Quadrangle Books, Inc., 1960), p. 261.

13. Phillip V. Tobias, "Early Man in East Africa," *Science*, 149 (1965), 25–26; Buettner-Janusch, *op. cit.*, p. 350.

14. C. A. Williams, Jr., "Immunochemical Analysis of Serum Proteins of the Primates: A Study in Molecular Evolution," in John Buettner-Janusch (ed.), *Evolutionary and Genetic Biology of Primates*, Vol. II (New York: Academic Press Inc., 1964), pp. 25–74; Morris Goodman, "Man's Place in the Phylogeny of the Primates As Reflected in Serum Proteins," in Washburn, *op. cit.*, pp. 204–234.

15. Coon, *op. cit.*, pp. 173–175.

16. Harold P. Klinger *et al.*, "The Chromosomes of the Hominoidea," in Washburn, *op. cit.*, pp. 236–239.

17. John and Vina Buettner-Janusch, "Hemoglobins of Primates," in Buettner-Janusch (ed.), *op cit.*, p. 84.

18. Sarel Eimerl and Irven DeVore and the Editors of *Life*, *The Primates* (New York: Time Inc., 1965), pp. 160–163, 173.

19. G. D. Hsiung, F. F. Black, and J. R. Henderson, "Susceptibility of Primates to Viruses in Relation to Taxonomic Classification," in Buettner-Janusch (ed.), *op. cit.*, pp. 1–23.

20. Schultz, "Age Changes, Sex Differences, and Variability . . . ," pp. 78–81; Frederick S. Hulse, *The Human Species* (New York: Random House, Inc., 1963), p. 153.

21. G. A. Harrison *et al.*, *Human Biology* (London: Oxford University Press, 1964), p. 46.

22. Bertram S. Kraus, *The Basis of Human Evolution* (New York: Harper & Row, Publishers, 1964), p. 189; Hulse, *op. cit.*, p. 169.

23. Le Gros Clark, *The Antecedents of Man*, pp. 218–219.

24. Harrison *et al.*, *op. cit.*, pp. 48–50.

25. Schultz, "Age Changes, Sex Differences, and Variability . . . ," p. 65.

6

Primate Sociality

To be human is to be social. From conception until death, social relationships are an integral and essential ingredient of the human condition. The behaviors which distinguish humans from nonhumans can be acquired only through social interaction. Most needs can be satisfied only in a setting of group membership.

How did man become social? Our best chance to find an answer is to search for clues among living nonhuman primates. They, too, are unusually sociable mammals. With but relatively few exceptions, apes, monkeys, and even prosimian species habitually associate with their own kind. The vast majority apparently spend their lifetime as members of at least one structured group, such as the family or the troop. Our ancestors, it would appear, were social long before they became human.

If our ancestors were indeed social at a nonhuman level, it is probable that they associated and lived in groups for reasons not unlike those of present-day primates. Their environments and biological makeups were presumably similar to those of living animals. Genetic inheritance then, as now, necessitated—and permitted—social life. How such inheritance encourages sociality (the tendency to form social groups) among higher primates today is the subject of the section that follows.

BIOLOGICAL BASES FOR SOCIALITY

What causes two or more animals to remain in continuous association? Fish and some mammals seemingly aggregate because there is greater safety in numbers. While the solitary animal may be ready prey, its chances for survival are often enhanced simply by living with others of its kind. Thus, the individual may associate because it is dependent upon the aggregation itself.

In some instances, as we saw in Chapter 4, association is assured by the dependency of one individual upon another. Each party to the association may depend upon the other (mutualism), or the dependency may be one-sided (commensalism). Dependency upon an individual, except in some cases of cooperation, usually stems from biological differences. The animal depended upon is equipped to perform a function the other cannot. Among mammals, association may be continued after physical dependency is outgrown because emotional or psychological needs have been acquired. This is quite evident in the relationships of humans and is probably true to some extent among other higher primates.

Two kinds of biological differences among higher primates suggest themselves as bases for sociality: differences between the immature and the mature, and sexual differences. There is also a possibility that primates may find safety in numbers. Let us look at each of these factors separately.

Dependency of the Young

A characteristic of the order Primates is a tendency toward prolongation of all periods of life. Compared with most mammals, higher primates have longer periods of gestation, mature less rapidly, and live longer. The ape or monkey infant, like the human infant, is born immature but with the capacity for making certain responses. Among these responses are reflexes or reflex-like patterns of sucking and grasping. The latter is of particular importance among monkeys. Since the mother must move from place to place in order to find food or escape danger, it is essential that the young monkey hold on to her. A bonnet macaque infant is able, on the first day of life, to cling tightly and be carried under the mother's belly even when she makes jumps of eight or ten feet.[1] A baboon mother gives some initial support to her infant, but within a day or two it fastens itself to her belly when she travels several miles on the ground each day.[2] Within a few weeks, the baboon infant becomes a "jockey," riding on the mother's back.

Infant chimpanzees in captivity have a relatively weak grasp, though grasp duration is much longer than that of the human infant.[3] While the grasp may be stronger in the wild, it is believed that the infant clings to the mother by holding on with arms and legs when the mother moves about or climbs.[4] A gorilla mother supports her infant with one or both arms for the first few months. However, a month-old gorilla has been observed hanging on by itself long enough for the mother to ascend trees.[5] Ape infants also come to ride on their mothers' backs.[6]

One writer implies that the period of nursing is related to types of food that are available or eaten. Because the youngster's first teeth (the deciduous or "milk" teeth) are small, there are restrictions as to what can be bitten or chewed. As a consequence, some amount of nursing is carried on among great apes for two years or longer.[7] This may be true, but field observations indicate that the ingestion of solid foods often begins early in infancy, as early as two and one-half months among gorillas.* [8]

The mother is more than a source of food and a means of transport. Field observers report rather consistently that ape and monkey mothers clean their infants and protect them from danger.[9] Generally, as in the case of the gorilla, the infant is not allowed to wander more than a few feet. When alarmed, infants typically rush to their mothers and climb aboard or cling to them.

Since higher primates mature at a relatively slow rate, the enforced relation between mother and young is rather extended. Opportunity is afforded for nonbiological needs—if only a need for the companionship of one's own kind—to supplant biological needs. There is ample evidence that social and emotional bonds develop between the mother and her offspring. Great-ape mothers and young often feed together and remain physically close to one another for several years.[10] Among monkeys, the mother-young relationship is known to provide a basis for groupings within the larger band or troop. Members of these groupings feed together, groom one another, and otherwise maintain close social relationships.[11] Within the troop, attention is frequently given the young by adults other than the mother. Care and attention from females is not uncommon, and "paternal care"—care from male adults—has been noted in more than one primate group.[12]

Motherhood apparently has its rewards. The primate mother seem-

---

* According to James A. Gavan in a personal communication to the author, laboratory observations suggest that, at least in some apes and monkeys, the early ingestion of solid food may be related as much to an infant's ability to get away from its mother momentarily as to the size of its teeth. Captive mothers oftentimes do not permit their young to eat solid foods for a considerable time. This sometimes creates nutritional problems, for the mother's milk does not supply all the minerals and vitamins essential to growth. In natural habitats, mothers have more difficulty in controlling the eating habits of their developing offspring.

ingly enjoys social and physical contacts with her infant. But mother-hood is likely to have its perils, too. Carrying or caring for an infant often makes the female more vulnerable to predatory attacks. It is not uncommon, therefore, for her to depend upon another adult for aid or protection. The tree-dwelling mother may rely upon others to alert her to the presence of danger. The terrestrial monkey, as we shall see, may be protected by more than one male if she stays with the troop. If she is unable to keep up with the troop because of her infant, an adult male may drop behind in order to accompany her.[13]

The primate young obviously benefits from association with its mother; the infant could not live without maternal care. The mother's chances for survival are often enhanced by the presence of an adult male. But what might encourage the male to remain in association with the female? One rather prevalent belief is that she is able to keep him near by offering continuing sexual satisfactions.

Sex

Sexual activities among most mammals are confined to brief breeding seasons. Usually, though not always, a breeding season is determined solely by the female's estrous (reproductive) cycle. When ovulation (discharge of the egg from the ovary) occurs, she experiences estrus, or "heat." Then, and only then, is she sexually receptive. Only then, as a rule, is she able to attract or arouse the male sexually. Once mating is effected, the female is not receptive or sexually stimulating again for what may be several months. Bird and mammal males that do remain with the female beyond the breeding season apparently do so for reasons other than the release of sexual tensions.

The ape or monkey male, on the other hand, has been pictured as being attracted to the female for sexual reasons alone. The physiology of the female, according to this point of view, places no real limits upon sexual intercourse. The menstrual cycle is not identical with the general mammalian estrous cycle, in that there is no definite estrus.*

---

* The estrous cycle begins after a quiescent or "anestrous" phase with the devel-opment of an ovum (or ova in most mammalian species) within follicles in the ovaries. While the ovum is maturing, the membrane lining the uterus (the endo-metrium) thickens and hardens. Thickening and hardening of the vagina reaches a maxium at ovulation. When the mature ovum is discharged, the endometrium, which contains mucous glands and blood vessels, breaks down and estrus, or "heat" (behavioral manifestations), ensues. Estrus may be characterized by bleeding or, more often among nonhuman primates, by swelling and discoloration of the sexual skin around the external genital organs. Following ovulation, a hormone promotes renewed growth of the endometrium.

The menstrual cycle also has a pre-ovulatory phase during which the ovum ma-

Consequently, there is no physiologically-determined breeding season among any of the higher primates.[14] Nonhuman primates, like humans, are "prepared to mate at all seasons." If this is true, there is justification for the conclusion that "the powerful social magnet of sex was the major impetus to subhuman primate sociability." [15]

The foregoing, it should be stressed, is one point of view. A quite different conclusion emerges from primate field studies. Jane B. Lancaster and Richard B. Lee, who have analyzed several such studies (fourteen ape and monkey species), state: "It is clear that constant sexual attraction cannot be the basis for the persistent social groupings of primates." [16] The authors of a more recent survey agree. Only among humans, they conclude, is there an absence of estrous cycle in the female and a lack of marked seasonal variation in mating practices.[17]

The belief that there is no breeding season among monkeys and apes springs principally from observations of laboratory and zoo animals.[18] Variations in environment and relationships are more limited in such settings than in natural habitats; and variations, Lancaster and Lee point out, affect the patterning of conceptions and births. Mating and births among monkeys are often timed to coincide with such factors as availability of food, temperature changes, and hours of daylight. There are, in other words, discrete birth seasons or birth peaks (more infants are born in some months than in others) and seasonal variations in mating. Some species do not copulate at all during five months of the year.*

Lancaster and Lee do not believe that African apes have been sufficiently studied to determine whether or not they have birth seasons or birth peaks. It is known, however, that chimpanzees exhibit signs of estrus. As among monkeys, periodic changes in the external genitalia and sexual skin (swelling, coloration) are associated with increased

---

tures. There is, however, no breakdown of the endometrium at ovulation; it is postponed until the end of the post-ovulatory phase, when uterine bleeding occurs. No outward signs mark the onset of ovulation. See G. A. Harrison *et al.*, *Human Biology* (London: Oxford University Press, 1964), pp. 92–93.

* A study of Rhesus monkeys on Cayo Santiago, Puerto Rico, suggests that births and sexual activities among monkeys may be related to seasonal changes in the genitalia of the males. Testes of sexually mature males were found to be large in the warmer and wetter parts of the year and small in the cooler and drier parts. This cycle corresponded to the cycle of copulations and births. That is, copulations occurred when the testes were large; births, when the testes were small. The sex skin of the females brightened during the menstrual cycle and faded after ovulation presumably occurred. Coloration was most intense during the late summer and fall, at the time of year when males had large testes. See Donald Stone Sade, "Seasonal Cycle in Size of Testes of Free-Ranging *Macaca Mulatta*," *Folia Primatologica*, 2 (1964), 171–180.

sexual activities.[19] At such times the female chimpanzee, like the female monkey, may initiate sexual relations with the male.[20] Female gorillas lack a prominent genital swelling, but captive females have been known to exhibit intermittent periods of sexual receptivity.[21]

The weight of evidence indicates that the nonhuman primate female is sexually accessible for a relatively brief period unless she fails to conceive. Sexual activities of the female baboon, for example, are often limited to a few weeks within a one- to two-year period. They are limited mainly because the female does not mate while pregnant or lactating.[22] Does this mean, then, that sex has no effect upon primate sociality?

Reports of field studies leave little doubt that sexual activities are of importance to most monkeys—too important not to have some effect upon sociality. Sex play ordinarily begins early in life, and copulations are usually frequent when the female is in estrus. It has been observed, too, that dominant male apes and monkeys sometimes exclude (perhaps temporarily) other sexually mature males from their groups.[23] The exclusion of potential sexual competitors suggests that one way in which a male may extend sexual satisfactions is to have more than one female available to him. This may account, in part, for the fact that a number of ape and monkey groups that have been observed contained more females than males.[24] Differential mortality may be of equal or greater importance. Among nonhuman primate males, as among mammals in general, the death rate of males appears to be generally higher than that of females.[25] In at least some of the groups in which there are more females than males, copulations take place during all or most of the year.[26]

Year-round sexual relations are possible in areas where ovulation does not have to coincide with changes in environment. Where the food supply is more or less constant and climatic variations are minimal or absent there is no particular adaptive value to seasonal births. At one time, perhaps all primates lived in such areas. Seasonal births may, that is, be a fairly recent adaptation.

Sex, in and of itself, possibly does not account for "persistent social groupings" among all higher primates. On the other hand, there is little reason to discount it as a contributory factor. Perhaps sexual activities are frequent enough to provide the basis for some other sort of bond between the sexes. Mating is more extended among higher primates than among mammals in general, probably because of an unusually long period of female estrus—more than half the estrous cycle among some baboons. When a number of females with varying estrous cycles are part of the group, there may indeed be sex without season so far as the male is concerned.[27]

Another, simpler, reason for primate sociality is that numbers alone promote survival. Present-day primates still find safety in groups, although man has eliminated or diminished the numbers of several primate predators.

AID AND PROTECTION

The individual ape or monkey is not structurally equipped to defend itself against all potential predators. Its major defensive equipment, at most, consists of fairly long incisors and prehensile digits. The latter are sometimes employed in throwing things and wielding weapons (by apes, at least),[28] as well as in grappling. Size may discourage some predators, but not all. Keen eyesight, though of importance in sensing danger during daylight hours, is useless at night. The sense of smell is relatively poor; and the sense of hearing is not acute enough to perceive the presence of snakes, owls, or night-prowling cats.[29] Many predators can outdistance an ape or monkey on the ground, some can climb trees, and a few can fly.

Most of the primates that must cope with predators avoid—or attempt to avoid—attack by utilizing trees, cliffs, or other heights. The orangutan and many species of monkeys rarely come to the ground at all. Those that do spend considerable time on the ground usually retreat to safe heights when threatened.

If apes and monkeys can avoid danger by using trees or other high places, why is there safety in numbers? One obvious reason is that a predatory animal is less likely to go unnoticed by several primates than by one or two.* A brief distraction—for infant care, play, sexual activities—may be fatal if others are not present to emit warning signals. The young, in particular, benefit. They begin life with no understanding of environmental danger signs; they must learn to discriminate between what is a threat to life and what is not.

The young, and often adults, are able to profit from the experiences of other members of the group. A member who has been exposed to a dangerous situation is apparently able to communicate its fear to the rest of the group when a similar situation is encountered again. A pertinent illustration is the behavior of a troop of eighty baboons observed by Irven DeVore. When DeVore began his observations, the troop could be readily approached in a car. This was changed when a para-

---

* Phyllis Jay notes that all kinds of monkeys that have been observed emit alarm calls to warn group members that have not sensed a predator. Also, two species that live in the same area respond to danger signals from members of either species. See "Field Studies," in Allan M. Schrier et al. (eds.), *Behavior of Nonhuman Primates*, II, (New York: Academic Press Inc., 1965), 545.

sitologist shot two of the monkeys with a rifle. Eight months after the shooting, the troop fled at the approach of a car. Not all members of the troop had witnessed the killings, but all responded to the fears of those that had.[30]

Although availability of food and other factors may be of equal or greater importance, the adaptive significance of the group can be partially inferred from some of the variations in group size and social organization that have been observed.[31] Where there is little or no threat from predators, groups tend to be relatively small or loosely structured. Gibbons, for example, live in families of only one adult male, one adult female, and their young offspring. They do not seem to be threatened by predators; but if they were, the predators could be easily avoided by retreat to the tops of trees. Slender branches which support a brachiating gibbon would yield under the weight of a cat. Howler monkeys normally live together in groups that average about eighteen members. They are arboreal, like the gibbon, but they do not brachiate. Tree-climbing ocelots are therefore sometimes a threat. Baboons and other monkeys that live almost exclusively on the ground or spend much of their time in open country often live in much larger groups, sometimes in excess of one hundred.[32]

Common langurs of North India spend their lives in or near trees in groups that average from eighteen to twenty-five. The area in which they live is populated by potential predators, but they seemingly pose no serious threat—in part because the monkeys can quickly take to the trees, in part because there are other prey.* The langurs have what Phyllis Jay terms a "relaxed" type of social organization. A dominance hierarchy exists, but it does not obtrude into normal daily activities. Interaction among adults is free and easy, regardless of dominance status; aggression is rare. When danger threatens, individuals dash into the nearest trees. Sighting of a predator elicits warning cries from any member; but there is no dependence upon larger adult males for protection, as is the case among terrestrial monkeys.[33]

Terrestrial monkeys are of more interest to us than primates adapted primarily to arboreal habitats, for their way of life more nearly approximates that of our prehominid ancestors. The baboons of East Africa, in particular, are believed to face problems which may not be unlike those that confronted our ground-dwelling subhuman forebears.[34]

---

* Washburn, Jay, and Lancaster point out that predation is very difficult to study. Many predators have been eliminated by man, and others are active only at night. Thus, the seeming lack of threat from predators in some places may be more apparent than real. At one time, certainly, areas that sustained primates accommodated animals that preyed upon them. See "Field Studies of Old World Monkeys and Apes," *Science*, 150 (1965), 1541–1547.

BABOONS OF EAST AFRICA [35]

Baboons may eat almost anything that is available, from cultivated crops and insects to bird eggs and the young of other mammals. The latter are usually discovered accidentally. Baboons may surround and kill small mammals should they come across them, but they are neither active nor habitual predators so far as is known. The preferred diet is mainly vegetarian, grass being the single most important food. Food is obtained in daily forages across open country. Nights are spent atop trees or cliffs, safe from such predators as lions, cheetahs, and wild dogs.

On occasion, at least, a baboon troop assumes a definite structure as it moves across open country. The thirty to fifty members of a typical troop are so arranged in space that the females and young (half or more of the troop are "immatures"—infants and juveniles) are flanked by adult and subadult males (large juveniles). Males are distributed to the front and rear of the troop, and some are close to the females and young in the center. A consort pair (adult male and female in estrus) usually stays at the edge of the group. The forward males sometimes move rapidly ahead to a new feeding spot, while the rest of the troop moves slowly along.

Should a predator threaten attack, the females and infants hurry to the safety of trees (troop movement is so directed that safe refuges and water are never too far away). The males continue to walk slowly. Within a short time, the predator confronts a number of ferocious-looking male baboons, with long canines much in evidence and shoulder mantles standing out so that the animals appear larger than they are. This confrontation is usually enough to postpone a carnivore's desire for monkey meat.

The spacing of the troop during movement reflects in large measure the dominance hierarchy of the troop. The females and young, who are given the maximum protection by their central position, are subordinate to the larger, more muscular males (an average adult male weighs approximately seventy-five pounds; an adult female, about thirty pounds). Among the males, those who walk nearest the females and young occupy the highest positions of dominance. Less dominant males and the sub-adults, who apparently have the lowest rank among males, provide the van and the rearguard.

The manner in which members of the troop distribute themselves in open areas affords the greatest protection to those least able to defend themselves, the females and the young. The males exposed to the greatest danger are those who, from a biological standpoint, are most expendable—subadults and the weaker males. Perhaps because baboons do stay together or because of past experiences, most potential predators stay away from them. Baboons, seemingly unconcerned, have been observed near such predators as cheetahs, dogs, hyenas, and jackals. Lions, on the other hand, put them to flight.

Dominance depends in large part upon physical condition and fighting ability. Of considerable importance, too—and it may sometimes outweigh sheer physical strength—are relations among males. A dominant male must be able to elicit the cooperation of other dominant males when necessary. An established hierarchy tends to be quite stable because two or three males will stand together against challenges by younger males or will otherwise come to one another's aid.*

The social organization of a baboon troop not only lessens the possibility of destruction from without; it also serves to reduce the likelihood of disruption from within. Bickering and fighting between juveniles or females usually brings one or more dominant male to the scene to stop the altercation. Potential conflict over privileges or scarce "goods" is minimized, for they are allocated according to position in the hierarchy.†️ The highest-ranking male, for instance, copulates most frequently—or exclusively, in some cases—with females in full estrus.

The group setting shelters the developing young and exposes them to many things they will need to know. Among other things, they learn about grooming, sexual behavior, and patterns of dominance and submission. They learn what to eat, places to drink, where safe refuges are located, and what aspects of their environment are fraught with danger. Through play, the young develop muscular coordination and experiment with behaviors they have observed in others. Juvenile play is also of sig-

* A dominance hierarchy among female baboons has been difficult to identify, in part because there is a tendency for female status to be more variable. Estrous condition, for example, markedly alters the status of a female. She may be the target of aggression on the part of other females when in full estrus if mated by the highest-ranking male. Among other monkeys, female hierarchies not only develop but are directly relevant to the male hierarchies, in that an offspring's rank is in part determined by his mother's rank. See, for example, Donald Stone Sade, "Determinants of Dominance in a Group of Free-Ranging Rhesus Monkeys," in Stuart A. Altmann (ed.), *Social Communication Among Primates* (Chicago: University of Chicago Press, 1967), pp. 99–114.

† Dominance would presumably affect the distribution of food if it were scarce, but no shortage of food is reported in the field studies of baboons discussed here. However, it was observed that when food was thrown to some baboon groups, one and only one male in a group had a consistent priority of access to the food. Similar behavior has been observed among other monkey species. It seems evident that a dominant male will sometimes take food when other males are around even though he is not hungry. If this is the case, taking food could be one means of reinforcing rank. That is, the dominant male may not want the food; but to allow another male to take it would be an admission of weakness, a failure to exercise the rights of high rank.

nificance in preparing males for their adult roles, for it is in play that they learn how to fight.

Before the individual reaches maturity (the male reaches full maturity in the eighth year), he has learned fairly satisfactorily what he can and cannot do in relation to his social and physical environments. He has certain expectations of others because they occupy particular positions in the group organization, and he seemingly knows they have certain expectations of him. The individual is, in a word, socialized. Through group living, the young baboon is transformed into a social creature.

Was it thus with our ancestors? The details and the problems were no doubt different. There is little question, though, that group life was as essential to the survival of prehominids as it is to baboons. Even today, the isolated baboon—a youngster that has strayed, an adult too ill or hurt to keep up with the troop—is likely to be killed by a predator. Social organization of some kind was also essential among prehominids for them to cope with their environments and live together year after year.

FACTORS FACILITATING SOCIALITY

It seems safe to conclude that the biological makeup of higher primates encourages sociality. Infant immaturity and slow maturation necessitate a relatively long period of care from at least one adult. Sexuality requires further study,[36] but there is reason to suspect that it functions to some extent as a "social magnet" or cohesive force. Limited structural or sensory specializations for defense make group living desirable in some areas and essential in others. As a consequence of prolonged association, nonbiological needs develop which function as additional cohesive forces.

The primate biological makeup also *permits* behaviors which facilitate group living. The complex primate brain allows baboons and other higher primates to learn techniques for avoiding and reducing frictions that develop in group situations. The most striking example of this in the baboon troop is role-learning. Each baboon comes to know what is expected of him and of others in terms of age, sex, and dominance positions. Behavior thus becomes more predictable in recurrent situations; social relations can proceed more smoothly than otherwise. Learning of this sort involves self-control. The primate brain is structured to make the checking of inappropriate responses possible.

Self-control and social-control and the learning of social behavior require communication between group members. Apes and monkeys are equipped to transmit meanings in a variety of ways. They can make and hear a variety of sound signals, including vocalizations, beating of the chest, grinding of the teeth, and "drumming" (striking the ground or the base of a tree with the palm of the hand or foot). The number of sound signals varies from species to species and sometimes within species, but most species that have been studied have at least ten. Exactly what meanings are transmitted by such sounds is not fully known. It is known that they serve to maintain contact among members that are spread out and to communicate feeling states, such as distress, aggression, and annoyance.[37]

Visual communication is more complex and probably of greater importance in interpersonal relations. Postures and movements that utilize the entire body or parts of it are employed to communicate aggression, submission, willingness to mate, readiness to depart, uneasiness, and an invitation to groom. Mobile lips not only increase the range of sound signals but also the repertory of facial expressions. Such expressions include baring the teeth and movements of the eyes, lids, and brows. Lip positions, alone or in conjunction with other signals, can indicate threat, fright, friendliness, and perhaps sorrow.[38]

Meanings are undoubtedly transmitted through tactile signals, but these meanings are difficult to discover. The hands are used to initiate physical contact, to inflict pain (by pulling fur, for example), and in grooming. Grooming itself may reflect friendliness, sexual interest, or rank position. Physical contacts which may function as communicative techniques include biting, embracing, kissing, and nuzzling parts of the body.[39]

The foregoing should be considered as suggestive of communicative possibilities among higher nonhuman primates, not as an exhaustive listing. Little or nothing is known of the role of olfaction, which is of importance among other mammals; [40] and more intensive studies need to be made of auditory, visual, and tactile communication. There is little doubt, however, that apes and monkeys are capable of emitting and receiving a variety of signals that can be used to control and cement social relations.

POSSIBLE CONSEQUENCES OF SOCIALITY FOR BIOLOGICAL MAKEUP

Clearly, the primate biological condition has important consequences for group living and social behavior. Is it also possible that the reverse is true, that sociality has consequences for the primate biological makeup? Such a possibility is fraught with significance, but how can it be examined or proved? Perhaps if we look at other forms of life, we can come up with some clues. Let us begin with a brief examination of some of the lower primates.

Sociality Among Prosimians

Nocturnal prosimians are possibly solitary animals, though we are not certain. Most of the species that operate during daylight hours apparently live together in groups of at least family size.[41] The larger groups tend to be fairly stable despite fighting when the females are in estrus. Even the most primitive primates, the tree shrews, manifest a desire to be near one another. They have been known to crowd into very cramped quarters in order to sleep or rest together. Individuals of more advanced genera not only seek contact with one another (regardless of sex) but also engage in mutual grooming.[42]

The prosimians most thoroughly studied in the wild are species of Lemuroidea on the island of Madagascar. These lemurs sometimes live in troops which are, as among higher primates, comprised of individuals of both sexes and all ages. Like higher primates, they evidence affectional ties between mother and young; and newborn infants elicit attention from other members of the troop. Grooming (with protruding incisors, or "tooth-scrapers," rather than hands) and play occupy considerable time, as is the case with higher primates.[43]

Significant differences exist between prosimians and most higher primates in sexual activities and means of communication. Among lemurs, copulations are usually limited to two or three months a year.[44] One observer believes that the mating season of two troop-living species is only two weeks.[45] Presumably, females come into estrus at varying times during a two- to four-month breeding season. Prosimians communicate vocally and through visual signals. Unlike higher primates, seemingly, they also employ scent signals. Urine, feces, and the secretions of specialized glands mark territorial boundaries, distinguish rivals and females in estrus, and play a role in dominance-submission activities.[46]

Sexuality is hardly a "social magnet" among prosimians. Lemurs of both sexes are sexually quiescent most of the year; the male, as well as the female, has a seasonal cycle.[47] Tree shrews, which breed more frequently throughout the year than do lemurs, live in smaller, less stable groups.[48] Both tree shrews and lemurs are likely to exhibit aggressive behavior during mating seasons, indicating that sex is more likely to be a disruptive than a cohesive force.

Infant dependency is apparently a cohesive factor, at least among lemurs. Among the larger-sized lemur species, infants nurse for no less than five months.[49]

It is doubtful that prosimian grouping serves any protective function today, though it may have at one time. The prosimian species that have survived into modern times are generally free of serious predatory threat. Some, like the tree shrew, are small and quick, seemingly able to evade

108

most carnivores. Most prosimians are now established in areas where there are few if any predators. Lemurs, for example, live only on islands (Madagascar, primarily) where there are no large carnivores.

What can the prosimians tell us about the possible influence of sociality upon the higher-primate physical makeup? Fossil evidence suggests that the prosimian ancestors of the higher primates were physiologically and behaviorally similar to living prosimians. If they were, sociality evidently preceded the evolution of monkeys and apes. It would seem, then, that the biological factors which encourage groupings among higher primates today were not necessarily the factors which initiated primate sociality. The same conclusion emerges from observations of animals that have origins more ancient than the Primates. Species of terrestrial, diurnal insectivores found over most of Africa live in small groups. In some regions these small animals are thought to live in "colonies." [50] Birds, fish, and insects sometimes habitually spend most or all of their lives in a family group, school, or society.

The fact that sociality and limited breeding seasons occur together at the prosimian level implies that extended mating may be a *consequence* of social life, rather than a causal factor. Since infant immaturity is often less pronounced and generally less lengthy among lower animals, it, too, may be a consequence. Group life, in other words, possibly solved certain important problems which permitted these traits to appear. Once they appeared, extended mating and infant immaturity proved to be adaptive; they contributed somehow to the survival of monkeys, apes, and evolving man, and so they were retained.

Do we humans owe our ability to mate at all seasons to social living among our remote ancestors? Is the prolongation of human childhood a by-product of millions of years of group life? These are intriguing questions—but where do we find the answers? We have no alternative but to reason from the known to the unknown. From what we know about living animals, we should be able to make some reasonable deductions. First, let us try to discover what important problem or problems continuous association might solve which would permit extended mating to develop.

Group Life and Mating Problems

Continuance of a bisexual species is dependent upon contacts between sexually mature males and females. Generally contacts must be made during a relatively brief breeding season. When members of both sexes live together in more or less permanent groupings, a mate is at hand when the female ovulates. A solitary animal, on the other hand, must seek its mate. To locate a mate separated by space and possibly by natural obstacles to perception, such as trees, brush, grasses, and hills, requires highly developed sensory equipment. Attracting and perhaps identifying a potential mate may call for stereotyped behaviors, such as calls or songs, nest-building, or "dances."

It is obvious that mating problems are greatly simplified by group life. As a consequence, survival of the species is enhanced. Time and energy otherwise spent in mating can be devoted to the satisfaction of other needs. Too, fertilization is virtually assured. A solitary animal in search of a mate may be delayed beyond the breeding season by distance or obstacles; or it may be killed, captured, or seriously injured while searching.

Group living also alleviates the necessity for sensory and behavioral specializations to facilitate location and identification of mates. Sensory equipment, neural pathways, and areas of the brain can develop differently and be employed for other purposes. Neither a highly developed sense of hearing nor an acute olfactory sense, for example, is prerequisite to breeding. There is therefore a possibility that other senses will attain greater significance. Perhaps it was as a result of these circumstances of group living that primates originally began to rely more heavily upon vision, respond more readily to tactile stimuli, and develop greater brain complexity. Developments along these lines may have aided arboreal adaptation, which in turn furthered and hastened trends toward keener vision and a more complex neural makeup.

Chemical changes detectable by highly developed olfactory organs signal the onset of estrus in the females of many mammalian species. As dog owners well know, the scents may attract males from a considerable area. Mammals that live in heterosexual groups have no particular need for such cues. The males may, indeed, be insensitive to them. This is the situation typical of the order Primates. Even prosimians, which utilize olfactory signals to some extent, apparently perceive estrus only at very close range.[51]

Breeding among higher nonhuman primates is frequently linked with visual cues. Females of several species exhibit sexual swelling or coloration of the sexual skin when they are in estrus. At such times, the female may actively seek copulation with one or more males. Similar behavior is exhibited by females of species that experience no physical changes visible to human observers during ovulation. Still others manifest no outward signs of estrus, physically or behaviorally, except for permitting copulation.[52]

Such variability in manifestations of ovulation among apes and monkeys suggests an evolutionary trend which reached its climax in the human female. It implies that continuance of our ancestral line came to depend less and less upon estrus. By the time man appeared, all indications of estrus—physical and behavioral—had disappeared. According to Clellan S. Ford and Frank A. Beach, the human female in Western society is presently sexually more responsive at about the period of menstruation than at ovulation. Even this periodicity may be related to cultural patterns.[53] Accordingly, copulation must be regular and frequent if human females are to be fertilized.[54]

Extended mating, then, can be adaptive under certain circumstances. It assures a coincidence between ovulation and impregnation when mating is not dictated by hormonal changes. But the separation of estrus and sexual behavior could not have occurred unless mating was regular and frequent. Regular and frequent mating obviously requires more or less continuous association between members of both sexes. And so we are back to sociality once again. How did sociality permit this kind of mating to develop? Variations in primate estrous cycles offer what may be our best clues.

Bases for Extended Mating

Birth peaks, you will recall, are often associated with cyclic environmental changes. A major function of estrus, therefore, is to time conception so that the young will be born and develop when conditions are favorable to their survival. This function is not universal among higher primates. Some species, both ape and monkey, have no birth peaks. In some parts of the world, apparently, marked seasonal changes are either absent or, if present, pose little threat to the young. Estrous cycles are free to vary—or disappear.

Another function of estrus is twofold. It serves to attract a male, and it triggers a response in the male that allows copulation to be effected during the brief time the egg is in position for fertilization. Group living, as we saw, eliminates the need to attract a male. This means, then, that in some environmental settings the sole function of estrus is sexual arousal of the male. Elimination of this function would relieve the necessity of estrus.

How can a male be motivated to sexual activity if there is no estrus? There can be but one answer: He must *learn* to respond to sexual cues. He can learn because sexual behavior is not regulated by the autonomic nervous system. Rather, it is controlled largely by the cerebral cortex. Sexual behavior is subject to voluntary control. If cues must be learned, anything within the individual's experience can serve to motivate intercourse. When the intervals between copulations are relatively brief, memory of a prior encounter may be sufficient in itself. The variety of sexual cues that can be learned is quite evident among humans. Many cues have no direct connection with the female. The connection is

111

usually made in interpersonal learning situations and through exposure to a culture which attaches sexual significance to certain acts, events, and phenomena.

While nonhuman primates are not exposed to a culture (as usually defined), there is every likelihood that they learn to associate varied stimuli with sexual behavior. A young baboon, for instance, has frequent occasion to observe that sexual intercourse and swelling of the female's genitalia are related. Both males and females may learn that a certain posture or behavior on the part of the female is an invitation to mate. The female, as well as the male, learns through experience to associate tactile stimuli with intercourse. There is suggestive evidence that strong sexual response in the nonhuman female occurs during as well as prior to intercourse. Some male apes have reportedly learned to arouse the female by stimulating her genital area orally or with the hand.[55]

Sexual motivation may, on occasion, stem from social pressures. As we noted earlier, dominant baboon males tend to copulate more frequently at certain times than do males lower in the hierarchy. This could be considered a reward of dominance; it may also be somewhat of an obligation. That is, the dominant male may copulate more often than he desires—just as he may take food he does not want—in order to maintain or reinforce his rank. Two other facts may be of significance in this connection. Not all copulations terminate in ejaculation; and a common sign of submission, by both males and females, is assumption of the copulatory posture of the female.* In short, the group is a source of sexual learning and of sexual motivation. Individuals are constantly at hand to serve as models and to direct and check impulses. Sexual behavior is generally visible, and members of the opposite sex are nearby to stimulate sexual memories and appetites. Social pressures possibly encourage sexual behavior on the part of at least some members.

Given these conditions, estrus serves no adaptive function. Mating is then limited, not by hormonal changes, but by forces which impinge upon the consciousness. Psychological and emotional factors assume

---

* Such behavior has been observed not only among baboons but among other genera of monkeys. John E. Frisch, reporting on Japanese macaques, said: "Repeated observations lead one to believe that [mounting] is not necessarily connected with the satisfaction of a sexual urge but rather with the expression of dominance." Frisch tells of an adult male taking a tangerine "which belonged by right to an animal of higher rank. The offender fled but, unable to escape, he apparently chose to surrender and did so by assuming the attitude of receptivity of the female. The higher-rank male at once mounted the offender, and the whole incident was closed." Early in the morning, animals of higher rank briefly mounted those of lower rank "so rapidly that it amounts to little more than a salutation. Apparently this behavior serves constantly to re-emphasize the rank order and to make the whole group recognize and support the dominance hierarchy." See "Research on Primate Behavior in Japan," *American Anthropologist*, 61 (1959), 588.

greater importance. Even at the nonhuman level, females have been known to reject (when in estrus) the sexual advances of males they did not particularly like.

So far as we know—and our knowledge is incomplete—nonhuman primates still experience estrus. It seems evident, however, that estrus no longer serves its usual purposes and that there is a tendency toward sex without season. We can see this in the lengthy estrus and frequent mating of baboons.* In captivity, the female baboon experiences sexual swelling for ten to twelve days on the average before full estrus is reached. For about eight days, she is in full estrus, or maximum swelling. Deturgescence then takes place during the next one and one-half to five days.[56] In natural habitats, sexual intercourse may occur during any phase of swelling. It may be initiated when swelling is *not* visible.[57]

CONCLUSIONS

The order Primates is an unusually sociable category of mammals. Animals making up this order are, by and large, adapted to their environments not only in terms of biological makeup but also through groupings and social behavior. Some, as members of structured groups, are able to exploit hostile terrestrial habitats. Early primate sociality, it would appear, enabled our ancestors to make the transition from trees to the ground.

The relationship between biological makeup and group living is reciprocal. Primate sociality is necessitated by some aspects of the makeup and encouraged by others. It is facilitated by sensory equipment and an inherent ability to make and respond to varied signals, most of which seem to be learned. The biological makeup is affected by group living in that the latter mutes and eliminates some of the selective factors normally detrimental to the biological success of the solitary mammal. Genetic changes which might have been maladaptive to less social animals were able to become established among primates. Because they did, the course of primate evolution was somewhat unique.

Among the possible evolutionary changes associated with group existence was a lessened dependency upon the sense of smell, with consequent improvement in visual efficiency. Other factors were also involved in furthering improvement of the sense of sight, as we shall see in a later chapter. However, living in heterosexual groups eliminated one of the major selective factors for highly developed olfactory equipment,

---

* Baroness Jane van Lawick-Goodall reports that the "sexual attraction" of a chimpanzee female normally lasts about ten days. But there are exceptions. This attraction persisted in one female she observed for almost five weeks. "During that time, most of the males we know were her constant escorts" (*My Friends the Wild Chimpanzees* [Washin n, D.C.: The National Geographic Society, 1967], p. 134).

the need to locate a mate. The group may also have afforded some protection to those animals unable to pick up the scents of distant predators.

With the loss of olfactory acuity, scents of estrus could no longer sexually arouse the primate male. Visual cues—sexual swelling or coloration, or behaviors—were utilized. Responses to such cues had to be learned, but the group provided a setting in which the learning of several types of behavior was encouraged. There were models to imitate and teachers at hand to impel and direct actions through tactile, vocal, and visual signs.

Learning was no doubt encouraged and furthered by the mere fact of association. One organism is always a potential source of stimulation or stress for another organism. Relationships are less conflictive and more satisfying if the animals involved are able to anticipate responses—that is, learn that certain signs precede certain behaviors. Smoother relations also ensue if group members learn what to do, or to avoid doing, in recurring situations.

As the ability to learn increased, more and more behaviors—including sexual behavior—came under the control of the central nervous system. Concomitantly, copulations or attempted copulations became more frequent. Sexual excitement was prompted less and less by cyclic hormonal changes, so memory or appropriate external cues could initiate sexual activities at any time. Cortical control of sexual behavior created a unique opportunity: sex could be used for nonsexual ends. Humans have exploited this opportunity to the fullest. Baboons and other monkeys may exploit it to some extent by employing sex as a means for emphasizing and reinforcing positions of dominance.

Frequent sexual intercourse eliminated a need for any indication of estrus. When mutations occurred which did away with sexual swelling or behavioral manifestations of ovulation, species could still be continued. Sexual relations were regular enough to insure fertilization of an adequate number of ova. Some suggestion of this tendency is found among nonhuman primates today, suggesting that sex without season probably predates *Homo sapiens* by millions of years.

If human sexuality is, in large measure, a consequence of group living, as our analysis leads us to believe, there is a possibility that other human traits are also consequences. Infant immaturity, we suggested earlier, may be among the by-products of sociality. In the next chapter, we shall explore this possibility.

NOTES

1. Paul E. Simonds, "The Bonnet Macaque in South India," in Irven DeVore (ed.), *Primate Behavior: Field Studies of Monkeys and Apes* (New York: Holt, Rinehart & Winston, Inc., 1965), p. 192.

2. K. R. L. Hall and Irven DeVore, "Baboon Social Behavior," in DeVore, *op. cit.*, p. 83; Sherwood L. Washburn and Irven DeVore, "Social Behavior of Baboons and Early Man," in Washburn, *Social Life of Early Man* (Chicago: Aldine Publishing Company, 1961), p. 96.

3. William A. Mason, "The Social Development of Monkeys and Apes," in DeVore, *op. cit.*, p. 519.

4. Vernon Reynolds and Frances Reynolds, "Chimpanzees of the Budongo Forest," in DeVore, *op. cit.*, p. 420.

5. George B. Schaller, "The Behavior of the Mountain Gorilla," in DeVore, *op. cit.*, p. 350.

6. Jane Goodall, "Chimpanzees of the Gombe Stream Reserve," in DeVore, *op. cit.*, p. 458.

7. Adolph H. Schultz, "Some Factors Influencing the Social Life of Primates in General and of Early Man in Particular," in Washburn, *op. cit.*, pp. 69–70.

8. Schaller, *op. cit.*, p. 350.

9. See, e.g., Clarence Ray Carpenter, "Societies of Monkeys and Apes," in Charles H. Southwick (ed.), *Primate Social Behavior* (New York: D. Van Nostrand Co., Inc., 1963), p. 46.

10. Schaller, *op. cit.*, p. 351; Reynolds and Reynolds, *op. cit.*, p. 421.

11. Sherwood L. Washburn, Phyllis C. Jay, and Jane B. Lancaster, "Field Studies of Old World Monkeys and Apes," *Science*, 150 (1965), 1541–1547.

12. *Ibid.*; Junichiro Itani, "Paternal Care in the Wild Japanese Monkey, *Macaca fuscata*," in Southwick, *op. cit.*, p. 92.

13. Hall and DeVore, *op. cit.*, p. 86.

14. John Buettner-Janusch, *Origins of Man* (New York: John Wiley & Sons, Inc., 1966), p. 357.

15. Marshall D. Sahlins, "The Origin of Society," *Scientific American*, 203 (September, 1960), 76–87.

16. Jane B. Lancaster and Richard B. Lee, "The Annual Reproductive Cycle in Monkeys and Apes," in DeVore, *op. cit.*, p. 513.

17. Washburn, Jay, and Lancaster, *op. cit.*, p. 1544.

18. Lancaster and Lee, *op. cit.*, pp. 486–487.

19. Clellan S. Ford and Frank A. Beach, *Patterns of Sexual Behavior* (New York: Harper & Row, Publishers, 1951), pp. 208–209.

20. G. A. Harrison *et al.*, *Human Biology* (London: Oxford University Press, 1964), pp. 92–93; Reynolds and Reynolds, *op. cit.*, pp. 417–419; Goodall, *op. cit.*, pp. 449–450.

21. Schaller, *op. cit.*, p. 352.

22. Irven DeVore, "The Evolution of Social Life," in Sol Tax (ed.), *Horizons of Anthropology* (Chicago: Aldine Publishing Company, 1964), p. 31.

23. Clarence Ray Carpenter, "The Howlers of Barro Colorado Island," in DeVore, *Primate Behavior* . . . , p. 268; Schaller, *op. cit.*, p. 339; Harrison *et al.*, *op. cit.*, p. 94.

24. Charles H. Southwick, Mirza Azhar Beg, and M. Rafiq Siddiqi, "Rhesus Monkeys in North India," in DeVore, *Primate Behavior* . . . , p. 127; Phyllis Jay, "The Common Langur of North India," in DeVore, *Primate Behavior* . . . , p. 207; Irven DeVore and K. R. L. Hall, "Baboon Ecology," in DeVore, *Primate Behavior* . . . , p. 40; Clarence Ray Carpenter, "The Howlers . . . ," p. 267; Schaller, *op. cit.*, pp. 334–335; Harrison *et al.*, *op. cit.*, p. 95.

25. Schultz, *op. cit.*, p. 77.

26. Lancaster and Lee, *op. cit.*, pp. 494–495; DeVore and Hall, "Baboon Ecology," p. 51.

27. Carpenter, "Societies of Monkeys and Apes," p. 43.

28. Adriaan Kortlandt and M. Kooij, "Protohominid Behavior in Primates (Preliminary Communication)," *Symposia of the Zoological Society of London*, No. 10 (August, 1963), pp. 65–75.

29. Schultz, *op. cit.*, p. 61.

30. Sherwood L. Washburn and David A. Hamburg, "The Study of Primate Behavior," in DeVore, *Primate Behavior* . . . , pp. 3–4.

31. Cf. J. H. Crook and J. S. Gartlan, "Evolution of Primate Societies," *Nature*, 210 (1966), 1200–1203; J. M. Warren, "Discussion of Social Dynamics," in Stuart A. Altmann (ed.), *Social Communication Among Primates* (Chicago: University of Chicago Press, 1967), p. 255.

32. M. R. A. Chance, "The Nature and Special Features of the Instinctive Bond of Primates," in Washburn, *op. cit.*, pp. 18–19; Clarence Ray Carpenter, "The Howlers . . . ," pp. 268, 278.

33. Jay, *op. cit.*, pp. 216–217, 248.

34. Irven DeVore and S. L. Washburn, "Baboon Ecology and Human Evolution," in F. Clark Howell and François Bourlière (eds.), *African Ecology and Human Evolution* (Chicago: Aldine Publishing Company, 1963), p. 365.

35. Materials presented in this section are drawn from Sherwood L. Washburn, "The Social Life of Baboons," *Scientific American*, 204 (June, 1961), 62–71; and from articles previously cited: Hall and DeVore, "Baboon Social Behavior"; Washburn and DeVore, "Social Behavior of Baboons and Early Man"; DeVore, "The Evolution of Social Life"; DeVore and Hall, "Baboon Ecology"; and DeVore and Washburn, "Baboon Ecology and Human Evolution."

36. Washburn, Jay, and Lancaster, *op. cit.*, p. 1544.

37. Peter Marler, "Communication in Monkeys and Apes," in DeVore, *Primate Behavior* . . . , pp. 555–569; Thomas T. Struhsaker, "Auditory Communication Among Vervet Monkeys (*Cercopithecus aethiops*)," in Altmann, *op. cit.*, pp. 318–323.

38. Marler, *op. cit.*, pp. 569–580; R. J. Andrew, "The Displays of the Primates," in John Buettner-Janusch (ed.), *Evolutionary and Genetic Biology of Primates*, II (New York: Academic Press, Inc., 1964), 294–299.

39. Marler, *op. cit.*, pp. 550–555.

40. *Ibid.*, pp. 547–550; Andrew, *op. cit.*, pp. 259–270.

41. François Bourlière, "Patterns of Social Grouping Among Wild Primates," in Washburn, *op. cit.*, pp. 3–5; Buettner-Janusch, *op. cit.*, pp. 181–242.

42. Andrew, *op. cit.*, pp. 241–243.

43. Alison Jolly, "Lemur Social Behavior and Primate Intelligence," *Science*, 153 (1966), 501–502.

44. A. Petter-Rosseaux, "Reproductive Physiology and Behavior of the Lemuroidea," in Buettner-Janusch, *op. cit.*, p. 130.

45. Jolly, *op. cit.*, p. 502.

46. Jean Jacques Petter, "The Lemurs of Madagascar," in DeVore, *Primate Behavior* . . . , pp. 253–255; 259–264.

47. Ernest P. Walker *et al.*, *Mammals of the World*, I (Baltimore: The Johns Hopkins Press, 1964), 401; Petter-Rosseaux, *op. cit.*, p. 100.

48. Walker, *op. cit.*, p. 396.

49. Petter-Rousseaux, *op. cit.*, pp. 124–125.

50. Walker, *op. cit.*, p. 138.

51. Andrew, *op. cit.*, pp. 268–269.

52. Simonds, *op. cit.*, p. 193; Carpenter, "The Howlers . . . ," p. 279; Schaller, *op. cit.*, p. 352.

53. Ford and Beach, *op. cit.*, pp. 208–211.

54. Andrew, *op. cit.*, p. 249.

55. Bernard G. Campbell, *Human Evolution* (Chicago: Aldine Publishing Company, 1966), pp. 258–260.

56. Hall and DeVore, "Baboon Social Behavior," p. 71.

57. Thelma E. Rowell, "Female Reproductive Cycles and the Behavior of Baboons and Rhesus Macaques," in Altmann, *op. cit.*, p. 29.

Infant Dependency and Infant Care

Primates are by no means unique in producing young which must be fed and protected. Among higher primates, however, the period of immaturity and care is unusually long. The fact that these primates are more sociable than most other animals suggests a cause-effect relationship. Was prolongation of infant dependency a consequence of many generations of group living? If the answer is yes, then a slowing of the maturation process must have adaptive significance. Of what sort?

In asking such questions, we raise other, more basic, questions. Since the mother and infant must stay together for some length of time, could it be that the need to nurture infants was the original impetus for primate sociality? The mother-infant relationship appears to be a likely nucleus for a family group, which in time could give rise to larger groupings. But how did this relationship become established? How could an infant become dependent if there was no adult to protect it?

There is no evidence to which we can refer which will give direct answers to our questions. We must again reason from known facts about living animals. One fact is the universality of infant care among mammals. All mammalian young depend upon the mother to furnish nurture for at least a brief period of time. Infant care, it would appear, existed before mammals evolved. We begin, therefore, with a brief look at infant care among non-mammals.

INFANT CARE AMONG LOWER ANIMALS

Except for members of the class Aves (birds), the typical non-mammalian vertebrate reaches maturity with no assistance from either parent. An occasional female fish carries eggs or live young on her body, as do some toads and some marine invertebrates. A few female snakes and lizards brood their eggs, and female alligators reportedly guard their nests. Most, however, seemingly forget their offspring once the live young or eggs are ejected from their bodies.[1]

When fish eggs or young are given any attention at all, it is usually the male who performs the "nursery" duties.[2] Some, such as the Florida pipefish and the sea horse, carry the eggs in a pouch until they hatch. The males of some species carry the eggs in their mouths. Others guard and aerate the eggs; a few remain nearby after the fry emerge from the eggs.[3]

Why is there so little parental care? The simplest answer is that the young can meet their needs without such care, for few non-mammals have to feed their young. Vertebrates that are hatched usually obtain enough food from the egg to sustain them until they can find food for themselves. Microscopic organisms, ordinarily plentiful in fresh and salt water spawning grounds, supply nourishment for immature fishes, whether hatched or born alive. Fish eggs, insect larvae, and other kinds of food are readily accessible to the young of several vertebrate species.

Feeding of the young is also rare among invertebrates. Larvae and grubs usually begin life in an environment where food—but not mother —is close at hand (several marine forms have no true mother). Many adult females, particularly among insects, deposit eggs on or in plant and animal life—living, dead, or decaying. Marine forms and some insects deposit eggs in water. A few insects hatch in soil and find their way into host animals, such as the earthworm. In some instances nests are constructed in which eggs and sometimes food are placed.[4]

The so-called social insects present a different picture. Unlike most non-mammals, these insects do remain in continuous association with others of their kind; and care is given to the eggs, the young, or both. Termites tend only the eggs. The young metamorphose from small termites into large ones; they are able to look out for themselves.[5] Care of the young is largely limited to the order Hymenoptera, which includes the ants, bees, and wasps.

A wasp queen-to-be constructs a small nest and lays a few eggs. She

119

brings food to the larvae when they emerge. When the young wasps reach a certain stage of development, they take over the duties of nest construction and care of subsequent larvae. The queen then devotes full time to laying eggs. Interestingly, the larvae subsist upon insects chewed into a paste by the workers.[6] Somewhat similar patterns are found among bees and ants.[7] Solitary wasps and bees also keep their larvae supplied with food.[8]

Within an insect society, eggs and the immature young are sheltered and cared for. Social arrangements obviously further species survival. Yet, as we have seen, many species manage to survive despite the lack of attention to offspring. Is it possible that *lack* of infant care also contributes to the survival of some species? Apparently it does, for the simple reason that the adult females of such species can more adequately perform their vital function, the production of new members, if the new members are not dependent upon them.

Mortality among most species of lower animals is generally high. Species survival is therefore contingent upon the production of large numbers of offspring during the female's lifetime. Quite obviously, then, the less time and the fewer resources she must spend in other activities— such as meeting her own needs or tending young—the greater her reproductive potential. Furthermore, the longer the female lives, the more offspring she can produce.

The nonsocial female that does not have to brood eggs or meet the daily needs of immature young is not restricted to one location. She can move when danger threatens, and she is less likely to attract predatory attentions to herself or her offspring. It is significant in this connection that the male fish is more often the guardian of the eggs than the female. He is more expendable. One or a few females can continue the species despite heavy loss of life among males, eggs, or young; some species can continue without any males.

After eggs or young are produced, the female who has no maternal responsibilities can immediately begin to store up nutriments within her body for the next pregnancy. She need waste none of her time and resources taking care of her offspring. Furthermore, mating is not delayed by a wait for the young to maturate to the point where they can fend for themselves.

Social insects have evolved structures and behaviors which allow the adult female to devote virtually all her time and energies to continuing the species. She and her offspring are often shielded from many environmental hazards by the location or construction of the nest, mound, or hive. "Soldiers" or other members of the society repulse trespassers. All the queen's needs, as well as the needs of the immature, are satisfied through the efforts of workers.

Sociality and Infant Dependency

Care of the young is not necessary among many species—nor is it feasible. The costs would be too high. The number of offspring that can be cared for is necessarily limited, so there would be fewer eggs or live young at any given time. To provision and protect offspring would shorten what is usually an already relatively brief reproductive period by lengthening the time between births. Nutriments or other resources necessary for the reproduction of new members would have to be diverted to the sustenance of the immature. The consequent reduction in offspring—per pregnancy and per lifetime—could only result in an excess of deaths over births.

If the costs of infant dependency are high, how did it become established? The organization of insect societies suggests one possibility: care of the immature became possible when the risks and burdens of motherhood were reduced through social mechanisms. The queen ant, bee, or wasp (and termite of some species) is less exposed to environmental hazards than a solitary female insect. Protected through efforts of other members of the society, the queen's life-span—hence her period of reproduction—is lengthened. Others also free her of any need to seek food for herself or her young.

Arrangements evolved by the social insects are, of course, somewhat unique. But any sort of grouping ordinarily provides some amount of protection and aid to the reproducing female. Associational life is also likely to reduce mortality among the immature. If a high proportion of the young reach sexual maturity, the imperative to reproduce large numbers is lessened. Our guess, then, is that infant dependency developed after animals began to live in proximity for relatively long periods of time. Group life did not make infant dependency inevitable, but it provided a favorable situation for its inception.

We are suggesting that sociality preceded infant dependency. This does not appear to accord with earlier observations that solitary wasps and bees feed their young. Such behavior would seem to indicate that infant dependency was the prior phenomenon. Let us take a closer look at these insects.

Several species of solitary wasps have no contact with their hatched young. The relationship between mother and offspring terminates when the former deposits her eggs in a nest. She does provide for their sustenance, however. Along with the eggs she deposits live spiders or insects, immobilized by her sting. Thus the larvae have fresh food when they emerge from the eggs. Other solitary species bring insects to the larvae or grubs. Why this variation in the satisfaction of nutritional needs? The adult wasp, you may remember, chews insects up for the grubs.

121

Insects, however, are not adult food. The adult can swallow only liquid foods, and herein may be the key to sociality.

A commonly observed practice among the Hymenoptera is *trophallaxis* ("food exchange"), the practice of passing a droplet of fluid from one insect to another. This appears to be all the nourishment some kinds of ants need. The wasp grub secretes a liquid that is eagerly licked up by the adult wasp (bees and ants do likewise). If trophallaxis supplies a part of the mother's nutritional needs, the time and energy she would otherwise spend obtaining food are reduced. Should all her nutritional needs be satisfied through trophallaxis, the relationship between mother and young is not strictly one of dependency-care. It is mutualistic; the mother benefits as much as do her young. It is not improbable that she supplies her young with food in order to feed herself. Perhaps the adults of some species learned that grubs were sources of food, just as ants somehow or other discovered that aphids can be "milked." When this happened, infant care began.[9]

Significantly, many, or perhaps all, of the so-called solitary wasps and bees that feed their young actually live in colonies or families. In one such species, the mining bee, the mother feeds her young until they are able to fly. The female young then stay on with the mother, sharing the work of collecting food and protecting the nest. When they themselves produce offspring, each female feeds her own and the cycle is repeated.

Among other species of bees, some of the females—for reasons unknown—fail to mate. Instead of striking out on their own, they continue to live in the maternal nest, becoming more or less full-time workers. In one such species, the unmated females are smaller and more numerous than their fertile sisters, as is also the case in the larger insect society.[10]

Each of these arrangements—which may be representations of earlier evolutionary steps in the direction of the insect society—obviously contributes to the reproductive efficiency of the fertile female. Once she establishes a family or colony, activities essential to her survival and the preservation of her young are soon shared or assumed by the more mature offspring.

Infant Care Among Birds

The class Aves provides a test of sorts for what we have just said. Since care for eggs or immature young, or both, is almost universal among species of this class, it is likely that birds have evolved means for negating the need to reproduce in large numbers. They should exhibit traits or characteristics which contribute to reproductive efficiency.

One characteristic is quite evident. The ability to fly—an ability which has been lost by some species—enables birds to avoid or escape many dangers to which small terrestrial animals are normally exposed. Nests can be located in trees, on cliffs, or in remote areas—places where eggs are not likely to be crushed by walking or running animals, and where eggs and infants are less subject to predation. The flying animal can often locate foods more readily, and some foods are more accessible to it than to quadrupeds of similar size. The ability to fly, in short, contributes to lowered mortality at all stages of life.

Cooperation between or among individuals, which is fairly common, directly or indirectly reduces the burdens of motherhood for the females of several species of birds. Members of a number of species, for example, are known to hunt food collectively, thereby assuring greater safety and perhaps more nourishment to individuals. Members of other species communicate the discovery of unusual food finds—that is, more food than the discoverer can eat.[11] During brooding it is not unusual for the male and female to spell one another; while one tends the eggs, the other takes care of its own needs.

Some species have evolved a division of labor between the sexes. For example, the female mallee fowl fixes a nest-mound in which she deposits her eggs. From then until the eggs hatch, the male spends more than five hours a day regulating the temperature of the mound. The male emperor penguin incubates the female's single egg with his sagging skin and feathers as the egg rests on his feet. The female, meanwhile, seeks out food for herself. After the egg is hatched, the well-fed female takes over the feeding of the infant while the male recuperates from the two-month ordeal he has completed (he loses a third of his weight).[12]

Biological mechanisms have also evolved (or been retained) which lessen demands upon the mother. Among these is rapid maturation. The young of some birds (such as quail, chicken, ostrich, and several acquatic birds) are able to leave the nest or hatching place a few hours after emerging from their shells. The mother may protect her young, but they are able to meet their own nutritional needs.[13]

The number of eggs produced at one laying or during a female's lifetime has apparently been regulated during the evolution of the various species. Seemingly, no more eggs are produced than are necessary to maintain a certain population balance—a balance man has upset in several instances. Birds subjected to the greatest hazards, in other words, normally tend to produce the greatest number of eggs. According to one writer, the number of eggs a bird lays is an index of its life expectancy.[14]

In sum, there is ample evidence that infant dependency is feasible among the Aves. Species have evolved means to compensate for the reproduction of limited numbers of offspring. Again, as with insects, we find that social arrangements are among these means. Is it possible, then, that sociality was a causal factor in the inception of infant dependency among birds? We shall return to this question in the next section.

ORIGINS OF INFANT DEPENDENCY

Our observations and reasoning lead us to believe that social existence was a necessary, although not sole, condition for the establishment of infant dependency. Generally speaking, the combined demands of self-maintenance, reproduction, and care of the young appear to be too great for the non-mammalian female to bear alone. These demands can be alleviated to some extent through the efforts of other members of the species. The mere presence of others (or of a single male, as among birds) may relieve the mother of a need to protect herself or her young.

If social existence was a necessary condition for the establishment of infant dependency, why don't all birds and mammals live in groups of some sort? One answer is that sociality developed selectively. Some species evolved the capacity for social life while others did not. One is tempted to use the Primates as a model and assume that sociality was an accompaniment of more recent evolutionary developments, such as greater neural complexity. But we know that this is not a safe assumption. Manifestation of a trait or characteristic in an advanced form does not necessarily mean that the trait or characteristic is recent. The five-fingered appendage predates the appearance of mammals. Social insects very probably became social long before higher primates evolved.

The fact that some insects are social implies that sociality is a primitive, rather than a recent, phenomenon. If we make this supposition, the answer to the question of why all birds and mammals are not social might be: some species of birds and mammals *lost* the capacity for sociality. That is, the ancestors of the Aves and the Mammalia may have lived in social units of some sort long enough to allow the young to become dependent. Later, genetic and environmental changes forced or encouraged the break-up of many of these units. *Not* living in groups, in other words, came to have adaptive value. Food shortages, the appearance of more efficient competitors or predators, destruction of habitats or shelters—these and other changes could have impelled evolving species to disperse as individuals. Again, genetic deviants that were unable to adjust to group life may have moved into some of the several vacant niches that were available. There is no direct evidence to support our supposition. However, geologic and fossil data give it some measure of plausibility.

Survival During the Mesozoic—A Speculative Reconstruction

The seeds of infant dependency were sown some 280 to 225 million years ago during the Permian Period.* The Permian was a period of momentous changes. The most pervasive of these were upthrusts of land and glaciation. The Appalachians, the Urals, and other mountain ranges were formed. Continents became fully emergent, and deserts were created in many parts of the world. Before the period ended a severe and widespread glaciation was experienced. The Permian was, in the words of one writer, "a time of reckoning" for existing forms of plant and animal life.[15]

Many evolving or evolved reptiles, the most advanced vertebrates of the time, were unable to meet the demands of Ice Age conditions. Being cold-blooded—with their body temperatures regulated by external temperature—they were torpid and helpless when temperatures dropped to near freezing. Numbers probably perished because they were unable to seek or obtain food, while others were too sluggish to mate. In areas where mating was achieved, eggs formerly incubated in hot sand or dirt failed to hatch.

One of the reptilian orders that did survive the Permian was the Therapsida. A very important survival factor may have been the acquisition of mammal-like traits. Fossils found in South Africa seem to indicate, from the shape of the pelvis, that the young were born live rather than hatched; and the teeth were divided into incisors, canines, and cheek teeth.[16] Perhaps, also like mammals, they were warm-blooded— maintaining a constant internal body temperature. This we cannot tell from the fossils.

The Triassic, the geologic period which followed the Permian about 225 million years ago, marked the beginning of the Age of Reptiles. Evolving rapidly, reptiles became adapted to varied terrestrial environments, and some began to invade the sea. Dinosaurs, most of them bipedal, made their appearance and eventually outnumbered other kinds of reptiles. By the end of the Triassic, some 190 to 195 million years ago, dinosaurs were the dominant form of terrestrial animal.[17] Small mammal-like reptiles persisted in spite of the dinosaurs and became widely distributed during the Triassic and succeeding Jurassic periods.

* The Permian was the final period of the Paleozoic Era (the Cambrian was the first period). The Paleozoic Era was followed by the Mesozoic Era (the "Age of Reptiles"), which is divided into three periods: Triassic, Jurassic, and Cretaceous. (See Geologic Time Scale.)

Evidence for the appearance and evolution of predecessors to the Aves is scant. Flight possibly enabled birds and birdlike reptiles to avoid some of the conditions that resulted in the fossilization of other animals. Many that might have been preserved—those whose bodies fell into water—were not because their bodies floated for a while. Instead of sinking to the bottom of a pond, lake, or stream to be fossilized, the dead birds were eaten by reptiles or fish. Such remains as have been found indicate that reptiles had invaded the air by the Jurassic. Creatures more reptile than bird, but feathered, were alive late in the period.[18]

Life for most of the reptiles that failed to develop along the more typical dinosauric lines was no doubt fraught with peril. Those that did survive the competition and predation of the large animals were adapted —or became adapted—to somewhat atypical niches. Some, for example, acquired mechanisms and body coverings that allowed them to be relatively active when temperatures dropped. This was adaptive in areas where the difference between daytime and nighttime temperatures was rather extreme. In the cool of the night, when the large reptiles were sluggish, small furred and feathered creatures were able to seek food and satisfy other needs.[19]

A number of reptilian variants avoided dinosaurs, during daylight hours or altogether, by the occupation of certain kinds of habitats. Late Triassic mammal-like reptiles of Wales seemingly evaded contacts with large animals by living in crevices and crannies of the rocky uplands.[20] Some possibly hid in or under bushes. For those that could climb or fly even for a short distance, the trees provided a haven; and several varieties of Triassic or Jurassic reptiles took to the trees for some part of the day or night. Among the arboreal invaders were winged, bipedal egg-layers that built crude nests (as do some present-day reptiles) and quadrupeds that give birth to live young.

Part-time occupation of the trees did not solve the problem of survival for all. Food, water, nesting materials, or other necessities could be obtained only by returning to the ground; and many that ventured onto the ground were destroyed. Their biological makeups proved inadequate for the detection of and proper responses to terrestrial danger signals. Others were not well equipped to maintain equilibrium on what may have been a hard—certainly an occasionally unsteady—surface. Falls were commonplace among these; mating and escape from attackers (possibly flying reptiles or carnivorous cousins) were well-nigh impossible.

Eggs and live young were especially vulnerable to arboreal hazards. Untended eggs, incubated by heat from the sun, were likely to be cracked, crushed, and knocked from nesting places by scurrying animals. Live young were toppled from perches by adults preoccupied with flight or sex. Winds, rains, and the actions of dinosaurs dislodged eggs, young, and even adults. Still other animals perished because they lacked equipment to accurately judge distances and speeds—their own and others—on the limited arboreal surfaces.

Those best equipped to meet the demands of an arboreal way of life became even better adapted through genetic changes and learning experiences. The general impact of such changes was to reduce the amount of time that had to be spent on the ground and to increase the safety of eggs and live young. Nutriments in the trees became more available or more accessible to some animals. Improvements in grasping ability, for instance, may have allowed quadrupeds to maintain their footing while obtaining insect larvae, insects, leaves, or other foods. Alterations in the skull and teeth possibly permitted others to reach or ingest new foods, such as boring insects, grubs, and bark. A few possibly discovered that they could subsist largely or wholly upon eggs or live young—of their own or of another arboreal species.

A factor that favored the preservation of eggs was an inclination to sit on nests. There is a possibility that nesting began more or less accidentally; later, perhaps, it became fixed, patterned, "instinctive" behavior. That is, evolving birds may have been poorly equipped for roosting, and resting in a nest may have been the simplest way for them to maintain equilibrium. If this were the case, the male stood to benefit as much as the female; so the present-day brooding behavior of male birds may have very remote origins. On the other hand, nesting may have begun on the ground or resulted from genetic changes that occurred after occupation of the trees.

Adaptation to an arboreal existence was aided and furthered by the association of two or more animals. Then, as now, there was a measure of safety in numbers. The arboreal predator that had a choice was more likely to prey upon isolated eggs and young than upon those in the proximity of even one adult. On the ground or in the trees, the actions of one individual in a group were likely to alert others to imminent danger. Patterns of association may have preceded invasion of the trees. Again, it may have been impossible for some animals to avoid more or less continuous sensory contact with one another. Trees and forests were limited during the Triassic by a semiarid climate that was widespread over much of the world, and by volcanic actions and inundations by water and mud in some parts.[21]

Sex, of course, brought males and females together. During courtship or mating perhaps mutual benefits to be derived from staying together were realized. Cool nights or dampness, for example, might have made warmth from another body desirable. Remaining together might also have made life more secure. An arboreal predator would be less inclined

127

to attack two adults than one, and two adults could possibly discourage encroachment upon a bit of territory—a limb or a tree. Offspring of the union may have remained near their parents for a time because it was safer to do so, because there was no need to go elsewhere for need-satisfiers, or because they were gregarious.

At some point in evolutionary time, biological and environmental circumstances became such that descent to the ground was unnecessary for infants, if not for adults. In the tree were all the requisites for life—food, water (from leaves and insects), nesting materials, space for play and other activities. An animal left one tree only to climb another, usually at mating time. This combination of circumstances, plus associational life, permitted certain genetic changes to become established—changes that would have been maladaptive, even lethal, earlier or to animals living in isolation. Since mother and young were subjected to fewer perils, it was less imperative that several offspring be produced at one time or that maturation be rapid. Gradually, mutations resulted in few offspring per pregnancy and the periods of gestation and infancy were lengthened. As a consequence of these changes, other alterations in biological makeup became possible.

Among the more significant alterations was an enlargement of the brain to accommodate and coordinate better muscular and sensory equipment. To maintain equilibrium and navigate sometimes narrow, sometimes unsteady, branches or limbs with speed and surety required finer muscular control than running on the ground. The sense of sight was important in the location of food and enemies, particularly to evolving birds. Improvements in the tactile sense possibly gave some evolving mammals an advantage over their kin, for greater sensitivity in the area of the digits made for more efficient grasping. The sense of smell of these animals possibly sharpened to some extent, enabling them to locate mates in other trees and to avoid danger when moving on the ground from one tree to another. Olfaction may have been important in the delineation of territories also; living prosimians rub urine or glandular secretions on a limb to notify others that a particular area is occupied. Along with these developments, association areas in the brain developed or expanded which linked different kinds of stimuli emanating from the same object. Visual cues were associated with tactile cues, tactile cues with auditory cues, and so on.

As the brain enlarged, close ties between and among animals became a likelihood. More memories could be stored, including experiences with others. The number and variety of stimuli that could be perceived and responded to increased. One consequence was that the behavior of animals living in association came to be anticipated. A gesture, a scent, a sound, or a preparatory act, for example, could not only be recalled but could sometimes be associated with subsequent actions. In other words, communication—non-purposive though it might have been—was extended, thereby enhancing the potential for coordination and cooperation.

Each change that persisted among members of arboreal species prepared the way for further changes. Once the young no longer had to look to their own safety and nutritional needs from the moment of birth or hatching or shortly thereafter, certain changes in biological makeup altered and enlarged behavioral possibilities which, in turn, provided bases for additional biological modifications.

Millions of years after the first reptilian variants took to the trees, accreted changes resulted in the sporadic production of young that were helpless for short periods after birth or hatching. Most probably perished. In some instances, however, the mother (or maybe another adult) fed these offspring for some reason or other. The mother may have been impelled by some innate neural mechanism set in motion by hormonal activity; perhaps she or another adult accidentally fed the helpless young —in a spirit of play, for instance. There may even have been a feeling state, somewhat akin to pity, that motivated succorable behavior. However the feeding began, these offspring survived in greater numbers than did helpless offspring that received no attention. Eventually an association between helpless young and feeding was established in the female's neuromuscular system. When this happened, the way was prepared for longer and longer periods of feeding.

A major restriction upon the length of the period of helplessness was the ability of the mother to provide food. The amount of food a single adult could carry was limited to what could be held in the mouth or beak. To feed even a few rapidly growing infants necessitated frequent trips to and from sources of food. This posed no particular problem so long as the period of helplessness was brief. Before rates of maturation could be slowed to any great extent, however, means for lightening the mother's load had to evolve or appear.

One such means resulted from environmental changes during the Jurassic. The most significant, so far as infant dependency is concerned, was an increase in the number, variety, and sometimes size of insects.[22] Food became more readily available for both evolving birds and evolving mammals. The former were especially benefitted. Food in relative abundance was usually near at hand, in the air if not in the trees. Numerous trips to and from the nest could be made without undue strain.

Matters were somewhat different with the quadrupeds. They could not fly, so food still had to be transported bit by bit up and down trees or from one part of the tree to another. To keep her young supplied with nutriments day after day for any length of time would have di-

verted an undue amount of the female's time and energy from reproductive and self-maintenance functions. Some species possibly became
extinct for this reason. Among mammals-to-be, the problem of extended
feeding was solved by biological changes. The female became equipped
to manufacture food for her young within her own body. The appearance of mammary glands not only reduced the burdens of motherhood,
it forced a greater intimacy between mother and infant. This sort of
maternal care provided a basis for further changes—physical, social,
and psychological.

There is no concrete evidence for the progression of events we have
sketched. The idea that mammals evolved in the trees is not widely
held today, but such a possibility seems as likely as a return to the
trees by evolving primates. A few years ago the late Earnest A. Hooton,
who is sometimes referred to as the "father of American physical anthropology," observed: "A considerable body of fossil evidence points to
an arboreal or tree-dwelling ancestry for all mammals with the exception
of the egg-laying duckbills and the spiny echidna, the lowly monotremes
of Australia." Furthermore, he wrote, "Even in modern terrestrial mammals the structures of the wrist and ankle point to an arboreal ancestry." [23]

Dr. W. D. Matthew, whom Professor Hooton cited with approval,
argued that the mammalian descent from trees occurred toward the
close of the Cretaceous period, which ended about 65 million years ago.
The growth of flora at that time, he said, greatly increased the territory
available to mammals.[24] Of equal or greater importance was the extinction of the large reptiles, which was completed many years after
a considerable variety of flora was conspicuous.[25] With the disappearance of these animals (from causes as yet unknown), the major competitive and predatory pressures of terrestrial environments were removed.
Environmental opportunities abounded, and the stage was set for the
radiation of mammals.

THE ADAPTIVE VALUE OF PROLONGED INFANCY

Although infant dependency has its costs, it is found among a variety
of species. In some instances the period of postnatal care is rather long.
The costs are evidently balanced or outweighed by certain advantages.
What are these advantages? At least a partial answer is suggested by two
evolutionary trends. In most lines of descent among mammals and in
other groups of non-flying animals, there has been a general trend toward
successive increase of body size; and there has also been a tendency toward greater neural complexity.[26]

The first mammals were small animals. Some living species are perhaps equally small, but others have evolved in the direction of greater body size. A probable impetus for this trend was an absence or relaxation of the imperative to produce in great numbers. Such may have been provided by arrangements and events we have just discussed, including protection and care for infants and the opening up of terrestrial niches relatively free from competition and predation.*

As we have seen, infant care ordinarily limits the number of offspring a female can produce. Obversely, adequate care of infants—facilitated by environmental circumstances—obviates the necessity for a large number of progeny at one time or during the female's lifetime in order to assure perpetuation of the species. There is a possibility, then, that the one or few that are born will be larger. Uterine space and nutriments that would otherwise be devoted to several embryos and fetuses can be utilized in the gestation of a more limited number of infants. This, in itself, possibly furthered an increase in body size among early mammals. Later, it furthered greater body size among some mammalian groups (such as horses, cattle, and elephants) more than among others.

Not all mammals, of course, evolved anatomical structures which permitted the females to produce infants of any great size. Carrying a large fetus was probably maladaptive for yet others. However, when conditions permitted, infant care allowed the establishment of mutations which resulted in considerable growth after birth. Where extended care was feasible, such growth could be attained at a relatively slow rate.

If infant care did contribute to the evolution of larger mammals, it was adaptive in many—if not most—instances. When larger varieties or species compete with smaller varieties or species, Bernhard Rensch has observed, the former have higher selective value for a number of reasons. Among other things, larger animals normally show greater physical strength, better resistivity to diseases, higher absolute speed in attacking or fleeing, and a longer duration of life.[27] It might also be noted that largeness tends to discourage attacks by many would-be predators. Some of the largest adult mammals are rarely if ever preyed upon, except by man.

Larger mammals, Rensch says, normally show a better learning capacity than smaller ones; the most complicated part of the cortex is both relatively and absolutely larger. This brings us to the second evolutionary

---

* If mammals evolved in the trees, it is very likely that there was selection *against* the more fecund female or her offspring. A large litter of slowly maturing infants would be difficult for non-marsupials to care for in the trees. The mother would probably find it impossible to manage her own safety and the safety of several young at one time. This may explain the small litter size (normally two) of the primitive tree shrew. After mammals descended to the ground, other factors (predators, for example) could have encouraged increases in the number of offspring per birth.

trend: increase in neural complexity. Significantly, birds and mammals—the animals that typically care for their young—have more highly developed brains and nervous systems than other animals. Thus they are able to perceive, respond to, and integrate a greater number and variety of stimuli. Among higher mammals, where the period of infant dependency is most prolonged, neural complexity is greatest. Behavior is, for the most part, under cortical control; it can be produced more or less voluntarily. This means that behavior tends to be less stereotyped, more flexible, than among lower animals. Adjustments to change need not necessarily depend upon alterations in biological makeup. Neural complexity, it would seem, is adaptive. But is it?

Each of us knows that the simultaneous impingement of several stimuli upon consciousness can be distracting, confusing, even frustrating. When action is called for, we may be unable to act at all or we may respond to the wrong stimulus. We must, therefore, learn to discriminate between stimuli and to associate them with situations and behaviors. Since we can respond in different ways to the same stimulus, it is also necessary to learn how to select among alternative courses of action.

In short, neural complexity is adaptive if there is proper learning; without learning, it can be maladaptive. The survival of higher species, then, depends upon there being situations conducive to the right kind of learning. Association between the young and the more mature—association required because of dependency—provides such a situation. Even if teaching is not deliberate, the maturing young have successful models to imitate.

There is ample evidence that young animals do learn from adults. The mother sea otter, for example, shows her pup not only how to open shellfish by hitting the shell on a rock and to select foods, but also how to swim. Black bear cubs learn from their mother where and how to obtain food, to coat themselves with mud to discourage biting insects, and to avoid certain hazards and unpleasant animals.[28] Lions learn from their parents the techniques of the hunt; only after ten months or so of watching do the young lions begin to hunt their own prey.[29]

A relatively long period of association between young and mother or other more mature members of the species provides an opportunity for the former to learn complex skills. Among primates, the care of infants apparently constitutes one set of these skills. Experiments demonstrate that patterns of behavior associated with care of the young have to be learned; a female ape or monkey reared in isolation does not know how to meet the needs of her offspring. To be a good mother requires practice and role-learning. Immature female apes, like little girls of our own species, spend considerable time playing at being mothers.[30]

132

Social skills are also important among primates. Apes, monkeys, and humans must learn how to get along with individuals of both sexes and of different ages. Each member of a group must learn what he or she can and cannot do relative to others as individuals and as representatives of categories (for example, male adults). Cooperation between or among individuals is often required. Higher primates can learn these and other social skills because they do live in groups. The obverse is equally true; they can live in groups because they learn such skills.

The survival of many—perhaps all—primate species is contingent upon the successful transmission of skills from one generation to the next. Among no other mammalian order do individuals have to learn so much in order that the species will be perpetuated. Even techniques and skills for satisfying basic needs must be learned. It has been repeatedly observed, for instance, that apes raised apart from other apes do not know how to handle their sexual impulses when they reach sexual maturity.[31] A male rhesus monkey raised in isolation, though paired with an experienced female, is unable to achieve intromission. Rarely is even a patient, experienced rhesus male able to impregnate a female that was deprived of a mother during infancy.[32] Reproduction, at least among some primate species, would virtually cease but for the learning situation which prolonged infancy provides.

The major advantage of a prolongation of preadult life among primates, it would appear, is that it makes considerable learning possible. If this is true, then cortically controlled behavior must be adaptive. How so? The answer has already been given: genetically patterned ("instinctive," "innate") behavior tends to be inflexible. Such behavior, if ineffective or maladaptive, must await modification or displacement through mutations and natural selection. Behavior that is learned, on the other hand, can be modified rather quickly so that adjustments can be made to changing situations. New challenges are more likely to be successfully met and new opportunities can be more readily exploited if cues and responses are linked through learning rather than by heredity.

Would man have evolved had most behaviors of earlier primates been genetically patterned? Obviously, he would not have. The shift from an arboreal to a terrestrial environment demanded major alterations in behavior patterns. Cooperation among individuals was no doubt essential. Had prehuman primates lacked the capacity for considerable learning, they would either have perished or evolved into something other than man.

NOTES

1. J. Z. Young, *The Life of Vertebrates*, 2nd ed. (New York: Oxford University Press, 1962), pp. 265, 382.

2. Christopher W. Coates and James W. Atz, "Fishes of the World," in *The Animal Kingdom*, ed. Frederick Drimmer, Vol. III, Bk. IV (Garden City, N.Y.: Doubleday & Company, Inc., 1954), p. 1399.

3. F. D. Ommanney and the Editors of *Life*, *The Fishes* (New York: Time Inc., 1963), pp. 105–118; Brian Curtis, *The Life Story of the Fish* (New York: Dover Publications, Inc., 1961), pp. 218, 267–268.

4. J. L. Cloudsley-Thompson, *Animal Behavior* (London: Oliver and Boyd, 1960), p. 117; V. B. Wigglesworth, *The Life of Insects* (New York: The World Publishing Company, 1963), p. 118.

5. Wigglesworth, *op. cit.*, p. 240.

6. Cloudsley-Thompson, *op. cit.*, pp. 117–118.

7. *Ibid.*, pp. 119–121; J. T. Bonner, *Cells and Societies* (Princeton: Princeton University Press, 1955), pp. 63–64.

8. Wigglesworth, *op. cit.*, pp. 327–328.

9. Facts in this paragraph are from Cloudsley-Thompson, *op. cit.*, p. 118; Wigglesworth, *op. cit.*, p. 238; and Peter Farb and the Editors of *Life*, *The Insects* (New York: Time Inc., 1962), p. 163.

10. Wigglesworth, *op. cit.*, pp. 238–239.

11. Roger Tory Peterson and the Editors of *Life*, *The Birds* (New York: Time Inc., 1962), pp. 137–141.

12. *Ibid*, pp. 141, 145–146.

13. Alexander Wetmore, *The Smithsonian Series*, IX (New York: Smithsonian Institution Series, Inc., 1944), 91–97.

14. Peterson and the Editors of *Life*, *op. cit.*, p. 142.

15. Carl O. Dunbar, *Historical Geology*, 2nd ed. (New York: John Wiley & Sons, Inc., 1963), p. 244.

16. Hartmut Bastian, *And Then Came Man* (New York: The Viking Press, 1964), pp. 156–157.

17. Dunbar, *op. cit.*, p. 287.

18. *Ibid.*, pp. 309–312.

19. Bastian, *op. cit.*, p. 171.

20. Dunbar, *op. cit.*, p. 289.

21. *Ibid.*, pp. 284–285.

22. *Ibid.*, pp. 304, 306.

23. Earnest Albert Hooton, *Up From the Ape* (New York: The Macmillan Company, 1937), pp. 66–67.

24. *Ibid.*, p. 67.

25. Dunbar, *op. cit.*, pp. 332–337, 345–348.

26. Bernhard Rensch, "Trends Towards Progress of Brains and Sense Organs," *Cold Spring Harbor Symposia on Quantitative Biology*, XXIV (Cold Spring Harbor, N.Y.: The Biological Laboratory, 1959), 291–297.

27. *Ibid.*, p. 291.

28. Sally Carrighar, *Wild Heritage* (New York: Houghton Mifflin Company, 1965), pp. 66–76.

29. Richard Carrington and the Editors of *Life*, *The Mammals* (New York: Time Inc., 1963), p. 147.

30. Sherwood L. Washburn and David A. Hamburg, "The Implications of Primate Research," in Irven DeVore (ed.), *Primate Behavior: Field Studies of Monkeys and Apes* (New York: Holt, Rinehart & Winston, Inc., 1965), p. 620.

31. Heini P. Hediger, "The Evolution of Territorial Behavior," in Sherwood L. Washburn (ed.), *Social Life of Early Man* (Chicago: Aldine Publishing Company, 1961), p. 45.

32. Harry F. Harlow and Margaret K. Harlow, "A Study of Animal Affection," in Charles H. Southwick (ed.), *Primate Social Behavior* (New York: D. Van Nostrand Co., Inc., 1963), p. 181.

CLUES FROM THE PAST

Eusthenopteron, a Devonian lobe-finned fish

8

From Fish to Mammal

Our focus thus far has been primarily upon the living. Animals of today offer several clues as to the problems and processes evolving man must have experienced. They furnish us with some inkling about the structure and behaviors of our prehuman ancestors at certain stages of development. By studying higher primates in particular, we can gain a better idea of how prehominids managed to survive in a hostile terrestrial environment.

What living animals cannot reveal are the details of the gradual transformation from primitive quadruped to bipedal *Homo sapiens.* For these details we must search the evidence of past life that has been preserved in the earth's crust. Most of our clues must come from fossils, and it is to the fossil record that we now turn.

Our survey begins with a brief sketch of developments that began over 360 million years ago and ended perhaps 70 or 75 million years before the present. During this period vertebrates moved into dry land and mammals evolved. In the following chapter we shall begin to trace the evolution of man from his most primitive primate origins.

Sometime during the Devonian Period (345 to 395 million years ago) several species of fish crawled out of lakes and streams—and continued to live. These fish, members of the order Crossopterygii, were the ancestors of the amphibians.

The crossopterygians were uniquely equipped to move onto land for brief periods. Unlike most fishes that were evolving at the time, they had nostrils that opened into the mouth, heavy scales, and paired sacs attached to the esophagus. The paired sacs functioned as rudimentary lungs, enabling the fishes to take in oxygen from the air through the nostrils. The heavy scales protected them from the drying action of the air. The crossopterygians were further distinguished by broad-based, paired fins and a sturdy skeleton. Bones in the paired fins were somewhat homologous to bones in the limbs of present-day terrestrial vertebrates. The fins permitted locomotion on land.[1]

Why did crossopterygians leave the water? They may have been chased onto land by predatory cousins. More likely, they left the water they were in, in order to search for more water. Lakes and streams they habited possibly dried up or became too brackish to support sources of food, so they sought other bodies of water.

To successfully traverse land demanded not only lung power but also mechanisms for overcoming the pull of gravity. A fish in water does not have to support its own weight or overcome a strong gravitational force in order to locomote. Those crossopterygians best able to solve the problem of gravity were no doubt the most successful on land. They could travel farther, if need be, to find water.

Those fish best able to solve the problem of gravity were equipped with digits for digging into the earth, thus aiding in balance and propulsion. They also had strong backbones to support their weight. In time, the more successful developed girdles to support a strengthening vertebral column. These girdles, the pectoral in front and the pelvic in back, were in turn supported by strong limbs and feet. This arrangement, which is found among early amphibians, not only lifted the body off the ground but also balanced it on four limbs.[2] Locomotion was a simple matter of moving the limbs. Movement of amphibians was probably slow, but much more rapid than that of the crossopterygians.

Thus two problems with which the terrestrial vertebrate must cope—obtaining oxygen from air and overcoming gravity—were solved by evolving and early amphibians. One problem they did not resolve was reproduction away from water. The fish must deposit its jelly-like eggs in water; out of water they dry up. In this matter the amphibian remained a fish. For over 300 million years, apparently, amphibians have deposited their eggs in water, and the young have gone through a fish-like stage during which they breathe through gills.[3]

Obviously a complete transition from aquatic to terrestrial environments was not possible until the appearance of a means of reproduction that did not restrict animals to watery habitats. This means appeared sometime during the Carboniferous, which began approximately 345 million years ago. The means was an improved egg in which the young developed beyond the fishlike stage of amphibian reproduction before they hatched.

The egg from which the animal hatched was so constructed that it did not have to be immersed in water. This, the amniote egg, first appeared among reptiles. Fertilized within the mother, the egg contained the embryo, a large yolk to nourish the developing embryo, and a sac to receive waste products. The contents were surrounded by a covering tough enough to prevent desiccation, yet porous enough to permit the intake of oxygen and the excretion of carbon dioxide.[4]

Exactly when the amniote egg was first used is not known. If this were known, dating the appearance of the reptiles would be much simpler. Unfortunately fossil eggs are rare. The oldest come from Lower (early) Permian deposits, which are several million years younger than definitely identified reptilian structures.* Complicating the establishment of dates for the appearance of reptiles is the fact that a number of amphibians were evolving in the reptilian direction at the same time. All these reptile-like amphibians have been classified as constituting the superorder Labyrinthodontia.† [5]

For many years reptiles were unable to fully exploit the potential the amniote egg offered them. The extensive Carboniferous swamps were better suited for amphibians. Not until drier lands became more available during the Permian, which began about 280 million years ago, did the diversification of reptiles begin in earnest. Among the first to radiate were mammal-like reptiles that had evolved from the earliest and most primitive order of reptiles (Cotylosauria). The mammal-like reptiles, or synapsids (all are classified as members of the subclass Synapsida), were remarkably successful as a group. How successful can be inferred from their widespread distribution. Fossils of various genera have been found in North America, Brazil, western Europe, Russia, South Africa, and China. They were successful, too, in terms of numbers and duration of existence. Synapsids constituted the majority (and were the largest in size) of all known Permian reptiles, and they persisted for as long as 100 million years.[6]

In view of such success, the almost complete disappearance of all synapsids prior to the appearance of the large reptiles is a bit puzzling.

---

* The reader interested in diagnostic characteristics that distinguish reptiles from amphibians will find discussions in Edwin H. Colbert, *Evolution of the Vertebrates* (New York: John Wiley & Sons, Inc., 1955), pp. 110–111; and in Alfred Sherwood Romer, *Vertebrate Paleontology*, 2nd ed. (Chicago: University of Chicago Press, 1945), pp. 164–171. Morphological differences between mammals and reptiles are summarized by Colbert, pp. 228–231, and discussed in greater detail by Romer, Chap. 15.

† The names of a number of animal groupings are derived from characteristics of the teeth. Such names can be readily recognized by the suffixes *odont* and *odontia*. In the above instance, the combination of *labyrinth* and *odontia* refers to the complicated nature of the enamel surface of the teeth. The dentition of these animals, incidentally, was carried over practically without change from the Crossopterygii.

A likely explanation is that food chains were destroyed or disrupted by geologic events of the late Permian and early Triassic. Glaciation, inundations by seas, and continental uplifts that created arid and semiarid conditions destroyed both plant and animal life. The central stock of synapsids were carnivorous, and when plant life was destroyed, the herbivorous animals upon which they preyed also perished. Amphibian populations, another possible source of food, were also decimated by natural forces. If such was the case, adaptations that were probably largely responsible for their success—adaptations for catching and eating animals—contributed heavily to the demise of the synapsids. When their specialized diet vanished, few were apparently able to adjust to other types of food.

The carnivorous nature of the central stock is indicated, in part, by the early trend toward differentiation of the teeth into incisors, large canines, and laterally-placed cheek teeth. Such differentiation made easier the seizing of prey and the ripping of flesh. Another general trend was toward an overall anatomical structure adapted to walking or running efficiently over dry land.[7] Predaceous synapsids could evidently outrun their more clumsy prey.

The two trends reached their peak among members of the order Therapsida, more specifically among members of two suborders. The suborder Theriodontia appeared first in time, about midway through the Permian; the Ictidosauria evolved during the Triassic, while theriodonts still lived. Either suborder could be ancestral to mammals. Both contained members that were almost mammalian in structure. Except for two small bones, one in the skull and one in the jaw, some ictidosaurs would probably have been classified as mammals rather than as reptiles.[8]

There is still uncertainty as to the exact line of descent from Therapsida to mammals. Exactly when mammals evolved has not as yet been determined either. Such matters are in doubt largely because of a change in the nature of fossil evidence. Sediments laid down prior to the latter part of the Triassic contain a wealth of skulls and skeletons. After that, and throughout the remainder of the Mesozoic, mammal fossils are less complete. In many instances, teeth are the major source of data.[9]

Teeth, jaws, and partial skulls indicate the existence of four orders of mammals during the latter half of the Jurassic, which began some 180 million years ago. The major identifying criteria are the cheek teeth. In mammal-like reptiles, the cheek teeth—when preserved—are all alike or gradually increase in complexity from front to back. In mammals, they are clearly differentiated into premolars and molars. Teeth and other fossil fragments of Jurassic mammals are from animals that ranged in size from as small as present-day mice to no larger than house cats.[10]

None of the four mammalian orders persisted as such beyond the

Cretaceous Period, which began about 136 million years ago. One order possibly gave rise to the monotremes. From another, Pantotheria, came the marsupials and placental mammals. Marsupials closely related to the opossum and placental insectivores related to modern shrews and hedgehogs have been discovered in Upper (late) Cretaceous deposits. The egg-laying monotremes (platypus, spiny anteater, and so on) are unknown in the fossil record until the Pleistocene.[11]

The ictidosaurs were not the only reptiles to appear during the Triassic. Another important group, the Archosauria, also evolved. From the archosaurs came the reptiles that dominated most of Mesozoic history—dinosaurs, flying reptiles, and large aquatic reptiles.[12] With the advent of these reptiles, mammals were hard put to survive. They were few in number and limited in variety during the reign of the reptiles. Not until after the large reptiles died out before the Mesozoic ended (some 65 million years ago) did the mammals begin to multiply and diversify.

THE MAMMALIAN INHERITANCE

With the appearance of placental mammals, the basic biological makeup man was to inherit had evolved. The human fetus and embryo would draw nourishment directly from the body of the mother instead of from an egg yolk, for membranes that had surrounded the embryo within the egg of reptilian ancestors had become fused to the walls of the womb to form the placenta. The human infant, like the offspring of other mammals, would be born immature. It would need protection and would feed upon milk produced in the mother's mammary glands. This and other food would be quickly metabolized, for the human would maintain a constant and relatively high internal body temperature. A first set of teeth, the milk teeth, would be displaced by a second set, which would be differentiated into incisors, canines, premolars, and molars. With these teeth it would be possible to reduce food to a consistency which facilitates swallowing and digestion. Grinding and chewing actions would release nutriments from foods that digestive juices could not release. Like other mammals, the young human would grow true hair—on some parts of the body at least.

Many other features man was to inherit were but modifications of earlier vertebrate structures. The brain, respiratory apparatus, and circulatory system had preceded mammals by millions of years. In the mammals they became more complex, more efficient. The number of bones, on the other hand, decreased in number. Mammals had fewer vertebrae and fewer bones in the skull; the lower jaw became a single bone rather than several as in lower vertebrates. One of the reptilian jaw bones migrated upward to form part of the middle ear. The eardrum was sunk into the head instead of being on the surface as in reptiles. Pentadactyl appendages were carried forward from reptilian ancestors.

The additional structural changes that had to occur before the genus *Homo* appeared were relatively few. They were, for the most part, but modifications of the basic placental makeup. In brief, these were to be primarily changes which resulted in keener eyesight and stereoscopic vision, differential use of forelimbs and hind limbs, and bipedal locomotion. Expansion of the braincase to accommodate a larger, more complex brain—an early mammalian trend—was to be carried much further. The teeth, while conforming to the generalized mammalian pattern, were to be reduced in number and changed in size and shape. Changes in dentition would be accompanied by changes in the shape of the face and skull.

Why did changes of this sort occur? Why did nonhuman primates evolve in the direction of man while other mammals did not? The key to differential evolution, we observed earlier, is to be found in the adaptations to different environments. Most mammalian orders, as they evolved, did so in various terrestrial environments. The primates, on the other hand, evolved in the trees. Selective factors and opportunities to which primates adapted, therefore, were of a different nature than those to which other orders adapted.

If adaptations to an arboreal existence did contribute to the uniqueness of our species, we may be able to deduce how and why from the Primate fossil evidence. It is to such evidence that we now turn.

NOTES

1. James R. Beerbower, *Search for the Past: An Introduction to Paleontology* (Englewood Cliffs, N.J.: Prentice-Hall, Inc., 1960), pp. 477–479; Edwin H. Colbert, *Evolution of the Vertebrates* (New York: John Wiley & Sons, Inc., 1955), pp. 71–72.

2. Colbert, *op. cit.*, pp. 86–89.

3. *Ibid.*, p. 88.

4. *Ibid.*, pp. 106–107.

5. *Ibid.*, p. 107; Alfred Sherwood Romer, *Vertebrate Paleontology*, 2nd ed. (Chicago: University of Chicago Press, 1945), pp. 141–143.

6. Romer, *op. cit.*, Chap. 14.

7. Colbert, *op. cit.*, Chap. 9.

8. *Ibid.*, pp. 131–134.

9. Bernhard Kummel, *History of the Earth: An Introduction to Historical Geology* (San Francisco: W. H. Freeman & Co., Publishers, 1961), p. 326.

10. Colbert, *op. cit.*, pp. 231–232.

11. *Ibid.*, pp. 235–236.

12. *Ibid.*, pp. 147–148.

9

The First Primates

In this chapter we begin a survey of some of the major fossil evidence for Primate evolution. We shall be less concerned with descriptive details, important though they are, than with interpretation. The answers we seek are to the question: What does a fossil or collection of fossils tell us about the way to modern man?

The answers, we shall find as we proceed, can be varied. There is a lack of consensus as to the meaning of certain evidence—or lack of evidence. This is to be expected. The fossil record, you will remember, is a biased sampling of past forms of life. It does not contain representatives of all extinct species and genera, nor is it safe to assume that each specimen that is part of the record was typical of its species population. Populations may vary considerably in their makeup, and the remains preserved may be those of an individual least like the majority.

Quantitatively, the Primate fossil record is impressive. The number of extinct Primate genera that have been identified exceeds that of most other mammalian orders. Unfortunately, these genera are unevenly distributed in space and time. To date, there is an absence of evidence to connect a generalized mammalian or insectivore ancestor with several mid-Paleocene species. Almost all of the early Cenozoic (Paleocene and Eocene) prosimians—more than sixty genera—have been uncovered in North America and Europe. On the other hand, virtually all evidence for the earliest known anthropoids comes from Egypt. Another fossil void separates these early anthropoids from Miocene-Pliocene hominoids of Africa, Europe, and Asia.[1]

Interpretations are further complicated by the nature of much of the evidence. Relatively few complete or nearly-complete specimens have been discovered. Quite often only the hardest parts of the body, the teeth, have managed to survive weathering, soil acids, scavengers, and other destructive agents. Fortunately, scientists have been able to devise techniques for obtaining considerable information from teeth. Explanation of a few of the clues Primate teeth offer may help answer questions which will arise in our survey of the fossil record.

CLUES FROM TEETH

Before the Eocene Epoch ended, some 37 or 38 million years ago, a primate called *Amphipithecus* was living in Burma. Our only knowledge of this animal is a section of lower jaw which, when found, contained three premolars and one molar. Cercopithecoids (Old World monkeys), apes, and hominids typically have two premolars, rather than three. A primate that departs from the pattern $\frac{2.1.2.3}{2.1.2.3}$ * is ordinarily a prosimian or a New World monkey. The latter may have a third premolar, or it may have only two molars. The teeth of prosimians likewise vary. Most have a third premolar, and many have more teeth in one jaw than in the other.

Amphipithecus was obviously not a New World monkey, since it was found in Burma. Was it a prosimian? Dr. Elwyn L. Simons of Yale University does not think so. More likely, he says, it was a higher primate so recently descended from a prosimian ancestor that the extra premolar had not yet been lost. It was, as the name given it implies, a transitional form (*Amphi* means "before"; *pithecus*, "ape"). One basis for this conclusion is the structure of the horizontal ramus, the part of the jaw that holds the teeth. The ramus is deep and massive, as in the living apes.[2]

---

* The number of each kind of tooth is identical on either side of both jaws: 2 incisors, 1 canine, 2 premolars, 3 molars.

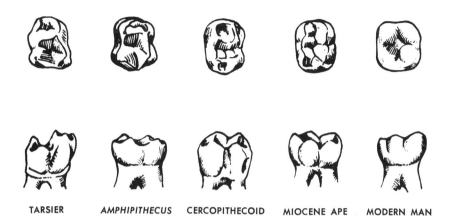

| TARSIER | AMPHIPITHECUS | CERCOPITHECOID | MIOCENE APE | MODERN MAN |

Figure 10. Primate molars (lower right). The cusp pattern of the tarsier molar is most like that of the earliest known primates. The "Y-5" pattern can be seen in the Miocene ape molar; the "±4" pattern, in the molar of modern man.

The single molar also suggests a transitional form. The cusps, or mounds of enamel, on the grinding surface of a prosimian molar form a pattern different from that of higher-primate cusps. The lower molar of a modern tarsier and several fossil prosimians, for example, has three cusps on the anterior portion and two on the back part. The distribution of enamel is considerably higher in the front. The *Amphipithecus* molar shows a similar distribution of cusps, but the front and rear of the tooth are of approximately the same height. In the latter respect, the molar is anthropoid-like.[3]

Molar patterns not only distinguish prosimians from higher primates, they also differentiate cercopithecoids from other Anthropoidea. Cercopithecoid molars (the first two and sometimes the third) are usually bilophodont (*loph* means "crest," therefore "two-crest tooth"). Two ridges or crests connect cusps which rise from each corner of the tooth. One ridge joins the two anterior cusps, the other links the rear cusps.[4] The lower molar of a living or fossil hominoid (Miocene and later), on the other hand, is likely to have a "Dryopithecus," or "Y-5," pattern. Five cusps are separated by valleys that somewhat resemble the letter Y. In modern man, the fifth cusp is often lost or reduced and there is a + instead of a Y pattern (referred to as "+4" or "+5").[5]

Hominid teeth are relatively smaller than the teeth of the great apes. This is particularly true of the canines, which among apes often overlap teeth in the opposite jaw. In the upper dentition of male apes (and some male monkeys), there is usually a *diastema* (a gap) between each canine and the incisor nearest it in order to accommodate the large canines of

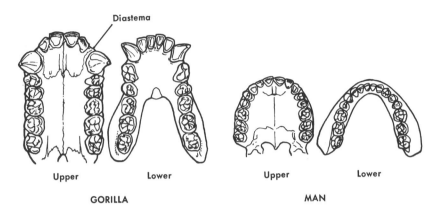

Figure 11. Characteristic differences between ape and human jaws. Apes typically have parallel rows of teeth and diastemata. The human dental arch is more rounded, and the canines and premolars are smaller.

the lower jaw. There may also be smaller gaps in the mandible for the same reason. As a rule, pressures from developing upper canines compress the first premolars of the mandible so as to form an oblique cutting edge. Such premolars (generally termed *sectorial*) have but one discernible cusp; the hominid premolar has two cusps. Because the canines interlock, movement of the ape jaw is restricted. As a consequence, the grinding surface of an ape molar is usually not worn as flat as that of most hominids.[6] Many other characteristics of teeth aid in the identification and classification of specimens.* Enough has been said, however, to indicate that teeth are a rich source of data.

PALEOCENE AND EOCENE PROSIMIANS

A tooth discovered in 1965 is thought to be a primate tooth. If it is, the Primate fossil record begins late in the Mesozoic.[7] Exactly when the order originated, presumably from an insectivore stock, is not known. The first Primates may have appeared before dinosaurs became extinct, or they may not have evolved until much later. There is little doubt that they were on the scene before the Cenozoic Era, or "Age of Mammals," began some 65 million years ago.

The first unquestionable evidence of Primates comes from mid-Paleocene deposits of about 60 million years ago in western North America, where the above-mentioned tooth was found. Fossils found in New

---

* A more detailed account of Primate dentition can be found in W. E. Le Gros Clark, *The Antecedents of Man* (New York: Harper Torchbooks, 1963), Chap. 3.

Mexico, Wyoming, Colorado, and Montana represent six prosimian genera. Seven other genera have been uncovered in later Paleocene deposits of North America and Europe. Teeth, jaws, partial skeletons, and a fairly complete specimen of one genus (*Plesiadapis*) indicate that primates of the Paleocene were much like squirrels and other rodents.[8]

The rodent-like prosimians were eventually replaced in the following epoch, the Eocene, by prosimians that resembled living lemurs and tarsiers. The new type is known from almost complete remains of two North American specimens (*Notharctus* and *Smilodectes*), skulls and limb bones of a European genus (*Necrolemur*), and other less complete remains. One family (Omomyidae) had wide distribution, for two genera have been uncovered in China, two in Europe, and several others in North America.

Fossils of Eocene primates reflect a number of significant evolutionary advances. Among the most significant were improvements in visual apparatus. The eyes were not separated by long snouts, as were those of

Figure 12.

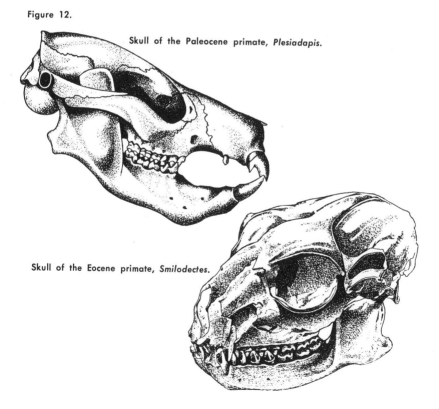

Skull of the Paleocene primate, *Plesiadapis*.

Skull of the Eocene primate, *Smilodectes*.

(Reprinted with permission from *Scientific American,* 211 [July,1964], pp. 56, 57.)

the Paleocene prosimians. Instead, the eyes were on the same plane, looking forward rather than outward. Therefore vision overlapped and stereoscopic sight was possible. A greater emphasis upon sight was accompanied by brain growth, hence an enlarged skull. The face, on the other hand, became proportionally smaller. The incisors were less slanting, less procumbent, than those of Paleocene primates; the jaws were shorter. Nerve fibers entered the skull of the Paleocene animals from the back, as is the case with quadrupedal mammals in general. The foramen magnum of the Eocene primate was to the rear of the skull, but on the underside, the ventral face of the skull. The Eocene animals appear to have had fewer claws on their digits; their hind limbs were longer in proportion to the forelimbs. Why were the Eocene types so different from their precursors? Why did the major Paleocene forms disappear? To answer these questions, let us attempt to reconstruct the course of events leading up to the changes.

MIGRATION—UP OR DOWN?

The higher-primate traits and trends found in Eocene prosimians, such as stereoscopic vision and an enlarging brain, found expression and became established as a consequence of generations of tree-dwelling. It is generally believed that they were acquired following an invasion of the trees early in Primate evolution. As two anthropologists have recently written, "The first Primates took to the trees with the sensory equipment of terrestrial animals." [9] In the trees, selective pressures for terrestrial sensory equipment were presumably lessened and the sense of sight became dominant over the sense of smell.

But why would the first Primates have taken to the trees? Conjecture has it that competition, or perhaps predation, increased on the ground. Vertical migration was a means of escaping such pressures. The fossils of the first Primates and their competitors or predators have yet to be discovered, so this idea can be neither proved nor disproved by reference to fossil evidence. What, then, is the basis for conjecture? One of the most explicit answers is furnished by Dr. Simons:

> Inasmuch as all living prosimian Primates are primarily arboreal, and since the anatomy of early Cenozoic prosimians (when known) also indicates tree dwelling habits, it is reasonable to assume that this was the broad ecological zone of ancestral members of the order. As has commonly been conjectured, however, Primates must orginally trace back to a somewhat more terrestrially oriented species, not necessarily definably a primate, existing at about the time when the order

initially differentiated. A probable indication of this is the fact that in many prosimians the olfactory sense (most effectively used among ground-dwelling species) remains highly developed.[10]

One basis for the notion of terrestrial origins, therefore, is the assumption, implicit in the last statement, that because the sense of smell is "most effectively used" on the ground, it is of little value to an arboreal animal. Indeed, Dr. Simons goes on to say, "a good sense of smell for a tree dweller has little value if the animal cannot 'see its way' to food sources. . . ."[11] We need only point out, in opposition, that olfaction may be adaptive for more than one reason. Among living Tupaiiformes, for example, the sense of smell appears to be of greater importance in reproductive behavior and in the delineation of territory than in finding food.

The biological makeup of living tree shrews provides another basis for the terrestrial-origins idea. Le Gros Clark, among others, believes it is probable that "the tree-shrews represent in their general structure a tolerably close approximation to the earliest phases in the evolution of the Primates from generalized mammalian ancestors."[12] Since the tree shrew's olfactory apparatus is better developed than that of more advanced primates, it is inferred that the generalized mammalian ancestors were terrestrial. On the other hand, the tree shrew has visual equipment superior to that of terrestrial insectivores. This difference is interpreted as an indication that ancestral tree shrews—and, by analogy, the first Primates—were changing from a predominantly smell-oriented (that is, terrestrial) brain to a sight-oriented (arboreal) brain.

Why, we wonder, did tree shrews not evolve further in the direction taken by other early prosimians? Why, once the smell-oriented brain began to show "some signs of retrogressions,"[13] were there no further advances in visual apparatus? More intensive studies of living tree shrews may be needed to answer our questions. Despite statements to the effect that *all* living prosimians are arboreal or primarily arboreal, it is possible that these primitive primates are not true tree dwellers. This possibility is suggested in the conclusion reached by three separate observers that the tree shrew (*Tupaia glis*) "probably" lives on or near the ground and climbs in low, fine-branched bushes.[14] The authors of a recent summary of information regarding mammals say much the same thing of the genus *Tupaia* without the use of "probably."[15]

Could it be that the tree shrew represents a once arboreal form that came *down* from the trees? It is as logical to suppose that traits adaptive to an arboreal environment were being lost as to assume that they were being acquired. But why might the early primates have come down from the trees? Generally speaking, animals do not abandon niches to which

149

they have become habituated unless they have to. What might have forced primates to change their way of life? The considerable variety and widespread geographic dispersal of early Cenozoic fossils appear to be relevant clues. By the early Oligocene, more than sixty genera of prosimians are known to have inhabited parts of three continents. At least seven genera of more advanced primates (to be discussed in the next chapter) lived on a fourth continent.

The diversification and dispersal of early primates are indices of reproductive success, occupation of varied niches, and migration. The three were related. As we see it, initial reproductive success eventually created an imbalance between prosimian populations and their customary need-satisfiers. Competition for food and space was inevitable. During the competitive process some animals perished. Others discovered that they could better satisfy their needs by vacating their usual niche or niches. The successful primates—those that managed to remain in the trees and retain their normal way of life—were better equipped in some way for an arboreal existence than were the animals that perished or migrated. There was, in other words, a selection for more advanced arboreal traits, traits reminiscent of a monkey or an ape rather than of a prosimian.

This selective process was probably more or less continuous for millions of years. Migrants found new forest habitats and multiplied, and the competitive process was repeated time and again. There were always some that remained in the trees and some that came down. Some of those ousted from the trees may have settled for niches on or near the forest floor. Others eventually had no choice but to venture into treeless habitats.[16] Later, they or their descendants may have regained access to trees in another geographic area. To do so possibly took many generations in some instances. During this time, structural adaptations to terrestrial niches may have been acquired; certainly, advances in the higher-primate direction were retarded.

What we are suggesting is that prosimian fossils from the Northern Hemisphere may be descendants of unsuccessful competitors for arboreal habitats and niches in another part of the world, probably Africa. Some—the more advanced Eocene forms—were descendants of ancestors that had been successful for a longer time than others. Again, the more advanced Eocene prosimians may have regained the trees earlier.

The Paleocene prosimians found in North America and Europe were possibly descendants of early arboreal failures. They themselves were apparently unable to compete with other arboreal or primarily arboreal mammals. Their dentition was adapted to rodent-like activities, such as gnawing and nibbling. True rodents invaded prosimian habitats late in the Paleocene, after which no more prosimians with predominantly rodent features evolved. Those which had already appeared seem to have been overwhelmed by expanding rodent populations.[17]

A NEW HAND

If there was competition for arboreal niches, what determined the outcome? What trait or traits differentiated the successful animals from those that descended the trees either temporarily or permanently? The former, it is reasonable to assume, were able to move about the trees with greater surety and probably with greater speed. They were therefore less likely to fall or to be captured by predators; they were better equipped to reach food at the ends of branches. Consequently, the successful primates lived longer and reproduced in greater numbers than did their less well-endowed kin.

The first Primates, like other early mammalian groups, inherited clawed, pentadactyl appendages from reptilian ancestors. By digging the claws into bark, primitive prosimians could run up and down tree trunks and along limbs. Climbing was accomplished by reaching and holding with the forelimbs while the hind limbs supported the body and provided upward thrust. The amount of thrust that could be exerted was contingent upon the structure of the hind limbs, and animals that experienced genetic changes which resulted in heavier leg musculature or longer bones in the leg or foot gained a competitive edge over others of their kind. Since the beneficiaries of such changes could ascend trees more rapidly, they were better able to elude predators and to reach scarce foods more quickly. In time, some of these primates learned to use the power of their legs for leaping from branch to branch. Leaping had its hazards, but it was a faster means of locomotion than climbing. In some areas, at least, selection for animals able to jump to safety or food then took place.

Another early selective factor is suggested by differences in the hands (manus) of living mammals. Digits of the typical mammalian hand are arranged in a fan. When the fingers are flexed to the palm, they converge. When extended, the fingers diverge from each other.[18] Such an arrangement allows a small climbing animal such as the squirrel to grasp wire, vines, or small branches by bringing the digits toward the palm. However, the grasping power of this type of hand diminishes as the fingers are extended; surety of the grip declines as the object to be grasped increases in size. Both hands are usually employed when food is brought to the mouth, and claws are essential to support when the forelimbs are employed in moving from one tree limb to another. In contrast, the human hand, and that of many nonhuman primates, is an efficient grasping instrument even when the fingers are extended to a considerable degree. This is due mainly to the fact that the first digit—the thumb, or hallux—diverges from the other digits and can function in opposition to them. Separation of the thumb from the fingers increases the total span of the hand and increases the power of the grip, particularly when the fingers operate parallel to one another. When something is grasped, the fingers encircle from one direction, the thumb from another. Thus fairly large objects can be held securely with or in the hand.

There is at present no evidence to indicate when the more human-like hand appeared. If the tree shrew manus is representative of the earliest Primate hand, the thumb may have begun to diverge shortly after the order evolved, if not before. The tree shrew hand is very similar to the typical mammalian hand (it has, in fact, sometimes been referred to as a paw), but there is a slight separation of the first digit from the fingers.[19] Fossil extremities of Primates and other mammals are scarce and, generally speaking, not too well studied. There is, however, ample evidence to show that some prosimians had acquired divergent thumbs and grasping hands no later than the Middle Eocene.[20]

The more human-like hand, whenever it appeared, was highly adaptive in an arboreal habitat. It afforded a grip that was not only more powerful but also more versatile than the grip of the typical mammalian hand. The separated thumb, operating somewhat independently of the other digits, allowed the hand to adjust to branches and limbs of varying size. This was of considerable value to leaping animals.

A number of consequences eventually stemmed from modifications in the hand. One, very possibly, was an increase in body size. More weight could be supported without any unusual increase in the strength of the digits, so animals that attained greater size through genetic changes suffered no untoward consequences on that account. On the contrary, a larger body probably had adaptive value, especially if the hands grew proportionally. Greater body size may have discouraged some predators, and larger hands could grasp larger limbs.

The new hand lessened selective pressures for claws. Animals born with mutant genes which foreshortened claws could often progress as efficiently as their normally endowed kin. Many may have moved with greater ease and speed, for they did not have to dig into a surface with their long claws and then extricate them as they progressed.

Shortening and eventual loss of the claws (or most of them) encouraged the employment of the hands for non-locomotor purposes. The forelimbs had long been used in bringing food to the mouth or nose. Primitive mammals and the tree shrew engage in this practice today, as did early dinosaurs; but both forelimbs are usually necessary to hold the food. A single human-like hand can do this job as well, if not better, and the other hand can be put to different uses. If necessary, for example,

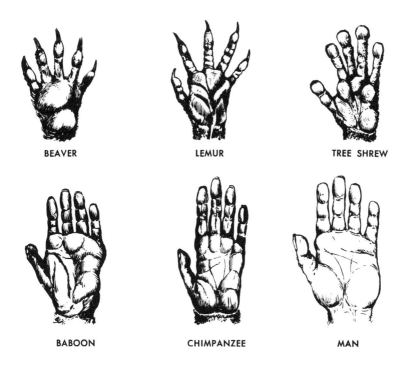

BEAVER   LEMUR   TREE SHREW

BABOON   CHIMPANZEE   MAN

Figure 13. Hands of living animals and man. (Not drawn to scale.) Note the clear separation of the thumb from the other digits in the lemur and higher-primate hands.

many primates can use one hand for support while plucking, grabbing, or catching food with the other.

The active motor variability shown in play by living prosimians and monkeys suggests the origin of other non-locomotor functions of the hand. When jumping from one limb to another, accurate employment of the hands is vital; the digits can only extend and close. But in play and exploration, the digits can assume new positions and engage in varied activities which exert no pressure for accuracy. During play a young prosimian or monkey will manipulate objects with its hands. Some of this manipulation—trying to pull a large object through a small hole, for example—serves no apparent practical purpose. Some, however, such as peeling a banana, can eventuate in the learning of adaptive behavior. Regardless of whether or not immediately adaptive behavior is learned, play increases variable usage of the hands. It may, as one writer suggests, have been a pre-adaptation for fine control. That is, when structural changes occurred which permitted the accurate manipulation of small objects, discovery of this inherent ability through play was inevitable.[21] Such structural changes included a heightening of tactile sensitivity, particularly in the terminal digit pads (volar pads). Tactile sensitivity in the digits contributed not only to fine control but also to the discrimination of objects through touch. Things could be perceived tactually while they were being seen or smelled.

Jumping and increased use of the forelimbs for non-locomotor purposes required—and encouraged—neural developments and modifications. A larger, more complex brain was a necessary accompaniment to increased and varied activities. Brain area was needed, too, to receive and interpret tactile stimuli and to make associations between the senses of touch and sight (and possibly touch and smell).

POSTURAL AND SENSORY CHANGES

Changes in the hind limbs did more than increase the speed of locomotion. Heavier musculature and lengthened limbs also resulted in a shift in total body weight, a shift in the center of gravity. Most of the animal's weight became concentrated in the rear half of the body, and a sitting posture was practical.[22] This shift in gravity contributed to the widening repertory of the hand. At the same time, increasing use of the forelimbs reinforced the tendency to squat on the hind limbs.

Frequent assumption of a semierect posture favored the establishment of genes which directed a shifting of the foramen magnum onto the ventral face of the adult skull. When nerve fibers entered the skull from underneath, rather than from the back, such a posture was simpler to maintain. Food could be brought to the mouth and other uses made of the forelimbs with less muscular strain, less bending of the backbone. It is possible, therefore, that movement of the foramen magnum prepared the way for an eventual reduction in the number of lumbar vertebrae—and attendant loss of flexibility in the lumbar region—among evolving Hominoidea.

Also related to the sitting posture and extensive use of the hands, very possibly, was a reduction in the length of the muzzle. A long muzzle usually increases sensitivity to odors—there is a greater area for chemoreceptor cells—and brings the nose and mouth of a quadrupedal animal closer to its food or source of food. In the deep forest, however, an unusually keen sense of smell is of no particular value in locating food. There is no wind to bring scents and provide directional clues; olfaction is of significance only in relation to what can be seen or touched.[23] Thus, if a forest animal is able to bring objects to the nose with its forelimbs, it suffers no great disadvantage by not having a long muzzle. Selection for genes which produced a long snout among many early prosimians was therefore lacking. Instead, there was very likely a positive selection for those genes which gave primates shorter muzzles in at least some settings.

A reduction in the size of the muzzle was accompanied by a decrease in the number of cells used for detecting odors. This meant that less of the brain was devoted to olfaction; more could be used for other purposes. As the number of cells in the upper portion of the nose decreased, the space between the eyes receded. Images picked up by each eye overlapped, and the world was seen, remembered, and interpreted in three dimensions. Prosimians with this sort of vision and brain were better able to accurately estimate distances when jumping from limb to limb. They survived longer and were reproductively more successful than their kin who failed to acquire mutations for such traits.

Differences between Paleocene and Eocene prosimians suggest that the jaw shortened at about the time the muzzle was being reduced. Shortening of the jaw implies a change in diet. The longer, more primitive jaw closed like a pair of scissors, from back to front. As the length of the jaw decreased, the point of the pivot—the point where the mandible fitted to the skull (mandibular condyles)—moved upward. The whole dentition came to meet simultaneously, so that the molars were equally effective as crushers and grinders. The shorter jaw also had greater compression power, simply because the distance between the point of pivot and end of the mandible was reduced.[24] With these changes, a considerable variety of food could be eaten; but experimentation with new foods likely preceded the changes.

Structural alterations in the eyes enabled primates to find many of the foods they could masticate and avoid some of the environmental hazards. Visual acuity, encouraged by behaviors and associations mentioned earlier, became an important selective factor as the mammalian radiation proceeded. Primates with keen eyesight could spot their increasingly larger and more numerous predators at a distance. They could locate food more readily and with greater safety. Along with acuity, the eyes of some primates also acquired sensitivity to hues. These animals could distinguish by color, as well as by shape, form, and texture. Fruits, in particular, were easier to locate.

The eyes—in conjunction with the sense of smell, perhaps—served to differentiate food from other parts of the environment. The forelimbs, as extensions of the body, served as instruments for obtaining food and conveying it to the mouth. The hands could extract insects and larvae from places not accessible to a short snout or an unspecialized tongue. Berries could be picked from thorny bushes, and fruits and leaves could be garnered from slender branches. Flexible fingers were used to seize crawling and flying insects, peel fruits, separate seeds from pods, and break some materials into bite-sized pieces. These activities found representation in the brain—in visual, memory, and association areas—and lessened the need for specialized dentition.

IN CONCLUSION

The changes we have discussed occurred among the prosimian ancestors of higher primates. While the remains of many prosimians have been found, the fossils of those ancestral to the higher primates have yet to be discovered; however, the changes are reflected in both living and extinct forms. When the remains of forms ancestral to the higher primates are found, they will exhibit traits and reflect trends which but needed to be carried further in monkeys, apes, and man. For instance, the hands of the fossil prosimians were not as flexible and the thumbs were not as opposable as they were to become among higher primates. The foramen magnum in postnatal life had begun to shift forward in Eocene primates; it was to move even farther forward in later forms. The muzzle was to be reduced still more. The brain would continue a trend toward larger size and greater complexity. Visual acuity and color vision were possibly to improve. The trend toward increased body size would also continue.

By and large, it would appear, the basic higher-primate structure was established by the Eocene. Evolution from then on consisted largely of continuing established trends, with variations from time to time. The basic structure developed in response to demands and opportunities of arboreal environments—furthered, we have suggested, by intraspecies competition.

NOTES

1. Elwyn L. Simons, "A Critical Reappraisal of Tertiary Primates," in John Buettner-Janusch (ed.), *Evolutionary and Genetic Biology of Primates*, I (New York: Academic Press Inc., 1963), 65–129.

2. Elwyn L. Simons, "The Early Relatives of Man," *Scientific American*, 211 (July, 1964), pp. 50–62.

3. W. E. Le Gros Clark, *The Antecedents of Man* (New York: Harper & Row, Publishers, 1963), pp. 81–86.

4. Carleton S. Coon, *The Origin of Races* (New York: Alfred A. Knopf, Inc., 1963), p. 134.

5. Michael Day, *Guide to Fossil Man: A Handbook of Human Paleontology* (Cleveland: The World Publishing Company, 1965), p. 24.

6. Le Gros Clark, *op. cit.*, pp. 113–114; G. H. R. von Koenigswald, "The Hominization of the Masticatory Apparatus, and Modifications of Diet," in William Howells (ed.), *Ideas on Human Evolution: Selected Essays, 1949–1961* (Cambridge: Harvard University Press, 1962), pp. 295–296.

7. Elwyn L. Simons, "Unraveling the Age of Earth and Man," *Natural History*, 76 (February, 1967), 52–59.

8. Information about fossils discussed in this section is drawn from Elwyn L. Simons, "A Critical Reappraisal of Tertiary Primates."

9. C. L. Brace and M. F. Ashley Montagu, *Man's Evolution: An Introduction to Physical Anthropology* (New York: The Macmillan Company, 1965), p. 108.

10. Elwyn L. Simons, "Fossil Evidence Relating to the Early Evolution of Primate Behavior," *Annals of the New York Academy of Sciences*, 112 (1962), 283.

11. *Ibid.*

12. W. E. Le Gros Clark, *History of the Primates*, 3rd ed. (Chicago: University of Chicago Press, 1961), p. 70.

13. *Ibid.*, p. 74.

14. Alison Bishop, "Use of the Hand in Lower Primates," in Buettner-Janusch, *op. cit.*, II, 162. The authors cited by Bishop are H. Hofer and H. Sprankel; their articles were published in 1957 and 1961.

15. Ernest P. Walker *et al.*, *Mammals of the World*, I (Baltimore: The Johns Hopkins Press, 1964), 396.

16. Cf. Elwyn L. Simons, "Fossil Primates and the Evolution of Some Primate Locomotor Systems," *American Journal of Physical Anthropology*, 26 (1967), 245.

17. Frederick Barth, "On the Relationships of Early Primates," in Howells, *op. cit.*, p. 295.

18. Bishop, *op. cit.*, p. 200.

19. *Ibid.*, p. 201.

20. Simons, "Fossil Primates and the Evolution of Some Primate Locomotor Systems," p. 243; William King Gregory, *Evolution Emerging*, I (New York: The Macmillan Company, 1951), 456 (illustrated II, 906).

21. Bishop, *op. cit.*, pp. 206–207.

22. Bernard G. Campbell, *Human Evolution* (Chicago: Aldine Publishing Company, 1966), pp. 90–91.

23. *Ibid.*, p. 218.

24. *Ibid.*, pp. 178–181.

Pre-Pleistocene Higher Primates

Human evolution included a prosimian stage. There is virtual agreement as to that. Consensus has not been reached, however, as to what the succeeding stages were. Did the line of human phylogeny stem directly from a primitive prosimian, from a monkey-like primate, or from a creature that resembled present-day apes? Each of these ideas and others have had some measure of acceptance in the past. Today, most authorities hold that the course of Primate evolution proceeded from a prosimian to a monkey-like stage. Then, from a generalized monkey group evolved the cerocithecoids and the ancestral stock of apes and hominids. The hominoid group eventually diverged, producing, among others, the forerunners of modern apes and of man.

The "anthropoid-ape hypothesis," the first view of human evolution to have any wide following, derives mainly from a comparison of the higher primates. Darwin's friend, Thomas Huxley, was among the first to conclude that "whatever part of the animal fabric" was compared, "the lower Apes [monkeys and prosimians] and the Gorilla would differ more than the Gorilla and the Man." [1] Darwin, in *The Descent of Man*, supported this conclusion. He declared that while man and the Old World monkeys had many characteristics in common, man and the "anthropomorphous apes" were even more alike. Among the apes, the chimpanzee and the gorilla "are now man's nearest allies." [2]

Comparative techniques have been increased and improved since the days of Darwin and Huxley. They have not, however, contradicted what these men said so far as many present-day scientists are concerned. George Gaylord Simpson, for example, has stated that the biochemical evidence "proves definitely" that apes are man's closest living relatives. Further, this evidence "seems to show quite conclusively that, among the apes, man is much the more closely allied to the gorilla and the chimpanzee." [3]

A minority view, which might be called the "generalized monkey hypothesis," is also based primarily on comparative evidence. Its supporters rely upon anatomical data; biochemical data are apparently ignored or are considered invalid or irrelevant. William L. Straus, Jr., who makes a good case for this point of view, argues that the apes— particularly the great apes—are too specialized to have come from the same stock as man. On the other hand, several important human traits that are essentially generalized find their counterparts in monkeys, prosimians, and even mammals of other orders. As an example of generalized characters, Straus points to the manner in which a human infant crawls about. The palm and extended fingers are placed against the ground or floor. This posture of the hands is typical of monkeys, not apes; the ape progresses quadrupedally by using the knuckles of the forelimbs for support. Relatively small canines, arms that are shorter than the legs, an absence of a "simian shelf" (bony plate that connects the two halves of the mandible at its base)—in these and several other ways man is more akin to monkeys than to apes.[4]

Why disagreements regarding the origins of the hominid line exist will become quite clear in the discussion that follows. The evidence is fragmentary and the record incomplete. It is impossible, therefore, to trace each primate group back to its point of origin. Comparative data from living animals must be relied upon, and voids are bridged with hypotheses. Hypotheses are based on the interpretations of comparative data and of fossils on either or both sides of the voids. At the same time, hypotheses influence the interpretation of data. A fossil fragment can mean one thing to a person who supports the "anthropoid-ape hypothesis." A different meaning may be assigned by someone who believes man derived from a monkey-like animal.

THE FIRST ANTHROPOIDS [5]

In the last chapter we saw that important advances in Primate evolution were made among Eocene primates in North America and Europe. Elsewhere, even greater steps in the hominid direction were taken during the same epoch. In Burma, we noted, at least one species was probably transitional to higher primates. Fossils recovered from Oligocene beds in the Fayum region of Egypt, about sixty miles southwest of Cairo, leave little doubt that higher primates had evolved in Africa before the end of the Eocene.

159

The Fayum fossils, mostly fragments and teeth, show that a variety of Anthropoidea or near-Anthropoidea lived in Egypt during some part of the Oligocene. The remains also suggest that most of the major Primate groups may have been evolving separately more than 28 million years ago. The oldest Fayum specimen, *Oligopithecus* (*oligo* means "small"; *pithecus* means "ape") *savagei* was living not long after the Oligocene began, roughly 36 million years before the present. It was apparently the first primate to have the same dental formula $\left(\frac{2.1.2.3}{2.1.2.3}\right)$ as the Old World monkeys, apes, and man. Dr. Elwyn L. Simons considers the ancestral position of *Oligopithecus* as "uncertain," but he suspects that this group may have given rise to a species from which both man and the African apes (chimpanzees and gorillas) eventually evolved.

Remains of at least five other higher-primate genera have been found in more recent Oligocene strata in the Fayum region. Only two genera, according to Simons, "are *not* apes": *Parapithecus* (*para* means "near"; hence, "near ape") and *Apidium* (after Apis, the sacred bull of Egypt). Both genera belong to a family (Parapithecidae) which, in Simons' opinion, may have been ancestral to the Old World monkeys. *Parapithecus* and *Apidium*, though stratigraphically more recent in time than *Oligopithecus*, have a more primitive dental formula $\left(\frac{2.1.3.3}{2.1.3.3}\right)$ than the latter. A fourth genus, *Aeolopithecus* (after Aeolus, god of the winds) is regarded by Simons as a likely Oligocene ancestor of the gibbon.

By the middle of the Oligocene, if not earlier, yet another primate group, *Propliopithecus* (*pro* means "before"; *plio*, "more") *haeckeli* (after Haeckel, a German scientist), was on the Egyptian scene. Details of this species' dentition, Simons has said, "make the animal seem more closely related to man's family, the Hominidae," than to any of the apes. However, Simons does not rule out the possibility that an as-yet-unknown species of *Propliopithecus* was the stock from which both the Hominidae and the African apes evolved.

The youngest (26 to 28 million years ago) of the Fayum genera is *Aegyptopithecus*. It is also the only group represented by a nearly complete skull, discovered in 1966. The jaw is more apelike than the jaw of *Propliopithecus*; the teeth are much like those of a gorilla. "Here," Simons says, "was an animal of the right form and the right age to be ancestral to the dryopithecine apes of the following epoch. It could thus occupy an early position in man's lineage and even perhaps be the direct forebear of apes such as the modern gorilla as well." He is inclined to believe that *Aegyptopithecus* descended from a *Propliopithecus* group.

The Fayum fossils strongly suggest, but do not definitely prove, that lines leading to the Old World monkeys and the Hominoidea became differentiated during the late Eocene or early Oligocene. These remains further suggest that early ancestors of man and the great apes were going their separate evolutionary ways before the Oligocene ended some 25 or 26 million years ago. If the Hominidae evolved directly from a *Propliopithecus* species, rather than from *Aegyptopithecus*, this separation of the Hominoidea probably occurred more than 30 million years before the present.

All of the Fayum primates were relatively small. *Aegyptopithecus*, the largest, was no larger than a gibbon. The smallest, *Parapithecus* and *Apidium*, seem to have been about the size of a squirrel monkey or a tarsier. The habitat of the Fayum primates was a forest of tall trees. Because of the tall trees, Simons believes, "early pongids were then more highly arboreal than at the present time." Their way of life involved "feeding on leaf buds and fruits near the end of branches," which "gave survival value to certain kinds of dexterity," such as climbing, clinging, and leaping. Such a way of life is practiced today by large lemurs, more so than by the chimpanzees and gorillas. It is possible, therefore, that the Oligocene anthropoids shared anatomical similarities with some of the living lemurs, as well as characteristics of the higher primates.

Since most of the Fayum genera were "apes," it would appear that hominoid characteristics proved to be advantageous quite early in Primate evolution. Such characteristics may have included a larger, more complex brain which enabled primitive hominoids to better adapt to changing conditions (for example, the radiation of other mammals) than their closest competitors (probably prosimians). They may have included structural features which permitted better vision or greater agility in the trees. Hominoid traits, whatever they were, apparently continued to be adaptive during the Miocene and the Pliocene, which began approximately 26 million and 7 million years ago, respectively. During these epochs, ape-like creatures became distributed on all the Old World continents—from Spain to China, and from the U.S.S.R. to Kenya.

MIOCENE-PLIOCENE HOMINOIDS *

The Miocene saw the appearance of a variety of hominoids. The exact number of genera and species that did evolve by early Pliocene times is currently in doubt. On the record, there are some thirty genera,

* The Miocene and the Pliocene are often discussed together because the boundary between the two epochs is not always clear.

most of which can be traced to the Miocene; but Simons argues that most of these categories are spurious. He attributes the proliferation of genera and species not so much to diversification among the primates as to some of the taxonomic practices of the past. Many of these practices were based on ignorance as to the distribution and range available for the primates concerned. For example, two quite similar jaw fragments, one from France and the other from East Africa, might be classified as separate genera. The similarities would be ignored because it was assumed that geographic distance or ecological barriers made it impossible for the two specimens to have been members of the same species or genus.

After considerable study, Dr. Simons has sorted most of the Miocene-Pliocene fossils into four major groupings: *Pliopithecus, Oreopithecus, Dryopithecus,* and *Ramapithecus.* We shall discuss each of these genera separately.

Pliopithecus

Pliopithecus ("more ape"), which lived during most of the Miocene and into the Pliocene, is generally regarded as part of, or very close to, the gibbon lineage. This conclusion is based on considerable evidence from Europe and Africa, including an almost complete skull and skeleton. Unlike the living gibbon, which has arms considerably longer than its legs, the limbs of *Pliopithecus* were of equal length. Since brachiators normally have longer arms than legs, the fossil animal presumably did not use its forelimbs as the primary means of locomotion.

Oreopithecus

Despite an abundance of fossils, recovered mainly from early Pliocene deposits, *Oreopithecus* has proved unusually difficult to classify. This difficulty highlights one of the problems associated with the reconstruction of Primate evolution. Fossil gaps and incomplete specimens make it impossible to formulate clear conceptions of primate structures at certain evolutionary stages. The earliest hominids would be expected to have several of the characteristics of the stock from which they sprang—but how many, and of what kind? If a fossil has monkey, ape, and hominid traits, should it be classified as a monkey, an ape, or a hominid? Should each trait be given equal weight, or are certain traits more diagnostic than others?

In 1872 the name *Oreopithecus* (*oreo* means "mountain") was given to a mandible with teeth that had been found in central Italy. Subsequent discoveries have shown its probable habitat to have been forested

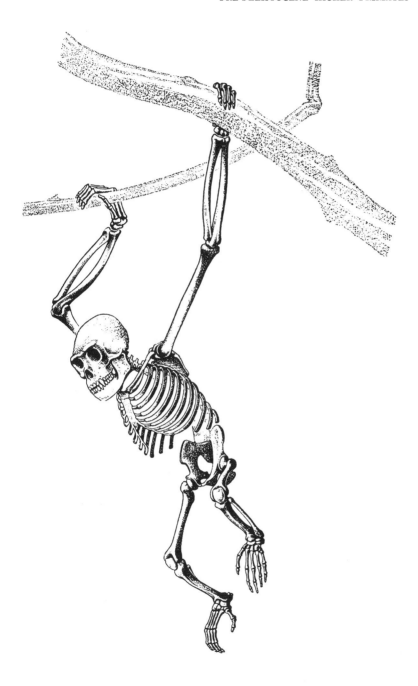

Figure 14. Reconstructed skeleton of *Oreopithecus*. (Reprinted with permission from *Scientific American*, 211 [July, 1964], p. 59.)

swamplands rather than the mountains and have led some to question its status as an ape. Prior to 1955 *Oreopithecus* was regarded variously as an Old World monkey, a great ape, a form transitional to apes, a separate ape family, and a primitive hominid. Lack of consensus was hardly surprising, for all studies were based on teeth and jaws or on casts —bad casts—of these parts. Between 1955 and 1958 the fossil collection was greatly enriched by skull and body parts of at least fifty individuals. In 1958 the better part of a young adult skeleton (badly crushed) was added.

The new *Oreopithecus* materials should have clarified matters. They did, but only to the extent that the idea that *Oreopithecus* might have been a cercopithecoid was abandoned. The several men who have studied the fossils still do not agree as to what kind of hominoid the fossils represent. *Oreopithecus* is still variously considered as a member of the family Pongidae (apes), the family Hominidae (hominids), or a family of its own.

The bases for confusion are quite evident in a summary presented by William L. Straus, Jr., who has made a thorough study of the *Oreopithecus* collection. Dr. Straus found only three cercopithecoid characters, two of which are shared by hominids (comparatively short hip bones, for example). Four characters are shared by cercopithecoids and pongids; five others are peculiar to living or fossil Pongidae. Some of the pongid features, Straus reasons, represent specializations connected with brachiation. The forelimbs, for example, are longer than the hind limbs, as is usual among brachiating primates. The total list of characters of *Oreopithecus* found among hominoids is twenty-six; thirteen of these seemingly apply only to the Hominidae.

Was *Oreopithecus* a great ape or a hominid? In terms of body size— it was as large as a present-day chimpanzee—it could have been either. The highest estimate of its cranial capacity, 529 cc., suggests an unusually large-brained ape or a primitive hominid. Even 400 cc., Straus' estimate, is not much outside the range of some of the earliest known hominids (435–700 cc.). *Oreopithecus* had a broad and shallow trunk, as do both hominids and great apes. However, it seems to have had five lumbar vertebrae, the number normally found in man and the gibbons (the great apes usually have less than five). Certain features of the face and skull are more hominid than pongid. The long protruding jaw of the ape is absent; the face is short and flat. The location of the foramen magnum also implies hominid status; it is farther forward than in the ape or monkey skull.[6] This suggests that *Oreopithecus* was evolving toward erect posture and bipedal locomotion. It might also indicate that *Oreopithecus* was in the process of losing adaptations to erect posture acquired by its ancestors. The second possibility seems

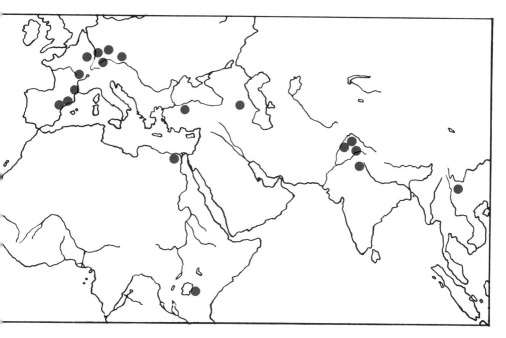

Figure 15. Range of dryopithecines during the Miocene and early Pliocene.

more likely if this group migrated to a swampy habitat or occupied an area which became swampy. In such case, they, like species of New World monkeys, would have been forced to remain in the trees.

The classification of *Oreopithecus* will probably continue to be problematic until more complete specimens—of other Miocene-Pliocene hominids, as well as of *Oreopithecus*—are found. More complete specimens might also tell us whether this primate represented a step forward in the hominid direction, or a step backward.

Dryopithecus

From the quantity of fossil materials found, the dryopithecines ("oak apes") appear to have been the most numerous, the most far-flung, and the most variable of the early hominoid groups. Remains of about 550 *Dryopithecus* specimens have been found in Miocene and Pliocene strata of Europe, Asia, and Africa. When alive, these animals presumably ranged from the size of a small chimpanzee to the size of a modern gorilla. Some were apparently quite similar to *Pliopithecus* in limb structure and dentition. This group, it is generally agreed, included ancestors of today's chimpanzees and gorillas. One *Dryopithecus* subgenus (*Sivapithecus*) was probably ancestral to the orangutan.[7]

165

The earliest of the known dryopithecines appear to be members of an East African subgenus, *Proconsul* * (originally classified as a genus). Most *Proconsul* fossils date from the early Miocene. One site in Uganda, where remains of a gorilla-sized ape (*Dryopithecus major*) were found, has been determined to be 19 million years old by the potassium-argon method. The Uganda materials, which include an excellent fossil palate and part of the face and lower jaw, appear to Simons and others to be from animals probably related to present-day gorillas.

The most complete specimen, *Dryopithecus africanus* (formerly *Proconsul africanus*), was discovered in Kenya. Its skull, almost complete in the facial portions, exhibits a mixture of higher primate features. Absence of a supraorbital torus (bony ridge over the eye sockets), for example, is more typical of monkeys and modern man than of the African apes. Impressions taken from inside the skull show that the brain resembled the brain of a present-day Old World monkey.[8] The dentition of this and other *Proconsul* specimens is pongid in its general features, but some incisors are hominid-like.[9]

A fossil hand and a few limb bones are of considerable interest to a number of scientists. These parts imply that *Proconsul* was not fully adapted to brachiation, at least not to the sort of brachiation practiced by living apes. The monkey-like structure of a forelimb indicates that the arm did not have the same range of motion as the arms of apes and man. At the same time, the thumb was not fully opposable to the other prehensile digits, a condition typical of a brachiating ape rather than a monkey.[10]

These few fossils from the limbs bear directly upon the disagreement regarding man's genetic ties with other primates. Many who hold that man and the great apes are most closely allied believe that the common ancestor of both was a brachiator. This belief or hypothesis is based on the fact that the arms and shoulders of man and the apes allow for free-swinging activities, while many monkeys apparently have difficulty raising their arms directly overhead. Furthermore, many believe, swinging through the trees encouraged bipedalism, for it brought the body into a vertical position. To opponents of this point of view, therefore, the *Proconsul* bones are evidence that man could not have had a brachiating ancestor—and perhaps no apelike ancestor. The limb bones and partially opposable thumb are interpreted to mean that Miocene apes passed through a "pro-brachiation" stage. That is, "an active quadrupedal form was developing the locomotor characteristics of a brachiator." [11] Full brachiation, when it finally evolved, would be too recent

---

* *Proconsul* means "before Consul." "Consul" was the name of a trained chimpanzee that performed in London music halls.

in time "to be considered as a possible preceding stage in the bipedalism of hominids." [12] In short, man and apes, to become the distinct creatures that they are, began evolving separately before structural specialization for brachiation developed.*

What is the true significance of the *Proconsul* fossils? Their meaning obviously depends upon one's point of view. They can, as we have seen, give indirect support to the "generalized monkey hypothesis." On the other hand, it can be argued with considerable justification that the limb and hand bones prove nothing. They may represent a species that was a side-branch in Primate evolution, or the bones may be from an animal that was quite atypical of its species. Again, the fossils can be interpreted as an indication that separate evolution of the Pongidae and Hominidae did not begin until late in the Miocene or early in the Pliocene—or that separate evolution began early in the Miocene, or even late in the Oligocene. Clearly, more complete specimens are needed before any definite conclusions can be drawn.

Ramapithecus

In 1934, G. Edward Lewis described a new genus and species of fossil primate uncovered in the Siwalik hills of India. The specimen, Lewis emphasized, possessed some hominid characters; but he cautiously classified his late Miocene find as an anthropoid ape, giving it the name *Ramapithecus brevirostris*. (Rama is a hero in Hindu mythology; *brevis* means "short"; *rostris* refers to a beak or beaklike part.) Also from Siwalik deposits came fossils of another genus, *Sivapithecus* (Siva is a Hindu deity).

Scant attention seems to have been paid Lewis' references to the hominid features of *Ramapithecus*. Nor did a 1938 paper by Lewis and two other scientists make much impression although they stated: "While the Siwalik genus *Ramapithecus* and the South African *Australopithecus* are still apes, by definition, they are almost on the human threshold in their known anatomical characters." [13]

It was not until the early 1960's that *Ramapithecus* began to receive serious consideration as a possible hominid. In the meantime, a number of candidates for the family Hominidae had been proposed. These candidates included *Proconsul*, various species of *Dryopithecus* (according to earlier classifications), *Sivapithecus*, and *Bramapithecus* (found at the initial *Ramapithecus* site). Each of these was eliminated. *Dryo-*

---

* Arguments regarding the role of brachiation in evolution, as well as observations of locomotor activities of living primates, are presented in Virginia Avis, "Brachiation: The Crucial Issue for Man's Ancestry," *Southwestern Journal of Anthropology*, 18 (1962), 119–148.

167

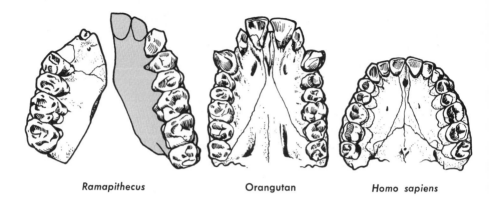

Ramapithecus   Orangutan   Homo sapiens

Figure 16. Upper jaws of *Ramapithecus*, orangutan, and *Homo sapiens*. (Not drawn to scale.) Curvature of the dental arc and relative tooth size suggest that *Ramapithecus* was an early hominid ancestor.

pithecus (including *Proconsul*), many scientists agreed, was too advanced in the pongid direction to have been in the human line of descent. Simons found *Sivapithecus* to be an Asian subgenus of *Dryopithecus*, and *Bramapithecus* proved to be part of the *Ramapithecus* specimen.

During the 1960's *Ramapithecus* gained acceptance as a possible late-Miocene or early-Pliocene ancestor to man, largely because of publications by Dr. Simons. The evidence, as described by Simons, is scanty—but rather convincing. The initial specimen consists of a portion of maxilla (upper jaw) containing two molars, both premolars, and the root of the lateral incisor (incisor immediately adjacent to the canine). In addition, the sockets for the canine and central incisor are preserved. As in later hominids, crowns of the cheek teeth are low (they are relatively high in apes). The incisors and canines, as reconstructed, are small compared with those of the dryopithecines and modern apes. The palate is arched, as is the palate of any member of the Hominidae. Of particular significance is the direction the row of teeth take. The cheek teeth and canines in one side of the ape or monkey jaw are more or less parallel to teeth on the opposite side. The human jaw, on the other hand, is curved, arcuate. So it is with the *Ramapithecus* jaw; the curvature of the row of teeth is hominid, and the muzzle is short.

In 1961 Dr. Louis S. B. Leakey reported the discovery of some other fossil maxillae, parts of either side of the upper jaw with teeth. These teeth are also similar to hominid teeth, and certain characteristics suggest facial foreshortening (a short muzzle). A comparison of this specimen, *Kenyapithecus wickeri*, with *Ramapithecus* convinced Simons and others that the two were very similar. The two genera were subsequently lumped together as a single genus, *Ramapithecus*. Potassium-argon dating showed the "Kenya ape" to be about 14 million years old. The estimated age of the specimen from India, derived from relative dating techniques prior to dating of the African find, is between 10 and 12 million years.

Dr. Leakey reported in 1967 the discovery of an even earlier (early- to middle-Miocene) hominid species, *Kenyapithecus africanus*. He also argued that although *Kenyapithecus* resembles *Ramapithecus*, the two are distinguishable genera.[14] Dr. Simons believes Leakey is in error; the specimens described are not hominids, but "apes of the genus *Dryopithecus*."

A dozen or so specimens of *Ramapithecus* are now known from North India, Kenya, and Yunnan, China. All consist of jaw fragments and teeth. Is it wise to conclude from such evidence that *Ramapithecus* was in the human line of descent? Simons seemingly believes that it is. As early as 1961, he stated that it would be somewhat illogical to assume that *Ramapithecus* was *not* a hominid. If the fossils are remains of apes, no such apes have been found or identified. And *Ramapithecus* is the type of creature that might be expected to have evolved by the Miocene in view of the nature of hominid evidence from the Upper Pliocene or Lower Pleistocene (see Chapter 11). More recently, Simons and David Pilbeam have stated that *Ramapithecus* is "best regarded as a hominid, not a hominid-like pongid, because it already exhibits the basic dental adaptations of *Homo* and *Australopithecus*." [15] (*Australopithecus* is discussed in the next chapter.)

CONCLUSIONS

Fossils found in Egypt seemingly indicate that higher primates were evolved from one or more prosimian groups before the Eocene epoch ended some 37 or 38 million years ago. Within the next 10 million years or so, during the Oligocene, separate lines leading to the Old World monkeys, the Pongidae, and Hominidae were possibly established. By then, too, the gibbons had diverged from other apes. Due largely to the fragmentary nature of most of the fossil evidence, the identity of man's Oligocene precursor is somewhat in doubt. Hominid-like features of the dentition of *Propliopithecus haeckeli* would seem to make this species the most likely candidate, and it is so regarded by some scientists. There is a possibility, however, that another *Propliopithecus* species gave rise to both the Hominidae and the great apes. In such case, the hominid line possibly stemmed from a species of *Aegyptopithecus*.

A gap of some 10 million years separates the Oligocene primates and the earliest Miocene fossils. Approximately 20 million years ago, ancestors of the gibbon (*Pliopithecus*) and the chimpanzee and gorilla (*Dryopithecus*) were on the scene. There is as yet no eivdence that a hominid-like creature had evolved by that time. Hominids (*Ramapithecus*) first begin to appear in strata that date from approximately 14 million years before the present.

Similarities in the molars of *Ramapithecus* and *Dryopithecus* species of equivalent size suggest to Simons and Pilbeam that both genera shared a common ancestry. On the basis of this and other evidence, they tentatively postulate that

> an early hominoid line gave rise to the ancestors of Pongo and the late Oligocene or early Miocene species of *Dryopithecus*-like apes, at present unknown, which were ancestral to *Pan*, *Gorilla*, and perhaps to *Homo*. During the first half of the Miocene the Hominidae became differentiated so that by late Miocene time pongids and hominids are clearly recognizable as separate throughout the Old World.[16]

We have no reason to suspect that any of the *Dryopithecus* fossils that predate *Ramapithecus* are hominid-like rather than apelike. It might be noted, though, that it is often assumed that the existence of a feature present in living apes but absent in man means that a specimen could not have been in the hominid line. A pongid specialization, in other words, usually eliminates a fossil specimen from consideration as an ancestor of man. One such "specialization," for example, is a projecting conical canine. Dr. Le Gros Clark points out that assumptions as to what constitutes a "specialization" are quite arbitrary. Thinking of this sort, he says, accepts the "false premise that even a slight degree of morphological specialization is not capable of undergoing an evolutionary reversal." Paleontology shows that it is not at all unusual for a character to be acquired, then lost, and there is evidence that a lost character can be reacquired.[17]

What happened during the roughly 40 million years we have discussed in this chapter is a matter of conjecture. There are no fossils to definitely link any prosimian group or groups with the Oligocene forms; there is no evidence which links the latter with Miocene primates. A gap of some 24 million years separates *Propliopithecus* and *Ramapithecus*. We know for certain that during these millions of years our ancestors became larger—as did all hominoids—and experienced changes in dentition. Changes in dentition suggest a departure from earlier dietary habits, which in turn suggests occupation of a different ecological niche.

What new or different niche might our prehominid ancestors have moved into? In view of later developments, it is reasonable to assume that they gradually learned to exploit opportunities on the ground. They were able to survive terrestrial hazards because they lived in groups. Initially, perhaps, the groups were loosely structured, somewhat like a number of arboreal monkey troops today. Gradually, foodstuffs available on or from the ground—grasses, roots, berries, various crawling and creeping things—became major sources of nourishment. As the prehominids became more experienced, better organized, and perhaps larger in size, they spent less and less time in the trees. Eventually, the arboreal habitat was vacated altogether.

Why did our ancestors vacate the trees? Answers to this question fall into one of two broad categories: (a) our forebears were forced out of the trees, or (b) they entered upon a terrestrial way of life on their own initiative. One current idea, for example, is that the prehominids became too large to subsist solely or primarily upon foodstuffs accessible to them in the trees. They, like living chimpanzees and gorillas, were forced to spend much of their time on the ground seeking food. One objection to this hypothesis is that our ancestors were completely, not just partially, divorced from an arboreal habitat. Apes still use trees as nesting places, if not as sources of food.

Some evolutionists are of the opinion that the transition to a terrestrial existence was initiated by dry spells during the Miocene. Trees were killed, the forests shrank, and arboreal habitats became quite limited. In the competition for arboreal habitats, our ancestors lost out to other primates. Professor Hooton thought this idea "ridiculous":

> Any change of climate involving deforestation of the ancestral area would either be sufficiently gradual to permit our arboreal ancestors to migrate to other forest zones, or, if of a sudden or cataclysmic nature, would have destroyed both the trees and the apes perching thereon. When the climate changes, most animals follow their congenial environment to a place where it remains fixed and constant.[18]

Hooton believed that our ancestors "saw and accepted the chance of a larger, more varied, and fuller diet; they wanted to live their lives more abundantly." [19] Whatever the reason, the fact that our ancestors did forsake the trees had far-reaching consequences. What these consequences were shall concern us in the next two chapters.

NOTES

1. Thomas H. Huxley, "On the Relation of Man to the Lower Animals," *Man's Place in Nature and Other Anthropological Essays*, authorized ed. (New York: D. Appleton and Company, 1898), p. 116. (Originally published in London in 1863.)

2. Charles Darwin, *The Descent of Man and Selection in Relation to Sex*, 2nd ed. (New York: D. Appleton and Company, 1889), pp. 153–155.

3. George Gaylord Simpson, "Biological Sciences," in Robert M. Hutchins and Mortimer J. Adler (eds.), *The Great Ideas Today, 1965* (Chicago: William Benton, Publisher, 1965), p. 301.

4. William L. Straus, Jr., "The Riddle of Man's Ancestry," in William Howells (ed.), *Ideas on Human Evolution: Selected Essays, 1949–1961* (Cambridge: Harvard University Press, 1962), pp. 69–104.

5. Except as otherwise indicated, factual materials used in the balance of this chapter are drawn from the following articles by Elwyn L. Simons: "Some Fallacies in the Study of Hominid Phylogeny," *Science*, 141 (1963), 879–889; "A Critical Reappraisal of Tertiary Primates," in John Buettner-Janusch (ed.), *Evolutionary and Genetic Biology of Primates*, I (New York: Academic Press Inc., 1963), 65–129; "The Early Relatives of Man," *Scientific American*, 211 (July, 1964), 50–62; "New Fossil Apes from Egypt and the Initial Differentiation of Hominoidea," *Nature*, 205 (1965), 135–139; "Unraveling the Age of Earth and Man," *Natural History*, 76 (1967), 52–59; "Fossil Primates and the Evolution of Some Primate Locomotor Systems," *American Journal of Physical Anthropology*, 26 (1967), 241–254; "The Earliest Apes," *Scientific American*, 217 (December, 1967), 28–35.

6. William L. Straus, Jr., "The Classification of *Oreopithecus*," in Sherwood L. Washburn (ed.), *Classification and Human Evolution* (Chicago: Aldine Publishing Company, 1963), pp. 146–177.

7. David Pilbeam, "Notes on *Ramapithecus*, the Earliest Known Hominid, and *Dryopithecus*," *American Journal of Physical Anthropology*, 25 (1966), 4.

8. M. F. Ashley Montagu, *An Introduction to Physical Anthropology*, 3rd ed. (Springfield, Ill.: Charles C Thomas, Publisher, 1960), p. 107.

9. W. E. Le Gros Clark, *The Fossil Evidence for Human Evolution*, 2nd ed. (Chicago: University of Chicago Press, 1964), p. 178.

10. John Napier, "The Locomotor Functions of Hominids," in Washburn, *op. cit.*, p. 185.

11. *Ibid.*

12. Gerhard Heberer, "The Subhuman Evolutionary History of Man," in Howells, *op. cit.*, p. 219.

13. Cited in L. S. B. Leakey, "An Early Miocene Member of Hominidae," *Nature*, 213 (1967), 155–163.

14. *Ibid.*

15. D. R. Pilbeam and Elwyn L. Simons, "Some Problems of Hominid Classification," *American Scientist*, 53 (1965), 238.

16. Elwyn L. Simons and D. R. Pilbeam, "Preliminary Revision of the Dryopithecinae (Pongidae, Anthropoidea)," in *Yearbook of Physical Anthropology 1965*, Vol. 13, p. 72.

17. Le Gros Clark, *op. cit.*, pp. 44, 181.

18. Earnest A. Hooton, *Up From the Ape* (New York: The Macmillan Company, 1937), pp. 114–115. Copyrighted, 1937, by The Macmillan Company.

19. *Ibid.*, p. 115.

II

Early Hominids: Finds and Problems

Fragments of what may have been hominids date back some 14 million years. For over 10 million years thereafter, until approximately 2 million years ago, the record is barren. Then remains begin to appear of not one, but of two or three possible hominid types. Each of three hominid types, all from South and East Africa, has been labelled "first man" in some publication. Most scientists, however, have seemingly adopted a wait-and-see attitude. There is reason for caution. New finds are constantly coming to light as a result of new discoveries or reinterpretations of known fossils. *Homo habilis*, one of the three hominid types reported to be "first man," was not described in a scientific journal until 1964; and, as we shall see, its taxonomic status has been questioned. Fossil materials for two other hominid types (usually referred to collectively as the Australopithecinae) are so vast that definitive analysis has not been completed. And there are the usual problems associated with fragments and incomplete skeletons. The first discoveries of these hominid types were made in South Africa. We will consider these finds, and then turn to the more recent East African discoveries.

THE SOUTH AFRICAN FINDS [1]

A number of significant fossil discoveries have been entirely fortuitous. Among these was the first evidence of manlike creatures in South Africa. As South African cities began to expand following World

173

War I, cement was needed for construction, and limestone sources in the Johannesburg vicinity were sought and located. Limestone deposits there, as elsewhere, were often interspersed with cracks and caves that had become filled with debris. The debris consisted primarily of a cement-like mixture of sand, soils, and pebbles that contained remains of animals. The mixture, known as breccia, had to be blasted before some of the limestone could be quarried. In the process of blasting, fossils came to light.

In 1924 one of these fossils, a baboon skull, came into the posssession of a student at Witwatersrand University at Johannesburg. She took the skull to a professor of anatomy at the University, Dr. Raymond A. Dart. Dart was impressed. The skull, which came from a quarry near Taung (about two hundred miles south and west of Johannesburg), was the first evidence that prehistoric primates had lived south of Egypt on the African continent. The professor learned that a miner had saved a number of fossil-laden rocks blasted at the quarry, and he immediately arranged to obtain these rocks.

After examining the rocks, Dart wrote: "I found the virtually complete cast of the interior of a skull among them. This brain cast was as big as that of a large gorilla; and fortunately it fitted at the front end onto another rock." Picking away at the second rock, there emerged "the complete facial skeleton of an infant only about 5 or 6 years old, which looked amazingly human." Dart painstakingly separated the specimen from breccia, and early in 1925 he issued a preliminary report describing the find. He stressed the human qualities of the face and the largeness of the brain capacity relative to apes of like size. "The specimen is of importance," he said, "because it exhibits an extinct race of apes intermediate between living anthropoids and man."

Reaction to *Australopithecus africanus* ("southern ape of Africa"), as Dart named the Taung specimen, was largely negative. It was of scientific interest because it indicated the presence of early primates in that part of the world, but few scientists accepted Dart's conclusion that the "southern ape" represented an "intermediate" stage. The general opinion was that the professor had exaggerated the human-like features of the skull. He had failed to take into consideration the fact that the young of apes and humans exhibit a number of structural similarities.

Misinterpretation of the data was but one of Dart's sins, so far as British scientists were concerned. He was also taken to task for publishing hastily, for failing to call upon an established authority for assistance and opinions, and for displaying ignorance in his "barbarous" combination of Latin- and Greek-based terms in the word "Australopithecus." The young professor, it appears in retrospect, was publicly chastised for his presumptuousness. He was an unknown in scientific circles, and, as such, he should have proceeded more cautiously. Above all, he should have sought the advice of older and wiser men.

But Dart refused to recant or retreat. He had examined the fossil; his critics had not. The skull, he knew, was constructed somewhat differently from that of an ape. For one thing, the foramen magnum and occipital condyles (knobs that articulate with the first neck, or cervical, vertebrae) were farther forward. The occipital torus (the area where neck muscles are attached to the occiput, or rear of the skull) was lower. These two features indicated that the Taung child had probably balanced its head over the spine much as we do. Very probably, therefore, it had walked in a more or less erect position. The nose and orbits for the eyes were, like the milk teeth, comparable to features of a human child of about six, rather than a young gorilla or chimpanzee. The skull above the orbits, the cranial vault, was also higher and more human-like. The incisors had been worn down, a condition sometimes found among primitive peoples, but never in young apes.

The "Taung baby," or "Dart's baby" as some called it, was relegated to near-obscurity for over a decade. The prestige of Dart's critics was such as to make the find somewhat of a joke. An unbiased appraisal was virtually impossible. Too, discoveries were being made in other parts of the world during the 1920's and 1930's that tended to prove that the critics were right. The discoveries were not remains of creatures with ape-sized brains, but fossils that exhibited definite hominid characteristics.

Despite the unfavorable climate of opinion, two men of prominence were interested enough to examine the Taung skull for themselves. One was Aleš Hrdlička, the leading American anthropologist of his day. The other, Robert Broom, was a physician by training and a paleontologist by choice. Hrdlička felt that more evidence, particularly adult specimens, was needed to establish the taxonomic identity of the skull. Broom, who had himself made some significant fossil discoveries of links between reptiles and mammals in South Africa, was less cautious. The Taung skull, he concluded, "was practically the 'missing link'—the most important fossil find ever made." Broom did more than offer Dart verbal support; more importantly, he was to join the search for evidence within a few years. Until then, however, he had to practice medicine for a livelihood.

In the meantime Dart freed the lower jaw of the Taung child and, in 1929, the two men were able to see the crowns of the teeth. What they saw was definite proof that the skull was not from an extinct ape. Not only did the child have relatively small canines and incisors, as do humans, but the cusps of the lower milk molars were developed for

175

grinding in the same manner as the cusps of deciduous human molars.

At Dart's urging, General Jan Christiaan Smuts, then deputy prime minister of the Union of South Africa, offered Dr. Broom a post in the Transvaal Museum in Pretoria. Thus, at the age of sixty-eight, Broom's avocation became his profession; he was able to spend his time searching for fossils. For some months he searched limeworks near Pretoria, bringing to light remains of extinct rats, moles, and a small saber-toothed tiger.

Broom believed in cooperating with the press, and South African newspapers carried reports of his finds. Two of Dart's students read these reports and came to Broom with information about finds they had made, a number of small baboon skulls. The cave in which the skulls were found was at Sterkfontein, about thirty miles from Johannesburg. Of course Dr. Broom was interested in visiting the cave.

The students and Broom arrived at Sterkfontein in August, 1936. A few days later, with the cooperation of the quarry manager, Broom came into possession of another "ape-man" specimen. When all the fragments that could be found were cleaned and put together, Broom said, "we found we had most of the skull, except for the lower jaw, of a creature which we eventually called Plesianthropus transvaalensis" ("near-man of the Transvaal"). It, too, was "intermediate between living anthropoids and man." The brain size (about 560 cc.) was that of a gorilla, and the lower part of the face protruded somewhat in an ape-like manner. Other features, such as the position of the foramen magnum and characteristics of the teeth, were predominantly hominid.

Although the skull was from an adult, *Plesianthropus* failed to satisfy the skeptics. Like the Taung skull, it did not exhibit features which fitted in with prevailing conceptions of man's ancestry. Nor did the next specimen Broom was to locate meet exisiting specifications.

A New Australopithecine *

Quarry workers kept Broom supplied with fossils from the caves and quarry at Sterkfontein for the next two years. Bits of skull, parts of limb bones, and teeth of *Plesianthropus* were recovered. Fossils of animals *Plesianthropus* may have eaten—rats, moles, and jackals—were also found. Then, in 1938, the quarry manager handed Broom a fragment which Broom described as "a beautiful palate of a large apeman with one molar tooth in position." The material in which the jaw was embedded was different from breccia in the Sterkfontein cave. Where had

* Because the first find was named *Australopithecus*, it and other similar or related forms were to be considered by some as members of the subfamily Australopithecinae. "Australopithecine" (without capitalization) is used as a less formal reference.

it been found? Reluctantly, for Broom paid for his fossils, the manager referred the doctor to a schoolboy at a farm near Kromdraai, about two miles away.

The schoolboy not only gave Broom fragments he had found; he also helped in the recovery of other pieces. When the bits of bone were joined, Broom said, "it was found that we had the greater part of the left side and of the right lower jaw of a very fine skull, with many of the teeth well preserved." At the time, the cranial capacity of the skull was estimated to be 650 cc., larger than that of prior South African finds. (More recent estimates place the capacity at a maximum of 550 cc.) The molars were also substantially larger. "In some respects," Broom wrote, "it was more human; in a few, less human. We described it as a new genus named *Paranthropus robustus*" ("akin to man," or "near-man").

World War II stopped work at the limeworks, and Broom's supply of fossils was choked off. It was just as well, for time was needed to examine and analyze the data that had been accumulating. From study of the data came a book by Broom and an assistant, G. W. H. Schepers, *The South African Fossil Ape-Men*, which was awarded the Elliot Medal for the most important book in biology published in 1946. The scientific world was forced to take another look at the South African finds.

Bone-Tooth-Horn Culture

Students and another baboon skull drew Dart back into the search for fossil evidence in 1945. The students had found the skull in Makapansgat Valley, some two hundred miles north of Johannesburg. They led Dart to the valley and helped him collect fossils that were strewn about the hillside, washed there from caves. A financial grant allowed Dart to begin excavation of a cavern at an abandoned limeworks site at Makapansgat in 1947. Shortly after work was started, the remains of what Dart took to be a different species of *Australopithecus* began to show up. Along with fossil fragments were carbon traces, which Dart interpreted as evidence for the use of fire. Consequently, he christened the "new" species *prometheus*, in honor of the fire-bringer in Greek mythology. But Dart was in error. Further analysis was to show that *Australopithecus africanus* from Taung and *prometheus* were of the same species. Not enough carbon was present to have resulted from fires.

Among the fragments found at Makapansgat was a piece of pelvis bone. Its shape more closely approximated a corresponding part of the human pelvis than of an ape pelvis, another indication that *Australo-*

pithecus got about on his hind legs. More complete pelves were to turn up later, along with fragments of limb bones, all of which confirmed the upright posture of *Australopithecus*. Dart seems to have been more impressed by other fossils than by a scrap of pelvis. As he was to write in 1955: "The Limeworks gray breccia is significant not so much for the number and variety of man-apes found in it (only 19 fragments had been found before 1955), but for the numbers and variety of huge wild animals found alongside the man-apes; and chiefly for the relative numbers of their bones, teeth, and horns (i.e., their *osteodontokeratic*— if we wish to say 'bone, tooth, and horn' in one word—remains)."

The full significance of the bone-tooth-horn remains eluded Dart for some time. What seems to have impressed him initially was the presence of such large animals as antelope in association with the "man-ape" fossils. These led Dart to conclude that the "Makapansgat protomen . . . were mighty hunters." A second conclusion began to form as further baboon skulls came to light. Many of them had one feature in common, radiating fractures due to the impact of something that had depressed the skull or shattered the jaw. Some skulls had rounded openings, as if the brains had been forcibly removed.

What did the depressions, the holes, the fractures, mean? Were they caused by falling rock? Dart reexamined baboon skulls from Taung and Sterkfontein. They exhibited similar evidences of violence. Falling rock at three different locations seemed too much of a coincidence. Dart consulted with R. H. Macintosh, a professor of forensic medicine and medicolegal expert, and other medical men. In their opinion, "these cranial fractures were of too local and specific a character to be explained by rock falls or earth collapses . . . ; they had been caused by implements of some sort wielded by hands."

What were the implements? Stones? None that could have inflicted the fractures were to be found in the caves. Macintosh suggested that only a stick or a piece of bone could have made such depressions in the skulls. It was then that Dart saw a possible connection between the unusual collection of bones and the fractures. As he tried to match holes and depressions with horns and bones, he found a number fitted together. Many of the baboons and six "man-apes" had been killed with the joint end of upper arm bones of antelopes. Circular holes could have been made by shafts of broken bones or with horn tips. "Patently the thug technique of bashing heads in with any handy bone or rock had a heritage of at least a million years," Dart wryly observed.

As Dart took a closer look at the bones, teeth, and horns, he perceived that they could have been utilized for a variety of purposes. The lower jaw of a hyena, for instance, could rip the hide of an animal; it could be employed for skinning, for removing fat from a skin or flesh from a bone. Horns were probably used as daggers, pick axes, or digging tools.

The bone-tooth-horn culture, Dart postulated, enabled the pigmy-sized *Australopithecus* group to survive in a rather hostile environment. There has not been too much support for this idea. While many pre-historians seemingly have little objection to the notion that such objects may have been utilized as tools, few are convinced—as is Dart—that the bones were fashioned for such purposes. Some even doubt that the australopithecines occupied the caves where the bones were found.

Scant attention has been paid another of Dart's ideas—that *Australopithecus* moved from a bone culture to a stone culture. This idea was based on the recovery of several thousand "stone pebble artifacts" found alongside bone fragments and a small fragment of what Dart believed to be the upper jaw of an *Australopithecus*. The fossils and artifacts were in a higher stratum—one reason they did not create much excitement. Another dampening factor was that stone implements had already been discovered in East Africa.

Further Post-War Finds

After World War II General Smuts urged Dr. Broom to continue his explorations. Before Broom could begin, Smuts left South Africa for a visit to England and the United States. In his absence the newly created Historical Monuments Commission of South Africa issued directives that excavations could be made only under certain conditions. This greatly aggravated Broom. Rather than be restricted by men who knew less than he, he decided to do no work at all. But when General Smuts returned, he told Broom to proceed. Broom was assured that a permit would be issued. In April 1947, three months after Broom resumed work at Kromdraai, the permit arrived. The doctor immediately ceased operations at Kromdraai and ostentatiously began to blast at Sterkfontein, a site not covered by the permit. It was Broom's way of protesting against petty bureaucracy. His defiance paid handsome dividends in terms of fossil materials.

Sterkfontein had been abandoned as a lime quarry, so Broom and his crew were able to dynamite as they saw fit. A number of fossils were brought forth including, in Broom's words, "the finest fossil skull ever discovered." The skull, uncovered by a lucky blast, was dubbed "Mrs. Ples." According to Broom: "This was the skull of a being not yet man but nearly man. The skull is practically human in all respects, except that the brain is small—only 480 cubic centimeters. . . ." Mrs. Ples was indeed a fine specimen, and she created a sensation both in South Africa and abroad.

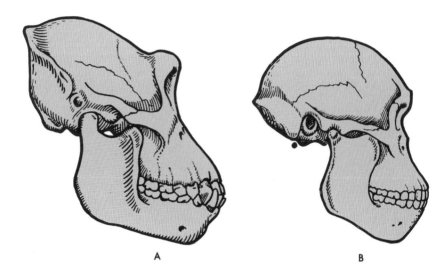

A　　　　　　　　　　　　　　　B

Figure 17. Comparison of a female gorilla skull (A) with the skull of a female australopithecine, "Mrs. Ples" (B).

In 1948 Broom's group found an almost perfect male jaw. More important was the discovery of a nearly perfect pelvis. The *Plesianthropus* pelvis was shaped very much like the human pelvis. There was no doubt that it came from an erect, bipedal primate. Even the skeptics agreed it was hominid, but some explained it as they had explained human-like thighbone fragments that had been discovered earlier. Somehow or other, the argument went, human bones had become intermixed with ape skulls. The skeptics, however, were diminishing in number.

Several other fossils were uncovered in the years that followed. Most were parts and fragments of earlier finds; but two other distinct specimens were found at Swartkrans, a mile or so from Sterkfontein. The first Swartkrans find was a jaw with teeth almost fifty per cent larger than those of *Paranthropus robustus* from Kromdraai. Because the teeth were so large, Broom labelled the find *Paranthropus crassidens* ("coarse-toothed"). Another large *crassidens* jaw was discovered in 1949 by Dr. J. T. Robinson, Broom's assistant. The second distinct specimen was also discovered by Robinson, who gave it the name *Telanthropus capensis* ("far-off man of the Cape"). *Telanthropus*, it was generally agreed, was a more advanced hominid form than the Australopithecinae.

PROBLEMS OF INTERPRETATION

In accordance with anthropological tradition, textbooks of the mid-1940's referred to the South African finds as extinct apes. Today, they are usually recognized as hominids. Such recognition has not resolved all controversy regarding the status of *Australopithecus* and *Paranthropus*. There is far from complete agreement as to how the two groups are related to one another and to other hominids.

Dr. Robinson proposed that all the South African specimens, with the exception of *Telanthropus*, be classified as members of the same subfamily, Australopithecinae. This subfamily was comprised of two genera: *Paranthropus*, the larger forms; and *Australopithecus* (see Table 1). Other authorities interpreted these specimens as representatives of two species of the same genus, *Australopithecus*. More recently, there has been some tendency to classify *Paranthropus* and *Australopithecus* as species of the genus *Homo*.[2]

Reluctance to accept the australopithecines as Hominidae and the taxonomic confusion they wrought reflect one of the problems that was bound to arise when such finds were made. The problem is one of diagnostic characters: What traits actually distinguish members of the family Hominidae from other higher primates? When a specimen exhibits traits supposedly peculiar to modern man (or his established hominid ancestors) in combination with supposed ape traits, how is it to be classified? As Pongidae, or as Hominidae? Like *Oreopithecus*, the australopithecines provided a taxonomic puzzle.

Table 1. Taxonomy of the South African Australopithecinae

SITE OF DISCOVERY	ORIGINAL DESIGNATION	J. T. ROBINSON'S VERSION	ERNST MAYR'S VERSION *
Taung	*Australopithecus africanus*	*Australopithecus africanus*	*Homo transvaalensis*
Sterkfontein	*Plesianthropus transvaalensis*	*Australopithecus transvaalensis*	*Homo transvaalensis*
Makapansgat	*Australopithecus prometheus*	*Australopithecus africanus transvaalensis*	*Homo transvaalensis*
Kromdraai	*Paranthropus robustus*	*Paranthropus robustus robustus*	*Homo transvaalensis*
Swartkrans	*Paranthropus crassidens*	*Paranthropus robustus crassidens*	*Homo transvaalensis*

* "Taxonomic Categories in Fossil Hominids," *Cold Spring Harbor Symposia on Quantitative Biology*, XV (Cold Spring Harbor, N. Y.: The Biological Laboratory, 1950).

What Is a Hominid?

Should a fossil primate structured for erect posture and bipedal locomotion be considered as a hominid or near-hominid, regardless of what other features it might have? That is, is such a structure diagnostic in itself? If the answer is yes, then the australopithecines must be considered part of the hominid line. Both the skull (position of the foramen magnum and occipital condyles) and post-cranial skeletal materials (pelvic parts, limb fragments) reflect a capacity for erect bipedalism. However, an affirmative answer assumes that man and his ancestors were the only primates to acquire this capacity. Were they? Some scientists do not think so.

Two kinds of evidence are possible indications that erect posture and bipedal locomotion are not peculiarly hominid traits. First, it is not at all unusual for nonhuman primates to stand up and even get about on two legs. The knees are usually bent, but apes have been known to stand upright with straight knees.[3] Second, *Oreopithecus* materials are sometimes regarded as reflecting the capacity for erect bipedalism. Taken together, this evidence implies that a number of extinct primates attempted to become habitually bipedal and that more than one group succeeded. Since such a possibility exists, it has been argued that erect posture or bipedalism per se does not distinguish the hominids, but rather a particular kind of upright posture and locomotion. The South African creatures were aberrant apes rather than hominids, the argument continues, because their pelves were not perfected for fully upright posture and walking (they could jog, but not stride).[4]

Of greater importance, so far as many scientists were concerned, was the criterion of brain size. How important this criterion was in the rejection of the australopithecines as hominids can be inferred from a statement by Marcellin Boule and Henri Vallois which appeared in 1957: "It cannot be denied that the fundamental human characteristic, that is the great development of the brain, the basis of all our psychological evolution, was never fulfilled in them. Human as they are in their dentition and posture, the Australopithecinae are none the less Apes in terms of their brain." [5]

But is brain size diagnostic of hominid status? Modern man does have a larger brain than the largest apes, and hence is supposedly more intelligent than they. But the difference in brain size between *some* men and *some* gorillas is not as great (about 100 cc.) as differences among living humans. Too, some very intelligent men have had braincases smaller than the average for modern man; there is no direct relationship between brain size and intelligence within the same species.[6]

When unrelated species are compared, absolute brain size is usually an even less reliable index of higher mental functions or intelligence. Brain size, especially among mammals, is often a function of body size —larger animals tend to have larger brains. The brain of an elephant, for example, is about four times the size of an average human brain; but no man is likely to consider an elephant superior to him mentally.

More meaningful, sometimes, is relative brain size, the relationship between brain weight and body weight. When brain-body ratios are compared, man usually has more brain per pound of body weight than any other mammal. The australopithecine brain was also relatively large. In fact, there is very little difference between the brain-body ratio of the Australopithecinae and of *Homo sapiens*—1:42 and 1:47, respectively. The former's brain-body ratio is even closer to that of some small monkeys, such as the capuchin monkey (1:43).[7]

The validity of absolute brain size as a diagnostic character has been questioned on other grounds, namely that "a comparison of forms based on cranial capacity is *not* a comparison of equal units."[8] The units may not be equal because the neural organization of two brains can be quite different. Creatures with gorilla-sized brains could have been capable of mental processes and behavior that would have been foreign to the great apes.

In addition, it might be noted that estimates of fossil skulls are not always precise. Cranial capacity is usually measured by pouring into a cranium something which can be measured in a calibrated vessel, such as sand, millet seed, lead shot, and the like. Most fossil skulls are not complete enough for this technique until they are reconstructed. A slight error in joining actual or reconstructed fragments can result in considerable variation in cranial capacity.[9]

Evidence of tool-making is another frequently used criterion of hominid status. The first tools, it has been often assumed, were fashioned from rocks or stones. While other materials may have been modified, as Dart proposed, they do not ordinarily preserve well. If preserved, they are difficult to recognize as ancient tools. So-called pebble tools—stones with the faces chipped for use as scrapers or choppers—were found in the area occupied by the South African individuals. As we have noted, however, such implements have been found in association with hominid fossils at only one location. Many authorities are therefore hesitant to conclude that the tools were used by the australopithecines. Le Gros Clark, on the other hand, considers it "obvious" that they did use tools. Those who have arrived at a contrary conclusion, he suggests, are men who may "find it difficult to suppose that creatures with such small brains would have been capable of making tools."[10]

Was There Time Enough?

Another factor which retarded acceptance of the Australopithecinae as members of our family was external to the fossils and artifacts. This was the time factor. As late as 1958 it was argued that since the Pleistocene began only 500,000 years ago there was hardly time for the South African "ape-men" to have evolved into *Homo sapiens*.[11] In 1962 it was still being said that the South African creatures were "too late" to be the direct ancestors of man, although improved dating techniques had almost doubled the length of the Pleistocene.[12] (More recent estimates place the beginning of the Pleistocene at between 1.5 and 3 million years ago.)

The beginning of the Pleistocene epoch is usually marked by evidences of a change in climate associated with the First Glaciation in Europe (Günz Glaciation). One type of evidence is the displacement of animals typical of the warm Pliocene climate by cold-adapted fauna. (A mixture of both types of fauna is often referred to as "Villafranchian" fauna, an assemblage which serves as a fairly universal marker for the Pliocene-Pleistocene border.) Unfortunately, this evidence is not clear-cut in South Africa. A number of Pliocene animals apparently migrated southward and outlived their kin in colder areas.

Geological clues which might indicate the onset of the Pleistocene in South Africa are difficult to find. According to one fairly well-accepted theory, there should be evidences of a "pluvial," or period of heavy rainfall. An unusual amount of precipitation supposedly fell on most parts of the world as the First Glaciation (and subsequent Pleistocene glaciations) began. In some regions this precipitation was gradually converted to sheets of ice; in Africa it was not. Such may well have been the case, but it has yet to be demonstrated that the First Glaciation—or any glaciation—was concurrent with an African pluvial. It is often impossible to tell when an increase in precipitation occurred in areas which normally experience heavy rainfall, and rainfall can vary considerably within quite short distances because of differences in altitude. Too, many potential clues were scrambled and buried by severe earth movements and volcanic activities during the Pleistocene.[13]

To complicate dating problems further, most of the South African fossils were preserved in limestone, which precludes dating by chemical or radiometric methods. And some cave deposits are not clearly stratified. It is hardly surprising, then, that estimates of the ages of the fossils range considerably. Authorities do agree that *Australopithecus* (as classified by Robinson) preceded *Paranthropus* by several thousand years.[14]

Prospects for locating the australopithecines in time, as we shall pres-

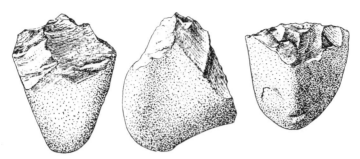

Figure 18. Oldowan tools. These earliest known stone implements were usually made by flaking two sides of a pebble to form simple cutting, chopping, and scraping tools. (By courtesy of The Trustees, British Museum [Natural History].) For a concise and readable description of Stone Age tools and tool-making techniques, see Kenneth P. Oakley, *Man the Tool-Maker*, 3rd Phoenix ed. (Chicago: University of Chicago Press, 1964).

ently see, have brightened considerably as a result of the dating of similar fossils found some sixteen hundred miles north of the main South African sites, in northern Tanganyika.

THE EAST AFRICAN FINDS

In the same year that Dart came into possession of the Taung skull, an African-born archaeologist, Louis S. B. Leakey, began a systematic study of East African prehistory. Among the sites he and his wife Mary investigated was a gorge at Olduvai (also spelled Oldoway) in northern Tanganyika (now Tanzania). The Olduvai Gorge, a kind of miniature Grand Canyon, had been discovered accidentally in 1911 by a German entomologist who was pursuing a butterfly. Fossils he found in the gorge and took back to Berlin prompted an expedition headed by Professor Hans Reck. Before much work could be done, World War I forced the expedition to return to Germany. Reck was unable to find funds to resume operations after the war, and he asked Leakey to take over.

Leakey and Reck visited the gorge in 1931, a five-hundred-mile journey over roadless country from the Coryndon Museum in Nairobi, where Leakey was curator. This first visit convinced Leakey that some sort of man or near-man had occupied the area. Many fossils of extinct animals were exposed on what had once been the shores of a lake. Also clearly visible were a number of crude stone tools. If there were tools, there had to be tool-makers. Leakey resolved to come back to the gorge as often as possible in order to locate the tool-makers.

Expeditions to Olduvai were difficult and costly. In the hot, dry seasons water had to be hauled from several miles away. Rains turned "roads" into seas of mud. Seven weeks of work a year was a major accomplishment. Nonetheless, the Leakeys gradually accumulated over a hundred species of animals, many of them extinct, and a variety of stone tools.

Different kinds of tools came from different strata. The more recently laid down layers contained implements which reflected complexity and craftsmanship. The tools became less complex, less skillfully made, as the floor of the gorge was approached. On the floor they were simple and crude. These crude tools the Leakeys named "Oldowan" (after Oldoway). Search as they would, though, they were unable to find evidence of anything like the South African Australopithecinae—"near-men," Leakey called them. It was as if "near-men" occupied one part of Africa and some unknown hominids had chipped tools in another part.

The long quest for an initial bit of hominid evidence ended on July 17, 1959. The day did not begin auspiciously. Leakey awoke with a headache and a slight fever. Mary, he says, was adamant in insisting that he stay at camp. Rather than risk a harrowing drive to the nearest hospital, Leakey agreed. The working days were running out, so Mary went off to their diggings. Some time later, Leakey heard the Land-Rover quickly approaching the camp. As he recalls, "I heard Mary's voice calling over and over: 'I've got him! I've got him! I've got him!'"

"Him"—"*our* man," as Mary called it then—was the much-publicized *Zinjanthropus boisei* specimen (*Zinj* is an old Arabic word for "East Africa"; the species designation honors Charles Boise, who provided financial backing). Mary, in searching the slope where Leakey had found some of the first Oldowan tools, spotted a piece of skull lodged in a rock slide. A little higher up were two immense teeth embedded in rock. When Leakey, headache forgotten, returned with Mary he concurred in her judgment: "The teeth . . . had belonged to a human."

After nineteen days of careful work, mostly with dental picks and small brushes, more than four hundred skull fragments plus an almost full palate and set of teeth were recovered. When the pieces were put together, only the lower jaw was missing. The molars, like the premolars, were unusually large; the other teeth were relatively small. Atop the skull was a slight crest of bone reminiscent of the sagittal crest of a male gorilla's skull. The lower jaw had evidently been heavy and the jaw muscles powerful.

The cranial capacity of the reconstructed skull was 530 cc., approximately that of the Taung child's skull. (The estimated capacity of the Taung skull at adulthood has been placed variously at 570, 600, and 624 cc.) [15] Obviously, *Zinjanthropus* failed to meet the brain-size criterion employed by some authorities with regard to the South African specimens. Nor, according to Leakey's dating—600,000 years ago at the earliest—did it and its kind have any more time than the Australopithecinae to become transformed into *Homo sapiens*. Still, Leakey argued that *Zinjanthropus* was more human than the South African "near-men," which the specimen admittedly resembled. What distinguished the two? The distinction, Leakey declared, was an ability unknown among the near-men and peculiar only to man—consistent tool-making.

Further excavation at the site of the fossil materials had revealed what was once a firm clay shore. Scattered about this "living floor" were tools of the Oldowan culture, the sort of artifacts the Leakeys had been turning up for years. Also scattered about were fossils of a variety of small animals—the young of "giant beasts he perhaps could not hope to kill as adults"—as well as birds, rodents, and reptiles. *Zinjanthropus* could not have torn the skin or fur from these creatures with his hominid teeth. He used the stone implements for such a purpose. Apparently, "*Zinjanthropus* must have begun making tools about the time he added meat to his diet."

These were Dr. Leakey's views as expressed in an article which appeared in the September 1960 issue of *National Geographic*. In this article, Leakey noted resemblances to modern man in features of the face and head, and he otherwise made a strong case for the humanness of his specimen. His views were given support shortly thereafter by potassium-argon readings that dated *Zinjanthropus* back 1.75 million ± 300,000 years. Many came to believe, as did Leakey, that the "world's earliest man" had been found.[16] It was a short-lived belief.

Man's True Ancestor?

Discovery of *Zinjanthropus* brought the Leakeys deserved recognition for years of dedication and hard work. It also brought financial backing for further exploration. Operations were expanded, and hundreds of fossils were uncovered in the next few years. Several of the fossils were hominid parts.

In December, 1960, Leakey reported the discovery of a number of fossil bones of the hand and the foot a few feet below the living floor *Zinjanthropus* had utilized. The hand bones were from a juvenile and an adult;[17] the foot bones were adult.[18] Two months later Leakey announced the finding of a juvenile hominid mandible and two skull fragments. The latter, he said, were from a skull larger than that of *Zinjanthropus*. Later, in 1961, he declared that the juvenile remains were of "a very remote and truly primitive ancestor of *Homo*," rather than of an Australopithecinae.[19]

No name was given the juvenile until 1964. In the meantime, it was referred to as "pre-*Zinjanthropus*" or "pre-Zinj." "Pre-Zinj" was formally christened in an article by Leakey, Phillip Tobias, and John Napier, which appeared in *Nature*, April 4, 1964.[20] The specimen, they maintained, represented a new species of *Homo*. At Dart's suggestion the species was given the name *habilis*, meaning "able, handy, mentally skillful, vigorous."

Other *Homo habilis* specimens, the authors said, were uncovered in deposits above the *Zinjanthropus* specimen, at the same level, and below it. The new species was generally characterized as being more human in its features than members of the genus *Australopithecus* (including *Zinjanthropus*; no other specimens are named). Some features were depicted as intermediate. The mean cranial capacity of *habilis*, for instance, was said to be larger than that of *Australopithecus* but smaller than the capacity of the next *Homo* species to evolve (*Homo erectus*). Other features, such as size of the jaws (mandible and maxilla), fall within the range for later *Homo* species. Implements of the Oldowan culture were reported as having been found in association with *Homo habilis* remains at three different sites.

Thus, *Zinjanthropus* was toppled from his position as the "world's earliest man." The authors were, however, reluctant to deny him hominid status: "While it is possible that *Zinjanthropus* and *Homo habilis* both made stone tools, it is probable that the latter was the more advanced tool maker and that the *Zinjanthropus* skull represents an intruder (or a victim) on a *Homo habilis* living site."

Dr. Leakey was still unwilling to deny *Zinjanthropus* hominid status at a symposium held at the University of Chicago in 1965.[21] By then, he also accepted the South African Australopithecinae as hominids. At the symposium Leakey dissociated himself completely "from any suggestion that you can use cultural evidence for any taxonomic purpose." This view was at complete odds with one expressed less than five years prior.

Why did Leakey change his mind? His own answer was, "We can no longer regard the making of tools as a criterion of man, since chimpanzees make tools to a set and regular pattern." The tool-making abilities of chimpanzees had been discovered by Jane Goodall in the Gombe Stream Game Reserve in Tanzania. Apes that Miss Goodall observed stripped leaves from twigs and used the twigs to fish for termites—an obvious modification of a natural object. Twigs were sometimes carried as far as half a mile for such use. Moreover, during the dry season, apes chewed leaves slightly to make them more absorbent, then employed them as sponges to soak up drinking water in boles of trees.

The criterion of upright posture, which Leakey had apparently never accepted, was also dismissed: "*Oreopithecus* certainly had a very upright position, as you can judge by his femur and his pelvic girdle." Another long-supposed difference between man and other primates was that only the former killed and ate other mammals, a criterion Leakey implicitly accepted in 1960. This distinction was also dismissed in 1965, for Miss Goodall had seen chimpanzees killing and eating mammals. Brain size, upright posture, meat-eating, tool-making—none of the old criteria were pertinent. How, then, could early man be distinguished from other hominoids? Leakey did not say. He implied that the only valid criterion is structural similarity to modern man, not any particular cultural manifestation.

CONTROVERSY

Judging from the publicity given Dr. Leakey and his finds during the mid-1960's, the general public accepted *Homo habilis* uncritically. The scientific community did not. The interpretations made by Leakey, Tobias, and Napier were challenged almost from the moment their paper was published. One of the challengers has been Broom's former assistant, Professor John T. Robinson.

Among other things, Robinson has sharply questioned the validity of the new taxon, *Homo habilis*. Both in print and at the 1965 Chicago symposium ("The Origin of Man"), he argued that the supposedly unique features of *habilis*, such as size of teeth and brain capacity, were within the range of *Australopithecus*, the South African group. The *habilis* braincases, he pointed out, are very incomplete and of such a nature as to make their capacities difficult to determine. Robinson concedes that there are differences between the Olduvai specimens and those from the Transvaal, but he believes that they are of virtually no significance; they can be accounted for by species variability and by changes through time. In short, *Homo habilis*, to Robinson's way of thinking, is simply an advanced *Australopithecus*.[22]

Dr. Tobias has expressed essential agreement with the interpretation of *Homo habilis* as an advanced australopithecine. Like Robinson and several others, Tobias considers "the *habilis* group . . . in so many respects intermediate between *Australopithecus* and *Homo*." But present taxonomic procedures are inadequate for handling "intermediates or transitional forms." *Habilis* had to be classified *either* as a species of *Australopithecus* or of *Homo*. The second alternative was selected because *Homo habilis* was evidently a tool-maker, while *Australopithecus* was not.[23]

One point upon which Robinson and Tobias disagree is the relationship between the South African australopithecines and *habilis*. Tobias believes the two groups were Lower Pleistocene contemporaries. The Australopithecinae were, therefore, "too late in time—and perhaps structurally a little too specialized—to have been on the direct human line." They were, it seems, "little changed survivors of a partially-hominized Upper Pliocene australopithecine population, which was ancestral to both the Pleistocene australopithecines and *Homo habilis.*" Robinson challenges this diagnosis. How do we know that the South African forms appeared later in time or contemporaneously with the Olduvai hominids? What concrete evidence is there to support such a conclusion? It is likely, he suggests, that *habilis* was a descendant of *Australopithecus.*[24] This suggestion is given some support by an analysis made by Kenneth P. Oakley, of the British Museum, prior to discovery of the East African hominids. According to Oakley's analysis, all the *Australopithecus* specimens (according to Robinson's classification) predated Olduvai Bed I, the location of the earliest East African fossils. The latter were of the same approximate age as *Paranthropus.*[25]

Others who have questioned the Leakey-Tobias-Napier diagnosis include some prominent anatomists and taxonomists. Le Gros Clark, for example, has been unable to find any great differences between *Australopithecus* and *Homo habilis.* He concludes that the latter is a "geographical variant," possibly a "local species," of the former.[26] Pilbeam and Simons say essentially the same thing,[27] and Bernard Campbell refers to *habilis* as an advanced form of *Australopithecus africanus.*[28]

CONCLUSIONS

The discoveries discussed in this chapter raised a question Linnaeus probably thought was settled for all time: What characters differentiate man from all other forms of life? The fossils found in South and East Africa have forced scientists to reexamine and reevaluate criteria used in the classification of earlier forms of man. These fossils have also made a number of people—including scientists—less prone to cling to the Linnaean notion that taxonomic categories are fixed and static. Fewer, we suspect, now think of our own genus or species as qualitatively different—different in kind—from all other genera and species.

Controversy and taxonomic confusion have been inevitable accompaniments of the finds. Consensus regarding the status of all the specimens has not yet been achieved. It may not be achieved for some time. Much depends upon further discoveries and probably upon further studies of what has already been found. There is ample room for disagreement at the present. Dates for the South African fossils have not been firmly established, and materials from the two areas are difficult to compare. Some of the Olduvai specimens are crushed and broken; none from either area is complete or nearly complete. Identical skeletal parts are often lacking. For instance, fossil extremities (foot and hand bones) have been found at Olduvai that cannot be matched with bones from the Transvaal; pelves have been located in South Africa but not in East Africa.

Despite considerable disagreement as to the interpretation of much of the evidence, there are a few important areas of near-agreement. Most scientists seemingly consider *Homo habilis* or *Australopithecus* or both as ancestral to modern man. Several believe that *Australopithecus* and *Homo habilis* are of the same lineage, if not of the same taxon. Finally, there is some measure of consensus that both the South African and the East African forms gave rise to more advanced hominids, fossils of which have been found in both areas (see Chapter 13).

As far as dating goes, it appears that the earliest *Homo habilis* specimen uncovered thus far lived approximately 1.8 million to 2 million years ago. A fossilized fragment of a bone discovered in northwestern Kenya since *habilis* was described has been interpreted as an arm bone from an australopithecine. The age of the fragment, according to potassium-argon dating techniques, is about 2.5 million years. How this bit of evidence will affect the interpretations of other fossils remains to be seen.

Some of the groups we have discussed may be reclassified and renamed in the future. A number of writers make no distinction between *Paranthropus* (including *Zinjanthropus*) and *Australopithecus*. These writers do not believe that differences between the two are sufficient to warrant separate taxa; the term *Australopithecus* is applied to both groups. Several scientists regard all the Lower Pleistocene specimens from both East and South Africa as members of the same genus, *Australopithecus*. Some authorities have proposed that all the specimens be classified as members of the genus *Homo*. Whatever the South African and East African hominids are called, they are apparently safely ensconced in the family Hominidae. How did they become hominids? This question will concern us in the next chapter.

NOTES

1. Materials in this section are drawn from the following: C. L. Brace and M. F. Ashley Montagu, *Man's Evolution* (New York: The Macmillan Company, 1965), Chap. 6; Robert Broom, "The Apemen," *Scientific American*, 181 (November, 1949), 20–24; Carleton S. Coon, *The Origin of Races* (New York: Alfred A. Knopf, Inc., 1963), pp. 231–277; Raymond A. Dart, "The Cultural Status of the South African Man-Apes," in *Smithsonian Report for 1955* (Washington, D. C.: Smithsonian Institution, 1956), pp. 317–338; Ruth Moore, *Man, Time, and Fossils*, 2nd ed. (New York: Alfred A. Knopf, Inc., 1963), Chap. 15; Ronald Singer, "Emerging Man in Africa," *Natural History*, LXXI (November, 1962), 10–21.

2. Michael H. Day, *Guide to Fossil Man* (Cleveland: The World Publishing Company, 1965), pp. 208–209.

3. Adolph H. Schultz, "The Physical Distinctions of Man," in William Howells, ed., *Ideas on Human Evolution: Selected Essays, 1949–1961* (Cambridge: Harvard University Press, 1962), p. 42.

4. John Buettner-Janusch, *Origins of Man* (New York: John Wiley & Sons, Inc., 1966), pp. 144–145.

5. Marcellin Boule and Henri V. Vallois, *Fossil Men* (New York: The Dryden Press, 1957), p. 92.

6. Buettner-Janusch, *op. cit.,* pp. 145–146.

7. *Ibid.,* pp. 146, 350–351.

8. Ralph L. Holloway, Jr., "Cranial Capacity, Neural Reorganization, and Hominid Evolution: A Search for More Suitable Parameters," *American Anthropologist,* 68 (1966), 103–121.

9. Buettner-Janusch, *op. cit.,* pp. 145–146.

10. Wilfrid E. Le Gros Clark, *The Fossil Evidence for Human Evolution,* 2nd ed. (Chicago: University of Chicago Press, 1964), p. 126.

11. J. Desmond Clark, "Early Man in Africa," *Scientific American,* 199 (July, 1958), 76–83.

12. Singer, *op. cit.,* p. 17.

13. Sonia Cole, *The Prehistory of East Africa* (New York: New American Library, 1965), Chap. 2.

14. Day, *op. cit.,* pp. 162–199, *passim.*

15. Phillip V. Tobias, "Cranial Capacity of *Zinjanthropus* and Other Australopithecines," *Nature,* 197 (1963), 743–746.

16. With the exception of the previous reference, materials in this section are drawn from: Brace and Montagu, *op. cit.;* Munroe, *op. cit.,* Chap. 16; and L. S. B. Leakey, "Finding the World's Earliest Man," *National Geographic,* 118 (1960), 420–435.

17. John Napier, "Fossil Bones from Olduvai Gorge," *Nature,* 196 (1962), 409–411.

18. M. H. Day and J. R. Napier, "Fossil Foot Bones," *Nature,* 201 (1964), 967–970.

19. P. V. Tobias, "The Olduvai Bed I Hominine with Special Reference to Its Cranial Capacity," *Nature,* 202 (1964), 3–4.

20. L. S. B. Leakey, P. V. Tobias, and J. R. Napier, "A Few Species of Genus Homo from Olduvai Gorge," *Nature,* 202 (1964), 7–9.

21. Quotations and paraphrasing of statements made at the symposium are from a transcript entitled *The Origin of Man* edited by Paul L. DeVore. The symposium was held April 2–4, 1965, and was sponsored by the Wenner-Gren Foundation for Anthropological Research, Inc.

22. John T. Robinson, "*Homo 'habilis'* and the Australopithecines," *Nature,* 205 (1965), 121–124; P. V. Tobias, "New Discoveries in Tanganyika: Their Bearing on Hominid Evolution," *Current Anthropology,* 6 (1965), 391–411 (see Robinson's views in the "Comments" section following Tobias' article).

23. Tobias, "New Discoveries in Tanganyika: . . . ," pp. 394–397.

24. *Ibid.,* pp. 405, 408.

25. Kenneth P. Oakley, "Dating of the Australopithecinae of Africa," *American Journal of Physical Anthropology,* New Series 12 (1954), 16–17.

26. Wilfrid E. Le Gros Clark, *Man-Apes or Ape-Men?* (New York: Holt, Rinehart & Winston, Inc., 1967), pp. 45–47; *History of the Primates,* 5th ed. (Chicago: University of Chicago Press, 1965), p. 76.

27. D. R. Pilbeam and Elwyn L. Simons, "Some Problems of Hominid Classification," *American Scientist,* 53 (1965), 251.

28. Bernard G. Campbell, *Human Evolution* (Chicago: Aldine Publishing Company, 1966), p. 336.

29. Bryan Patterson and W. W. Howells, "Hominid Humeral Fragment from Early Pleistocene of Northwestern Kenya," *Science,* 156 (1967), 64–66.

12

From Hominoid to Hominid

What were the circumstances and events which brought about the appearance of the family Hominidae? This is a difficult question to answer. Fossil voids separate potentially relevant data, and much of the evidence is fragmented and incomplete. Important morphological and behavioral changes necessarily occurred prior to the appearance of the first hominids, but the available evidence does not reveal exactly what these changes were.

Reconstruction of the transformation of a hominoid group to Hominidae is difficult, but it is not altogether impossible. The good scientist, like the good detective, does not rely solely upon knowledge and skills; he also exercises imagination. Thanks to the imaginative efforts of some scientists, we have plausible interpretations as to what might have taken place during this phase of human evolution. As we look at these interpretations (and add to them), it may be well to keep in mind that they are "educated guesses." Although the interpretations are derived from fossil data or what is known about the structure and behavior of living animals, they can be neither fully confirmed nor rejected by existing evidence and techniques of analysis.

TOWARD ERECT BIPEDALISM

Man is the sole primate that habitually moves about on his hind limbs. Our prehominid ancestors were the only primates to experience—or to persistently benefit from—a series of anatomical changes which resulted in erect posture and bipedal locomotion. The exact nature of these changes is not known. It is generally assumed, however, that the foramen magnum and occipital condyles moved forward and that there were modifications of the pelvis, hind limbs, and associated musculature. This assumption is based mainly upon the belief that prehominids were structurally similar to present-day apes or monkeys.

Whatever the anatomical changes, they were in a sense anticipated by existing behavior patterns among prehominids. The major difference after the changes occurred was that they did certain things more often and more efficiently. In a word, the prehominids were *preadapted* to erect posture or bipedalism. Within their environmental setting, temporary bipedalism and some degree of erectness furthered survival.

What sort of activities were preadaptive to erect posture? Brachiation is an answer offered by many who believe that the human and great ape lines derived from a brachiating ancestral stock. A primate that swings from limb to limb necessarily carries its body in a more or less perpendicular position. Therefore, the argument goes, the brachiator is likely to retain this position to some extent when progressing on the ground. As evidence that the hominids came from a brachiating stock, a number of similarities between man and the apes are noted. Sherwood L. Washburn, for example, notes a "profound similarity in the motions of the arms of man and apes," and says that "on any playground one can see humans brachiating from bars, hanging by one hand, and exhibiting a variety of motions and postures which are similar to those of the apes." Washburn points out that man and ape share a number of anatomical features—in the shoulder, thorax, and lumbar areas and in the elbow, forearm, wrist, and hand—which enable them to exhibit similar motions and postures.[1] Professor Hooton, who thought along somewhat the same lines, reasoned that the broad, flat thorax of the hominoids developed in association with brachiation. In quadrupeds, he observed, the weight of organs, fluids, and other thoracic contents tends to increase the distance between the vertebral column and the breast bone. Furthermore, movements of the forelimbs possibly compress the thoracic cage laterally. In a brachiating or habitually erect animal, on the other hand, gravity pulls the thoracic contents towards the central trunk area; and lateral movements of the arms outward from the body tend to broaden the shoulder girdle and result in a lengthening of the collarbone (a bone often absent in four-footed mammals).[2]

Other behavior that was possibly preadaptive to erect posture can be observed among a variety of animals. Such behavior includes the practice of rearing up on the hind legs in order to better exercise sensory equipment. Obstacles to vision, hearing, or smell are thereby surmounted to some extent; certain dangers and need-satisfiers are more likely to be perceived. Charles F. Hockett and Robert Ascher, who have constructed one of the more thorough hominoid-to-hominid schemes, believe that the prehominids spent some of their time in shoulder-high grass, above which they could raise their heads.[3]

Another widely distributed activity, found among both primates and non-primates, is the raising of the front part of the body in order to use the hands or paws. As a rule, animals that do this sit or squat on their hind limbs while feeding themselves with the forelimbs. In addition many primates, as we noted earlier, grasp and manipulate objects. They have apparently been doing this for millions of years, probably long before the prehominids appeared.

Living apes brachiate, raise their bodies to look around, and sit on their haunches while employing the hands in non-locomotor activities. Their ancestors very probably did the same things. Why, then, do none of the Pongidae habitually stand on their hind legs? Either of two possibilities can answer this question. First, it is possible that only prehominids experienced those mutations which furthered erect posture. Second, behaviors that were preadaptive for upright posture alone were not in themselves preadaptive for erect bipedalism. Remains of *Oreopithecus* specimens seem to negate the first possibility, for, in the opinion of Simons [4] and others, these fossils show indications of structural adaptation for bipedal walking. If, as indicated by the second explanation, behaviors other than sporadic upright posture were preadaptive to habitually erect posture, what were they? Most likely they were bipedal activities. But what might predispose a primate to run or walk on its hind legs? Among quadrupedal vertebrates in general, some suggest,[5] there are two impetuses for the development of the bipedal gait: to attain greater speed, or to free the forelimbs for purposes other than locomotion.

Animals that occasionally gain speed by running bipedally, such as lizards, have forelimbs that are shorter than their hind limbs. The length of the stride is therefore greater in the rear, and the front legs come to be a drag as speed increases. As the shift from four legs to two is made, the tail acts as a balance for the body. The body remains close to the horizontal axis while the animal runs, a position hardly conducive to the attainment of erect posture.

There is another way in which the hind legs can contribute to speedy movement—by providing propulsive power. A number of the Old World monkeys hurl themselves through space with a powerful thrust

195

from the hind legs, a means of progression often referred to as "semi-brachiation." Semibrachiation, John Napier contends, was preadaptive to bipedalism. At the moment of take-off, he points out, the hind legs are extended at both the knee and hip joints; while in flight, the fore-limbs are extended at the shoulder to grasp the limb when it is reached. During brachiation, on the other hand, the legs remain more or less flexed at the hips and knees; they contribute nothing to brachial locomotion, and their use in bipedal locomotion is actually discouraged. There is no evidence that ancestral baboons went through a semibrachiation stage, Napier says, which would largely explain why living baboons are quadrupedal in terrestrial habitats.[6]

If prehominids became temporarily bipedal in order to use their fore-limbs, to what use were these limbs put? Observations of gorillas and chimpanzees suggest that the forelimbs may have served defensive pur-poses. In coping with an intruder into its territory, the normally quadru-pedal mountain gorilla has been known to become bipedal. It threatens —bluffs—by running towards the intruder while thumping its chest. On the rare occasions when the gorilla attacks a member of another species, the forelimb serves as a weapon. One swipe can kill a man.[7] Chimpanzees also threaten or attack from a bipedal position, often throwing objects or wielding a club.[8]

A second kind of behavior preadaptive to bipedal locomotion, carry-ing, may have been an outgrowth of prior employment of the hands. Objects that were grasped with the hands or limbs, it was learned, could be carried from one place to another. Such behavior is not at all unusual among present-day apes and monkeys, who occasionally carry sticks, stones, food, and other objects for short distances when on the ground. Usually only objects that can be carried in the mouth are taken into the trees. Carrying is an essential ingredient in several of the recon-structions of the hominoid-to-hominid transition. Gordon W. Hewes, for example, believes that

> the only activity likely to have had the capacity to transform a mainly quadrupedal ground-dwelling Primate into an habitual biped would have been food transport from the places where food was obtained to a home base where it was consumed. Such carrying could only be ac-complished efficiently by an animal with arms and hands for grasping and holding.

The major food transported by the hominids-to-be was meat, mainly the remains of animals killed by the larger carnivores.[9]

Hockett and Ascher suggest that the transporting of scavenged meat may have begun accidentally. Perhaps a prehominid feasting on a carcass in the open country was suddenly surprised by the return of the killer. Without thinking, he ran from the scene, still clutching a piece of meat. When he realized what he had done, he and members of his group began to remove parts of other animals' kills to a safe place before the carnivores returned. Perhaps accidentally, also, a prehominid learned that a stone was a weapon. He was surprised by a predator while pounding something with a stone and ran with the stone in his hand. Finally cornered, the prehominid either struck out at the predator with the stone or threw it. In either case, he and his kind learned the value of carrying some sort of weapon.[10]

Hewes sees the first regular use of tools as having arisen out of the habit of carrying meat to a lair. As the practice of food transport continued, bones, antlers, mandibles with teeth, and other potential tools began to accumulate. Eventually, prehominids began to use these objects (and perhaps stones or sticks that were lying around) for butchering meat and removing marrow from bones.[11]

Environment for Bipedalism

An arboreal habitat offers opportunities for activities which incline the body away from the horizontal axis. While such activities—climbing, sitting, jumping or brachiating from limb to limb—were preadaptive to habitually upright posture, they apparently did not provide the necessary impetus for the attainment of habitual bipedalism. It is difficult to see how such erect bipedalism would serve any particular survival function among present-day arboreal primates or among our tree-dwelling ancestors. For this mode of locomotion to be adaptive, our ancestors certainly must have had to adapt to a terrestrial environment; they had to vacate the trees before they became fully bipedal.

If the prehominids were well adapted to an arboreal niche, it is not likely that they sought a new way of life without some compelling reason. One such reason suggested by several writers was a change in climate which reduced Miocene forests. Hooten, we noted in Chapter 10, rejected the notion that competition for space followed this change; arboreal animals would have remained in the retreating forests. Hockett and Ascher agree that some bands of hominids did just that. Others, however, were caught in isolated groves that gradually shrank in size. Our ancestors were among the latter.

Some of the primates caught in the shrinking groves may have managed to retain their prior way of life to a considerable extent. Our ancestors did not. Familiar foods and space in the trees eventually ran out for them, and they were fully exposed to hazards of the savannah. In the words of Hockett and Ascher:

197

There may not be much food, at least not of a familiar sort. There may be little available water, for the trees tend to cluster where the water is more abundant. And there are fleet four-footed predators, as well as herbivorous quadrupeds big and strong enough to be dangerous at close quarters. One cannot avoid these other animals altogether, since their presence often signals the location of water, or of food fit also for hominid consumption. The quest for food must be carried on constantly, no matter how pressing may be the drive to find a new grove of trees in which to settle. It is a wonder that any of the waifs of the Miocene savannah survived at all. Enormous numbers of them must have died out.[12]

The survival of our line, in the opinion of Hockett and Ascher, was due to the early discovery that carrying weapons and food was highly beneficial.

John Napier also believes that the open-grassland environment was extremely hostile. He takes exception, however, to the idea that bipedalism became habitual while prehominids were adjusting to new foods and terrestrial predators. Converting from quadrupedalism to bipedalism at that time, Napier implies, would only have compounded already immense problems. He concludes, therefore, that our ancestors became bipedal *before* divorcement from the trees was complete. A likely place for bipedalism to have developed was the "woodland savannah, which is neither high forest nor open grassland." This type of "halfway-house niche," which is occupied by many primates today (including some chimpanzees), provided familiar forest foods and trees for refuge. At the same time, it offered grassy spaces in which new behaviors could be practiced and new foods could be sampled. The woodland-savannah was, in short, "an ideal nursery for evolving hominids, combining the challenge and incentive of the open grassland with much of the security of the forest." [13]

From Gathering to Part-Time Hunting

Whether bipedalism became fully established before or after the trees were completely abandoned, the transition from an arboreal to a terrestrial environment was a gradual one. The prehominids were not suddenly thrust into an entirely foreign set of circumstances. Many generations of experiences on the ground preceded even the first ventures of any distance away from the trees. Like primates today, our ancestors sought food on or from the forest floor and in small open spaces. Searching for food in grassy areas near the trees required few modifications in established behavior patterns. Foods from the grassy areas were sometimes carried for short distances in the hands, just as fruits and nesting materials had long been carried in the forest. The employment of objects as crude tools in the forest (that is, digging or fishing for insects with sticks) was readily generalized to grassland situations. Warning signals emitted by individuals in the trees were equally effective in protecting animals on the forest floor or in nearby grassy areas.

In time, deeper and deeper penetrations of the grasslands were made. The supply of food available in and near the trees may have become insufficient, or our evolving ancestors may have been spurred by curiosity or the desire for a more varied diet. With deeper penetrations, the widening distance between trees and foragers lessened the effectiveness of the calls from the trees. New cooperative techniques had to be devised to insure survival. The most probable adjustment was a modification of the original warning system: alarms were still sounded by one or more individuals not engaged in eating—but from the ground, rather than from the trees. Without conscious planning, members of a foraging group would alternatively eat and watch. To see for any distance, it was necessary to rear up on the hind legs. At the first indication of danger, all members quickly retreated to the trees.

If carnivores were a serious threat to the prehominids—authorities do not agree that they were—lengthy stays in the savannah could have been hazardous even with some sort of warning system. Prehominids unable to run quickly (young children, pregnant females, the infirm) would have been able to do little if any foraging in grassy areas. In such case, carrying food back to the trees might have made the difference between extinction and survival of the hominid line. A quantity of food was essential—more than could be carried in the mouth; it was necessary, therefore, to clutch grasses or other foods to the body with the forelimbs.

Carrying was important in another context, the transport of infants. Both the ape and the human infant are able to grasp for only relatively short periods at birth (5 minutes and 2 minutes, respectively), and the strength of the grasp wanes within a few days after birth.[14] It is reasonable to assume, therefore, that a prehominid infant was carried by the mother, at least on occasion—for example, when the group moved any distance or when danger threatened.

Little by little, prehominids learned the comings and goings of the animals that frequented the grasslands. As the habits of these creatures became better known, ventures into the grasslands entailed less risk to life and limb. With knowledge, too, came added opportunities. The prehominids were not unfamiliar with meat; like higher primates today they had killed an occasional small mammal (probably primate) in the forests. In the grasslands, they observed, one animal would obtain meat by waiting until a successful predator ate its fill and moved on. Why couldn't they do likewise? And so they waited until the scavenger or scavengers left a carcass. The pickings were slim, but the prehominid hands could sometimes reach scraps of flesh not accessible to a four-footed animal. Brains and bone marrow could be obtained, they found, if the skull and bones were broken with a stick, a stone, or a bone. This finding may have been accidental, a consequence of frustration, or simply an extension of a prior practice of extracting the meat from seeds and nuts.

Pressed by need or inspired by insight, prehominids eventually entered into competition with the scavengers rather than waiting until they abandoned a carcass. Members of a foraging group may have frightened the animals away by yelling and bipedal charging. But hungry scavengers —say, hyenas—would be but briefly discouraged by such tactics. Sooner or later, prehominids began to use sticks, limb bones, stones—whatever was available—to ward off or beat off persistent competitors. Sometimes a direct blow or a missile thrown by a prehominid stunned or killed one of the scavengers. From such experiences, perhaps, came the realization that meat could be obtained by using objects in the environment as weapons.

To combat scavengers, eat, and depart the scene before the predator returned encouraged greater coordination among the foragers. It also encouraged the development of techniques to secure meat quickly. Perhaps prehominids tried to separate a carcass into pieces with their bone-cracking instruments and eventually discovered that rocks or bones with certain characteristics were more effective than others in piercing hide and flesh. Edged rocks and pointed bones or mandibles came to serve as severing and disjointing tools. While some members of a group staved off scavengers and kept an eye out for predators, others reduced the carcass to pieces that could be carried back to the trees.

The first grassland animals to be deliberately killed by weapon-wielding prehominids were victims by chance, not by reason of skills or conscious planning on the part of prehominids. Most likely a foraging party stumbled across immature young temporarily abandoned or separated from their kind. As their knowledge of life in the grasslands increased, however, prehominids learned to stalk small animals or surprise them away from burrows and groups. Practice in the wielding of clubs and the throwing of missiles, plus increased cooperation among members of a party, yielded handsome dividends. Slowly but surely, the flesh of other animals became a staple in the prehominid diet.

We have referred only to the successful, the prehominids whose genes were transmitted to ancient *Homo*. Many of their kin fell by the way-side in the progression from gathering to scavenging to part-time hunting. Among those eliminated were primates that were unable to stand up straight enough or long enough to perceive dangers in the grasses and that could not run while carrying food or weapons. These failed to experience, or experienced in lesser degree, mutations that resulted in modifications in the pelvis and muscles needed for powerful extension of the leg. Primates incapable of increasingly complex cooperative endeavors left few if any progeny, as did those that lacked the physical or mental capacity to use natural objects as tools and weapons.

Thus, during generations of living in a "halfway-house niche," our ancestors gradually acquired the adaptations necessary for occupation of fully terrestrial niches. When it became necessary or desirable to desert the trees, they were equipped—physically, mentally, and socially—to survive the perils of the open country.

TOOLS AND TEETH

We implied in the speculative reconstruction above that prehominids may have used tools before they became bipedal. Professor Washburn believes that they did, primarily because of the small canine teeth of the South and East African hominids. In contrast, among apes and monkeys, he says, the males have large canines. These teeth, backed by very large jaw muscles, provide a very efficient fighting mechanism. A display of the teeth by a group of male baboons (or sometimes by an individual baboon) has put cheetahs, dogs, and even leopards to flight. The absence of long canines among the australopithecines, Washburn reasons, indicates that protection of the group had shifted from a reliance upon teeth to a dependency upon tools long before the shorter forms appeared.[15]

When did the shift occur? *Ramapithecus* did not have large canines, which would suggest that tools were in use more than 14 million years ago. Since many nonhuman animals with supposedly less intelligence than the higher primates make some use of tools, such an early date is well within the range of possibility. The idea that short canines are an index of tool-using becomes somewhat problematic, however, when an even earlier specimen is examined. You will recall that *Propliopithecus* is considered as a possible ancestor to the Hominidae. If hominids did experience a reduction in canines, we would expect *Propliopithecus* to have had large canines. The Fayum specimen does not; its canines are shorter than those of the Lower Miocene *Dryopithecus* (*Proconsul*) *africanus* specimen.[16]

Nevertheless a single specimen does not disprove Washburn's idea. The individual may have been an aberrant or a female. The relatively short canines of *Propliopithecus* and the absence of large canines in some species of monkeys does, however, suggest an interesting possibility. Could large canines have evolved after the lines leading to man and the great apes separated? That is, could large canines be an adaptation acquired only by the great apes? If so, monkeys that acquired large canines could have evolved them independently, but perhaps for much the same reason or reasons.

One frequently mentioned adaptive value of large canines has to do with diet. Ashley Montagu, for example, states that their main function is to rip and shred the hard outer coverings of plant foods. Such teeth are required, he says, because all nonhuman primates, with the exception of the baboons, are vegetarians.[17] This may be true to some extent at present and might have been even more true in the past. But why, then, among female anthropoids did only the gibbons evolve canines as large as those of their male counterparts? Was the diet of females different in the past, or did the males rip and shred for them? Neither possibility seems very likely. Long canines are no doubt important in the defense of a group that must cope with terrestrial predators. But are they adaptive for the same reason among arboreal primates? At one time they may have been; but some arboreal primates, such as the gibbons, have virtually no contact with predators nowadays. Neither requirements of diet nor of defense against predators seem adequate explanations of the appearance of large canines among male apes and monkeys.

Large canines are put to another use: fighting or bluffing members of the same species. This, we suggest, was probably the determining function among most species. The male that experienced mutations for longer canines had an advantage over his smaller-toothed rivals and antagonists. He would inflict more pain and present a more fearsome appearance. He therefore had greater access to females in estrus and to food or other need-satisfiers that were in short supply. Thus his genes were transmitted to future generations in proportionately greater numbers than those of other males.

Mutations for larger canines possibly occurred from time to time among evolving hominids, as they do among humans today. There was, however, no persistent selection for them. If vegetable materials were ripped and shredded with the teeth, such foods afforded no particular advantage to those that ate them. If teeth were employed against predators or in quarrels among group members, the outcome was decided by factors other than long canines. Perhaps the manner in which the hands were used—in grappling, hitting, throwing or wielding objects—proved more effective than biting or baring the teeth. Perhaps social arrangements, derived by accident or as a consequence of environmental pressures, lessened the need, desire, or opportunity for extensive intragroup combat. Survival may have been largely contingent upon a fairly high order of cooperation between and among members of a prehominid group, particularly during the transition to terrestrial life.[18] This transition may have begun with—and been largely responsible for—the separation of the ape and hominid lines.

The demands of a hostile terrestrial environment probably encouraged, or demanded, cooperation. At the scavenger stage of development, Hewes suggests, meat-eating fostered some amount of sharing and cooperation. If enough of a carcass were carried to a lair, "the meal would tend to be unaltruistically and unequally 'shared' by the family or band members present, provided they were hungry and agile enough to snatch portions away from the individual who brought it home." Such inadvertent sharing "improved family nutrition, reduced infant mortality," and otherwise conferred biological advantages.[19]

Successful hunting, particularly of larger animals, would have required teamwork among the hunters. It would have been necessary, too, William Etkin believes, for males to cooperate in caring for the young. Females encumbered by infants and pregnancy were not efficient hunters or food-transporters. Mothers could not care for their babies alone, as they had in the forests where foods were readily at hand. The male had to bring meat to his mate and immature offspring, at least by the time of the australopithecines. Etkin presupposes monogamy at this stage in human development. It would have been impracticable, he says, for a single male to be protector and provider for many females.[20] Possibly, too, monogamy minimized friction generated by sexual rivalries.

Monogamous relationships were probably encouraged by physiological and anatomical changes experienced by the female. Estrus, if it had not disappeared completely, was of less importance in determining sexual receptivity. The female was sexually attractive for long enough periods to satisfy the male's sexual desires, thereby making him less inclined to seek intercourse with two or more females.

Another important change occurred as prehominids became adapted to bipedalism. With the tilting of the pelvis, the birth canal and external genitalia shifted forward. Concomitantly, a muscle important in bipedal locomotion, the gluteus maximus, enlarged to form the large buttocks. The posterior approach to coitus typical among quadrupeds became increasingly difficult. Face-to-face sexual behavior—which would probably have been impossible in the trees—was much more comfortable and practicable. Adoption of this position, more than one writer believes, encouraged individual attachments between male and female. As Ashley Montagu notes, male and female were brought closer together psychologically as well as physically. They could learn to embrace, exhibit tender emotions toward each other, and invent displays of affection (kissing, nose-rubbing, etc.).[21]

Attachments between male and female may have contributed to a division of labor between the sexes. Some writers have pictured the female as perpetually with child, hence unable to move freely into the savannahs. She could, however, gather vegetable foods and perhaps kill small animals in the vicinity of a relatively safe site (a clump of trees, a cave, or rock shelter) while the male ranged across the grassland in search of prey.

There is, of course, no concrete evidence for monogamy, attachments between male and female, and cooperation between the sexes; but they can be inferred from arrangements and behaviors found in present-day hunting and gathering societies. We have seen that there is evidence for the killing and eating of animals by nonhuman primates and by the early African hominids. The fact that australopithecines bashed in a number of baboon skulls demonstrates that they were able to kill relatively large animals. It also implies considerable cooperation among the hunters. A single hominid or a poorly coordinated group of hominids would have found it extremely difficult, if not lethal, to attack a troop of baboons.

Whether evolving hominids lacked large canines from the start or whether these teeth were reduced (which is the general belief), one fact seems evident: Factors selective for large canines were largely inoperative among the Hominidae not long after the ape and hominid lines parted. A somewhat unique biological makeup or environmental circumstances may have negated any advantages such teeth offered. Techniques developed quite early, particularly cooperative techniques, may have allowed prehominids to attain ends normally reached by means of long canines among other primates. Food-gathering might have demanded so much time and energy that there was little opportunity for serious intragroup combat. Yet another possibility, one with which Professor Dart might agree (see below), was the early discovery that natural objects were weapons that could be used to settle interpersonal differences. Positions of dominance went to those males that could wield a club most effectively or throw sticks and stones with accuracy. Later, it was learned, these weapons could be used in obtaining food.

CHANGES IN THE FACE, SKULL, AND BRAIN

Among the anatomical changes experienced during the hominoid-to-hominid transition, it is generally believed, was a decrease in the relative size of the face. The snout presumably retreated as the canines and incisors became smaller. In the opinion of several authorities, a reduction in the size of the front teeth was a consequence of tool-using and the eating of meat. This line of thought is based on the assumption that the prehominids had prognathous (projecting) faces, like today's chimpanzees and gorillas. As suggesed above, however, it is possible that facial lengthening was confined to nonhominids. Pilbeam and Simons propose that prognathism occurred, "at least in part, as a response to demands of ground living, defensive display and vegetarian diet." *Proconsul africanus* and *Oreopithecus*, they observe, were relatively orthognathous (straight-faced), while the terrestrial baboons and macaques have long faces.[22]

Primates with large bodies often have a larger masticatory apparatus relative to brain size than small primates. Joseph Biegert interprets this to mean that when primates became larger, their jaws increased at a greater rate than did their braincases. Therefore, increases in body size may have resulted in greater prognathism. A large olfactory organ or organs between the ventral spine and the mandibular symphysis (front of jaw, where the two halves fuse), such as the enlarged vocal apparatus of howler monkeys, can also "cause" facial lengthening. On the other hand, expansion of the brain can flatten the face.[23] It has also been suggested that assumption of upright posture contributed to facial flattening.[24]

Another explanation for reduction in length of the face is suggested by the small jaws and flat face of the young chimpanzee: mutations resulted in the retention of features that were formerly characteristic of the prehominid infant, features which had been lost as the body developed. *Neoteny* (or *pedomorphosis*)—the process by which embryonic, fetal, or infantile features are retained in later stages of development *—may account for a number of important features of the human face and skull. One such feature is the positioning of the foramen magnum and occipital condyles. At the beginning of the fetal stage, Adolph H. Schultz has observed, the head of an Old World monkey, ape, or human fetus is posed on top of the spinal column. The occipital condyles are forward on the skull base. As the ape or monkey fetus develops, the condyles shift toward the back of the skull; most of the skull projects forward of the spine. The human fetus undergoes no such change. Consequently, the human skull is balanced over the spine in postnatal life.[25]

Ashley Montagu [26] lists and discusses a number of other possible neotenous characters in man, such as hairlessness of the body, long neck,

---

* Neoteny is thought by some to have played a very significant role in several evolutionary developments. One theory, for example, holds that the free-swimming larvae of an echinoderm group (sea urchins) failed to progress beyond the larval stage—except sexually—and eventually gave rise to the first chordates, the ancestors of the vertebrates.

thinness of the skull, thin nails, and low birth weights. The milk teeth of young apes, Montagu notes, resemble human adult teeth more closely than they resemble the teeth of adult apes. Of greater significance, neoteny supposedly brought about the rounded, globular form of the skull (also evident in the young chimpanzee) and considerable brain growth after birth. Among apes, most brain growth occurs before birth. The gibbon, Montagu says, attains 70 per cent of its brain growth during gestation. The human brain, on the other hand, is only about 25 per cent of its adult size at birth. The human brain continues to grow until about the twentieth year of life, and the main sutures of the braincase (neurocranium) do not normally close until late in the twenties. The ape's brain expands little, if at all, after the first year or so; the sutures close within a few years after birth.

The foregoing suggests that man's unusually large brain is possible because neotenous mutations have allowed him to retain characteristics that are infantile, even fetal, in other primates. This does not mean, however, that such mutations made a large brain inevitable. As we saw in Chapter 2, every possibility offered by mutations is not exploited. Generally speaking, a marked change in structure or functioning brought about by genetic alterations must make an organism better adapted to its total environment; otherwise, the mutant genes—and the possibilities they offer—are lost. In short, a large brain had to prove adaptive. Its advantages had to outweigh its costs in order to become established.

The costs of a large brain appear to be considerable. In the words of Carleton S. Coon, the human brain is a "gluttonous organ." Even when the body is at rest, about 765 cc. of blood must be pumped to the brain every minute; physical exertion may almost double this amount. At rest, in other words, around 12 per cent of the body's total blood supply is used by an organ that occupies approximately 2 per cent of the body's bulk. Great amounts of oxygen and sugar must also be fed constantly to the brain. It is very sensitive to changes in temperature and must be kept warm in cool weather and cooled in hot weather.[27] Since blood must be pumped uphill much of the time, the human heart is placed under more strain than is the heart of a quadruped.

We can readily deduce from man's behaviors and accomplishments that a large brain can have adaptive value. There is also evidence from comparative studies and experiments with larger and smaller animals of related species that points in the same direction. It has been found that larger (hence larger-brained) animals can usually learn more, or learn more difficult tasks; and they can retain what has been learned for longer periods of time than the smaller animals. Bernhard Rensch, who reports these findings, believes the differentials in learning may be due to an alteration in neural makeup. Innervation of greater body areas requires "a relative increase of more complicated regions of the cortex" and an absolute increase of the number of nerve cells which "allow more complicated nervous connections and therefore a more plastic behaviour and an increased utilization of experience. We have also to consider that larger species normally have a greater duration of life." [28]

The animal that can learn more and remember longer has a greater capacity for adaptation to varied and variable situations. Its behavior is less stereotyped, more responsive to change or changing conditions. Adaptability, it seems safe to conclude, was a crucial factor in the survival of evolving hominids. We cannot assume, of course, that the first hominids had a brain as complex as ours. It is obvious, too, that most of the expansion of the hominid brain has occurred since the days of the South African and Olduvai forms. But the fact that the australopithecines had a brain-body ratio close to that of modern man does suggest that considerable brain growth was achieved during the hominoid-to-hominid transition. The only known nonhominid primate, living or extinct, with a larger braincase than the australopithecines is the modern gorilla, an animal several times the body size of any of the australopithecines or of *Homo habilis*.

The brain of the early Pleistocene hominids was not only relatively large, it was organized along somewhat different lines than the brain of a nonhominid. Components or subsystems within the brain had undergone reorganization. This can be inferred from the topography of the *Australopithecus* skull, which indicates a greater amount of neopallium ("new cloak"—that part of the brain which has to do with senses other than the sense of smell) than an ape has,[29] and from the tools that have been found. The manufacture of stone (and possibly bone) tools, if not their use, demanded a neuromuscular makeup unknown among other animals. The tools also indicate that the early hominids were capable of organizing experiences in a more human manner, as Ralph L. Holloway, Jr. has pointed out.[30] To fashion implements, however crude, is to exercise foresight; things are made for events which have yet to occur. To employ similarly made objects—or variously shaped ones (bones)—for a variety of purposes (killing, skinning, cutting) implies an ability to abstract, to recognize the persistency of qualities such as durability or sharpness in different contexts. It implies, in other words, a capacity for conceptualization.

Before evolving hominids could become deliberate and successful hunters, they had to have a brain that could discriminate, remember, and relate a variety of information. A reorganization of the brain was also necessary to change what Adriaan Kortlandt calls the "subjective world" or "world picture" of the subhuman primate. Observations and experiments have demonstrated that apes and monkeys define the character and identity of things primarily by their place and spatial relations. Zoo chimpanzees, for instance, tend to define and react to food as something entirely strange when the food is put in an unaccustomed place. They may even refuse to eat their meals. The primate subjective world is adapted to things which remain fixed, such as trees and vegetable foods; it is predominantly static. The carnivore, on the other hand, has to catch moving animals. Its subjective world therefore has a predominantly mobile character. Man has a brain which enables him to form static pictures *plus* the mobile type of world picture. The ability to integrate the two contrasting world pictures, Kortlandt says, "opens the road to the achievement of a mechanical technology. . . ."

Hunting, Kortlandt observes, demands concentration. A carnivore may spend several hours or even days following or waiting for its prey. Nonhuman primates lack this persistent motivation. As a rule, they can concentrate on one activity or object for half an hour at most. A carnivore would die of starvation if it was constantly diverted from its prey.[31] The significance of extended concentration, or persistent motivation, extends beyond hunting, of course. To manufacture anything, even the crudest of tools, requires some amount of sustained attention.

Hockett and Ascher are of the opinion that some form of language developed during the hominoid-to-hominid transition.[32] Pressures to cooperate, if they were as great as is generally thought, would certainly have encouraged the development of communicative techniques absent among nonhuman primates. In this connection it is interesting that wolves, which hunt cooperatively, have a larger number (32 to 36 per cent) of communication patterns than foxes, which hunt as individuals.[33] Even if the first hominids lacked what might now be called language, it is very likely that they transmitted a greater number—and probably greater variety—of meanings through utterances than their predecessors. In either case, changes in brain structure were involved.

It is not altogether improbable that the brain became structured to allow a social code of sorts to develop by the time hominids evolved. Assuming that cooperation between and among individuals was necessary to achieve a food supply and safety, fighting and discord would have exposed members of a group to starvation or environmental dangers. Possibly, then, an individual unable or unwilling to do his part, or one who created friction (by forcing himself upon another's mate, for example), was treated roughly. The fractured australopithecine jaws and skulls mentioned earlier may reflect the application of sanctions.

Professor Dart has a different interpretation of the jaws and skulls, for he believes the early hominids were asocial creatures—brutal, selfish, bullying, and sexually aggressive. To Dart's way of thinking, it is logical to conclude from "the consistency with which such fragmentary remains as isolated teeth and skulls or parts of them and of pelves, have been found in australopithecine deposits" that "cannibalism was a frequent occurrence." [34] This view does not seem to accord with field observations. To our knowledge, no competent observer has ever seen one great ape kill or eat another of its kind. All reports picture them as quite peaceable in their relations with one another. The notion that wild animals and "savages" are bestial is a myth. As Montagu points out, "savages" live cooperatively with one another and seldom bother anyone; and although civilized men behave like "beasts," the beasts of the field do not. The australopithecine fractures, Montagu suggests, were accidental. At worst, ritual canniblism was practiced—but not indiscriminate killing.[35]

SUMMARY AND CONCLUSIONS

The evolution of hominids from a hominoid stock began with the convergence of certain genetic and ecological changes. The latter altered the availability and distribution of need-satisfiers, thereby encouraging or necessitating modifications in habitual behavior patterns. Initially, such modifications consisted in more frequent occurrence of or slight variations upon familiar behaviors—such as rearing up on the hind legs higher, more often, or for longer periods of time. As environmental changes continued—the dry seasons possibly became progressively longer each year and forests scarcer—the search for need-satisfiers increasingly exposed prehominids to the demands and opportunities of a terrestrial way of life.

Among the first genetic changes, it is generally believed, were those which altered the shape and position of the pelvis. Assuming that the pelvis was shaped somewhat like that of a living great ape, prehominids experienced a widening and shortening of the hipbone (ilium). (See page 93.) Had this been the only change in this area, the size of the birth canal would have been greatly reduced. The size of the latter was maintained, however, by a "bending" of the pelvis; the point at which the hipbones articulated with the spine (at the sacrum) moved down, shoving the pelvic canal forward. The sacrum was brought nearer the acetabulum, the socket of the femur. Such alterations in bone structure affected the attachment and functioning of muscles associated with posture and locomotion. For example, the broader ilium provided a greater front-to-rear area for the attachment of muscles which balance the trunk on the lower limbs, and such muscles grew larger. Shortening of the pelvis brought the muscles that extend the leg closer to the acetabulum, making it easier for these muscles to contract; thus a maximum of movement, as in walking, was possible with a minimum of contraction.

Changes, it must be remembered, are interactive and reciprocal. One change affects another and provides the basis for yet other changes. The gradual shrinkage of forests may have required or encouraged exploration and exploitation of terrestrial niches. But so, too, did a gradual assumption of erect posture and bipedal locomotion—which were furthered by ecological circumstances. Alterations in the pelvic region fostered changes in the skull (position of occipital condyles and foramen magnum) and in the lower extremities, thus making erect posture and bipedal progression more feasible. Carrying possibly encouraged bipedalism; but bipedalism also encouraged carrying. When the forelimbs were freed from a need to participate in locomotion, more carrying of objects into and out of the grassland could take place. The hands, long accustomed to a variety of uses, could be put to even more uses with habitual erect bipedalism.

A more omnivorous diet was furthered in part by environmental changes. It was also encouraged by prior experiences with a variety of foods, by dentition that could masticate just about any edible substance, and by prehensile hands that could hold and manipulate animate and inanimate objects. Crucial, too, in an extension of the diet were alterations in neuromuscular systems. The brain and neural pathways were increased and reorganized to perceive and respond to more information and to adapt to the mobility and habits of other animals. An improved neural makeup also permitted a greater degree of cooperation and, concomitantly, the development of more efficient means of communication between and among group members. The relationship between neural makeup and behavior was, of course, reciprocal. Increased complexity in either affected the other.

It is probable that group life and cooperation, particularly between the sexes, provided situations which were safer for the immature young. The period of infant dependency became more and more extended, furthering an increase in body size and brain size. Slowly closing sutures of the braincase proved to be adaptive, for more time was necessary to learn to adapt to social and natural environments. The ground offered more opportunity for interaction among a greater number of individuals; too, it was a more varied and variable habitat than the forests. As evolving hominids learned to cope with their new habitat, more and more of what was learned was transmitted to the young—through example, interference with activities, gestures and expressions, calls, and eventually by means of what might be called symbols. Foundations for culture were established, in other words. Members learned increasingly more from one another—from experiences of the past as well as of the present—and depended less and less upon trial-and-error learning.

In sum, the pressures and opportunities of a terrestrial environment were selective for most of the physical and behavioral characteristics which distinguish *Homo sapiens* from his nonhuman kin. The nature of these selective forces is uncertain, for the ecology of prehominid-hominid environments is not fully known. It is very likely that the forces were varied and changed from time to time and from place to place.

Natural selection may have favored erect bipedalism and other hominid-like traits because the environment was hostile. Those unable to peer over grasses, carry foods and weapons, and cooperate, for instance, may have starved or been killed by predators. Again, characteristics not oriented in the hominid direction may have been eliminated through competition. For example, primates unable to maintain an erect posture or work with others may have been unable to locate food, or food in sufficient quantity, quickly enough. Many who were ill-equipped for terrestrial life may have spent so much time and energy in self-maintenance that they failed to reproduce themselves proportionately.

Some primates, for one reason or another, might have succumbed more readily to accidents or diseases. Perhaps they were not nimble enough or intelligent enough to avoid certain situations or certain parasite-infested areas of the savannah. An inability to learn or remember how to use tools, track animals, exercise self-control, cooperate with others, respond to communicative cues, and the like may have led to the destruction of many prehominid or early hominid cousins. Violent individuals or any who manifested behavioral peculiarities were possibly killed or isolated. On the other hand, individuals who exhibited hominid-like features and behaviors may have been more sexually attractive as well as socially acceptable.

Whatever the selective factors, most of the basic *Homo* characteristics were well established by the Upper Pliocene or Lower Pleistocene. The foot and perhaps the pelvis were to be modified slightly for more comfortable walking; [36] the hand was possibly to acquire greater dexterity.[37] There were to be further increases in body and brain size and in brain complexity. The relative size of the front teeth was to decrease, as was the length of the face. Self-control and social control, which must have been of importance during the hominoid-to-hominid transition, were to become more pervasive and more readily maintained as language evolved —and essential as the rudiments of culture expanded into true culture.

Another change—which may have occurred during the transition— was the acquisition of more efficient heat-dissipating mechanisms. Our ancestors became less hairy and developed more sweat glands, it

211

has been suggested, as a result of a hunting way of life.[38] Bipedal creatures with the ability to lose body heat rapidly could plod after large, furry quadrupeds until these animals dropped of exhaustion.[39]

Most of the changes that were to occur before modern man evolved, we shall see in the chapters which follow, were but a continuation of trends reflected in the fossil evidence from South Africa and Olduvai Gorge.

NOTES

1. Sherwood L. Washburn, "Behavior and Human Evolution," in Sherwood L. Washburn (ed.), *Classification and Human Evolution* (Chicago: Aldine Publishing Company, 1963), pp. 194–195.

2. Earnest A. Hooton, *Up From the Ape* (New York: The Macmillan Company, 1937), pp. 93–103.

4. Charles F. Hockett and Robert Ascher, "The Human Revolution," *Current Anthropology*, 5 (1964), 135–168.

4. Elwyn L. Simons, "Fossil Primates and the Evolution of Some Primate Locomotor Systems," *American Journal of Physical Anthropology*, 26 (1967), 251.

5. E. Lloyd DuBrul, "The General Phenomenon of Bipedalism," *American Zoologist*, 2 (1962), 205–208.

6. John Napier, "The Locomotor Functions of Hominids," in Washburn, *op. cit.*, p. 187.

7. Frank B. Livingstone, "Reconstructing Man's Pliocene Pongid Ancestor," *American Anthropologist*, 64 (1962), 301–305.

8. Adriaan Kortlandt and M. Kooij, "Protohominid Behaviour in Primates (Preliminary Communication)," *Symposia of the Zoological Society of London*, No. 10 (August, 1963), p. 73.

9. Gordon W. Hewes, "Food Transport and the Origin of Hominid Bipedalism," *American Anthropologist*, 63 (1961), 698–701.

10. Hockett and Ascher, *op. cit.*, pp. 140–141.

11. Hewes, *op. cit.*, p. 703.

12. Hockett and Ascher, *op. cit.*, p. 140.

13. John Napier, "The Antiquity of Human Walking," *Scientific American*, 216 (April, 1967), 64.

14. William A. Mason, "The Social Development of Monkeys and Apes," in Irven DeVore (ed.), *Primate Behavior: Field Studies of Monkeys and Apes* (New York: Holt, Rinehart & Winston, Inc., 1965), p. 519.

15. Sherwood L. Washburn, "Tools and Human Evolution," *Scientific American*, 203 (September, 1960), 69.

16. Bernard G. Campbell, *Human Evolution* (Chicago: Aldine Publishing Company, 1966), p. 332.

17. M. F. Ashley Montagu, *The Human Revolution* (Cleveland: The World Publishing Company, 1965), pp. 157–158.

18. Cf. Ralph L. Holloway, Jr., "Tools and Teeth: Some Speculations Regarding Canine Reduction," *American Anthropologist*, 69 (1967), 63–67.

19. Hewes, *op. cit.*, p. 704.

20. William Etkin, "Social Behavior and the Evolution of Man's Mental Faculties," in M. F. Ashley Montagu (ed.), *Culture and the Evolution of Man* (New York: Oxford University Press, 1962), pp. 137–138.

21. Ashley Montagu, *op. cit.*, p. 186.

22. D. R. Pilbeam and Elwyn L. Simons, "Some Problems of Hominid Classification," *American Scientist*, 53 (1965), 243–244.

23. Josef Biegert, "The Evaluation of Characteristics of the Skull, Hands, and Feet for Primate Taxonomy," in Washburn, *Classification and Human Evolution*, pp. 122–129.

24. Pilbeam and Simons, *op. cit.*, p. 244.

25. Adolph H. Schultz, "The Specializations of Man and His Place Among the Catarrhine Primates," *Cold Spring Harbor Symposia on Quantitative Biology*, XV (Cold Spring Harbor, N. Y.: The Biological Laboratory, 1950), 46.

26. Ashley Montagu, *op. cit.*, pp. 167–179.

27. Carleton S. Coon, *The Origin of Races* (New York: Alfred A. Knopf, Inc., 1963), pp. 77–78.

28. Bernhard Rensch, "The Relation Between the Evolution of Central Nervous Functions and the Body Size of Animals," in Julian Huxley, A. C. Hardy, and E. B. Ford (eds.), *Evolution As a Process* (London: George Allen & Unwin Ltd., 1954), pp. 189–197.

29. Biegert, *op. cit.*, p. 123.

30. Ralph L. Holloway, Jr., "Cranial Capacity, Neural Reorganization, and Hominid Evolution: A Search for More Suitable Parameters," *American Anthropologist*, 68 (1966), 113.

31. Adriaan Kortlandt, Comment on "The Essential Morphological Basis for Human Culture," *Current Anthropology*, 6 (1965), 322–323.

32. Hockett and Ascher, *op. cit.*, p. 144.

33. Kortlandt, *op. cit.*, p. 321.

34. Raymond A. Dart, "The Ecology of the South African Man-Apes," *Yearbook of Physical Anthropology 1964*, Vol. 12, pp. 34–40.

35. Ashley Montagu, *op. cit.*, pp. 152–154.

36. Napier, "The Antiquity of Human Walking," pp. 62–66.

37. John Napier, "Fossil Hand Bones from Olduvai Gorge," *Nature*, 196 (1962), 409–411.

38. Weston La Barre and M. F. Ashley Montagu, Comments on *The Human Revolution, Current Anthropology*, 5 (1964), 148, 161.

39. C. L. Brace and M. F. Ashley Montagu, *Man's Evolution* (New York: The Macmillan Company, 1965), p. 220.

13

Middle Pleistocene Man

"Missing link" was a joke, a derisive phrase among nineteenth-century opponents of Darwinism. Baron Georges Cuvier's dictum—"Fossil man does not exist!"—still held sway over much of the thinking about early man during the latter part of the century. Fossils of pre-*sapiens* hominids discovered before and after *The Origin of Species* was published were ignored or discounted as evidence for the existence of an earlier form of man. Darwin's ideas, so far as many people were concerned, were not only heretical but also intellectually unsound.

Among those who held views to the contrary was a German naturalist, Ernst Haeckle, who called Darwin the "Copernicus of biology." Using Darwin's ideas and his own knowledge of lower forms of life, Haeckle worked out a genealogical tree of animal life, from the initial microorganism (the "moneron") to the present-day complexity and diversity. He also assigned a name to the as yet undiscovered primate group that linked man with his nonhuman ancestry: *Pithecanthropus alalus* ("apeman without speech"). This subhuman group, Haeckle concluded from a comparison of ape and human embryos, resembled the gibbon, not the chimpanzee and gorilla as most Darwinians believed.[1]

Eugene Dubois, a young Dutch physician and anatomist, was another man who took the notion of a "missing link" quite seriously—so seriously, in fact, that he was determined to find it. But where to look? Dubois had read both Darwin and Haeckle. The first had reasoned that the climate and the presence of chimpanzees and gorillas made Africa the most likely place to search for human origins. Haeckle's belief that man's ancestors were gibbon-like pointed to southeast Asia. Africa was not very accessible to a Dutch citizen with no financial resources, but Holland did have colonies in southeast Asia. And so Dubois signed on as a health officer in the colonial armed forces of the Dutch East Indies.

PITHECANTHROPUS ERECTUS

Dubois was not yet thirty years of age when he took up a post at a hospital in Sumatra in December, 1887. More than a year passed before he found time to undertake any search for fossils. All he found then were teeth of orangutans. Dubois was perhaps disappointed, but not discouraged. He had become acquainted with published works on Indonesian paleontology and had seen some interesting prehistoric materials from Java. That island, he decided, was a more likely place to find evidence of the "missing link," so he sought a transfer to Java. In April, 1889, he was commissioned by his government to explore the deposits of Java.

The following year Dubois found a jaw fragment that contained two premolars and the socket for a canine. Dubois made reference to this fragment in the Government Mining Bulletin in 1890 and again in 1891. Then, strangely, no further mention was made of the fossil until he published a memoir in 1924. Perhaps he decided that the fragment was not after all "a remain of a not exactly determinable human species" of "another and probably lower type" than any known hominid.[2]

The jaw fragment had been exposed by the Solo River a few miles from the hamlet of Trinil, in central Java. From the same general area came two other finds, both reported in 1891. The first was a molar "of a chimpanzee (Anthropopithecus)." The second find Dubois regarded as "a fine skullcap which, with even less doubt than the molar" could be "attributed to the genus Anthropopithecus troglodytes. That both the specimens came from a great manlike ape" was "at once clear." Dubois was certain that the skullcap was from an extinct chimpanzee genus. Its "greater dolichocephaly" (long-headedness) distinguished it from the skullcap of an orangutan; and it lacked the "cranial crests" of the gorilla. The species to which the new "Pleistocene chimpanzee of Java" belonged was less clear, for the "skull differs from that of the living chimpanzee by its greater size and its higher vaulting."

Dubois furnished a species name for his "chimpanzee" the following year, 1892. Nearly fifty feet upstream from the place where he had found the skullcap, he discovered a femur (thighbone). "The characters of the bone make it certain that the Javanese *Anthropopithecus* stood and walked equally upright as man," thus freeing his arms and hands. Dubois therefore gave the specimen the species designation *erectus*. Quite possibly, he wrote, "man has evolved from this old-Pleistocene *Anthropopithecus erectus*. And thus is also furnished an adverse proof to the opinion, expressed by some, that India was the cradle of man."

Before excavations near Trinil came to an end in 1893, two more teeth, a molar and a premolar, were added to the collection. In 1894 Dubois turned his attention from searching to studying what he had found. After scrutinizing the fossils, he decided that they were not from an extinct chimpanzee after all. They were, according to the title of an 1894 report, from "a manlike transitional form," a form Dubois called *Pithecanthropus erectus*. Dubois estimated the cranial capacity of the skull to have been 1,000 cc. The skull was too large to be ape, too small to be human. The teeth and femur also exhibited characteristics that were neither completely apelike nor yet fully human. In an article published in 1898, Dubois reiterated his belief that the specimen he had discovered was a "link connecting together Apes and Man." This was his last public pronouncement for a quarter of a century.

Discovery of the "erect ape-man" was no doubt a source of considerable satisfaction to the young Dutch doctor. He had set out to find a form which bridged the gap between man and nonhumans, and he had succeeded. But the events which followed his return to Europe must have diminished his sense of satisfaction to a great extent. Although Dubois' finds were of considerable interest to the scientific world and were almost universally regarded as of great importance, there was a diversity of opinion as to how the fossils should be interpreted. The latitude for disagreement was considerable, but controversy centered on two matters. First was the question of the relationship of one fossil to another. Did the skullcap, the femur, and the two teeth come from the same individual? From the same type of individual? From different individuals or forms? No consensus was reached on this matter. Secondly, there was the question of classification. Again, opinion was fragmented. Some scientists agreed with Dubois that *Pithecanthropus erectus* was a transitional form, intermediate to man and his apelike ancestral group. Some interpreted the fossils as remains from a modern man, a microcephalic idiot. Yet others accepted the view of the prominent German pathologist and anthropologist, Rudolf Virchow, that the skullcap showed "the greatest resemblance with the skullcap of a Hylobates," or gibbon, that the femur, too, was from a giant gibbon, and the teeth were more apelike than human.

Dubois apparently had little stomach for the interminable controversy. He grew more and more silent, and eventually withdrew both himself and his finds from public view for more than two decades. Some say he hid the bones beneath the dining room floor in his house; others say he kept them stored in a museum in his home town (Haarlem). In either case, Dubois failed to respond to requests to see the specimens until 1923. Then, surprisingly, he extended to the American anthropologist Aleš Hrdlička the privilege of examining the fossils. Hrdlička reported that the materials contained not only the four parts from *Pithecanthropus erectus* but also another tooth, the initial discovery (the jaw fragment), and skeletons from Wadjak in central Java (now generally classified as *Homo sapiens*).

Dubois had three articles published in 1924. In these articles he de-emphasized the human-like features of the *Pithecanthropus erectus* fossils. In one he went so far as to say: "The form of the skull of the Pithecanthropus is on the whole not human; nor is it a transition of any type of manlike apes to the human type." His stress was primarily upon gibbon-like characteristics, an echo of Virchow's opinion that Java man was a giant gibbon.

Man or Ape?

Who was right? The young doctor, so confident he had found the missing link that he assigned the name Haeckle had coined for it to his find? The eminent Dr. Virchow—and Dubois after his years of silence? Or those who held that the bones were from a small-brained member of *Homo sapiens*? Dubois reported in an 1896 paper that only Virchow maintained that the femur "belonged to the ape, most probably a Hylobates." Most "were agreed that the femur was human and not simian in character." [3] There was little doubt that the thighbone came from a creature that could walk on two legs—which would seem to have eliminated the possibility that *Pithecanthropus erectus* was a giant gibbon. Because the femur was so human-like, however, some doubted that the femur and the skullcap could have come from the same individual; the two fossils were perhaps not even from the same period in time. (Fluorine analysis later demonstrated that the skullcap and femur are of the same relative age.) [4]

The skullcap (page 218) was less than human, yet not completely apelike. It was thick and lacked the human forehead. The flattened frontal area of the braincase led forward to a heavy brow ridge (supraorbital torus), and a heavy bony ridge ran across the rear of the skull (the occipital torus). The latter was not as inclined, not as high on the skull, as a gorilla torus. This indicated that although *Pithecanthropus*

217

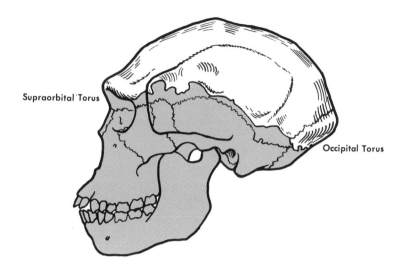

Supraorbital Torus

Occipital Torus

Figure 19. The *Pithecanthropus erectus* skull as reconstructed from the skullcap (unshaded area).

erectus had powerful neck muscles, they were not as powerful as those of a gorilla. The cranial capacity of the skull, about 900 cc. (the current estimate), was in excess of any ape skull, yet supposedly smaller than a normal human skull.[5]

Had the skull been more complete or had Dubois found any artifacts in association with the fossils, perhaps the "erect ape-man" would have created less confusion and controversy. As it was, the specimen remained somewhat of an enigma until after other significant fossils began to be uncovered in northern China.

SINANTHROPUS PEKINENSIS [6]

About the time Dubois was again making his finds available for international scrutiny, another physician and anatomist arrived in China. The physician, Dr. Davidson Black, a Canadian slightly past forty, accepted an appointment as professor of anatomy at the newly founded Peking Union Medical College. Black was keenly interested in prehistoric man. He had worked on the Piltdown man materials and knew the details of other fossil finds. Like Dubois, he aspired to make a significant fossil discovery himself. It was this hope which motivated him to seek the teaching position. Man, he believed, had originated in Asia; and Peking would serve as a place from which to search.

Unknown to Black at the time, two other men had already begun exploration of chalk quarries about twenty-five miles southwest of Peking, near the village of Choukoutien. One of the men, Dr. J. G. Andersson, a Swedish geologist, had visited the quarries in 1920 while acting as an adviser to the Geological Survey of China. Versions differ as to how Andersson discovered the site—he observed fissures filled with red earth that contained fossil fragments, or he noted that bits of quartz did not belong to particular strata. However the site was located, a paleontologist, Dr. Otto Zdansky, was brought in to assist Andersson. Once on the scene, Zdansky quickly discovered two teeth of very human appearance among the fossils that were dug from what the Chinese referred to as Dragon-bone Hill.

Andersson and Zdansky did not know what to make of the two worn, primitive molars. No other evidence of ancient man had been found in Asia north of the Himalayas, and the teeth were from deposits supposedly at least a million years old—much older than man was thought to be. Puzzled, the men took the teeth to Dr. Black. Black, who was certain that the molars were from a human of considerable antiquity, recognized the importance of the find. He was apparently able to convince others of their significance, too, for the Rockefeller Foundation agreed to provide funds for a thorough investigation of Dragon-bone Hill. Another Swede, Dr. Birgir Bohlin, was brought in to supervise the field work under the general direction of Dr. Black.

In April, 1927, the first scientific expedition organized to search for man's ancestors began operations. Digging was difficult, and tons and tons of material had to be moved and sifted for teeth and small bones. A vast quantity of animal fossils was collected, but the debris was barren of hominid remains. Then, on October 16, three days before the first season's work was scheduled to end, Bohlin discovered a hominid tooth close to where the other two teeth had been found.

Black and Bohlin examined the tooth, a molar from a child of about eight, for hours. It was compared with chimpanzee teeth, the teeth of Chinese children, the teeth of extinct hominids. The tooth differed from all of these to the degree that Black decided it represented a distinct hominid genus. He gave it the name *Sinanthropus pekinensis*, or "China man of Peking," later to be more commonly referred to as Peking man. In December of that year Black reported the discovery of *Sinanthropus* to the Geological Society of China. Long ago, he told the Society, there lived in China a prehistoric man closer to modern man than to the great apes. It was perhaps a rash conclusion to draw from a single tooth— but Black was right.

How right Black was became evident during the next two years. In 1928 Dr. W. C. Pei, who took over Bohlin's position, discovered several

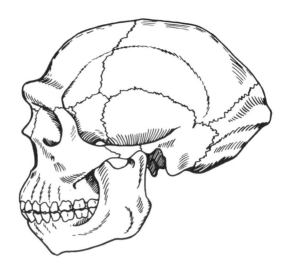

Figure 20. Reconstruction of a female *Sinanthropus* skull.

teeth, and jaw and skull fragments. On December 2, 1929—again just before work was scheduled to cease—Pei found a complete skull in a newly opened cave. It was uncrushed; only the face was missing. The specimen was such as Black had visualized from the child's molar.

Within a few days, news of the discovery was flashed around the world. The reception given the *Sinanthropus* skull was quite different from that given specimens from South Africa and *Pithecanthropus erectus*. There were few detractors, and little controversy arose, mainly because the new evidence fitted in with existing ideas about man's early ancestors. Nor did Black arouse much criticism when he stated, in a 1930 report, that the "morphological evidence so far available" placed *Sinanthropus* "not far removed from the type from which evolved the extinct Neanderthaler and the modern *Homo sapiens.*" [7]

A second adult skull, reconstructed from fragments, and a variety of other materials were added to the initial finds during the early 1930's. In 1934, Dr. Black died of a heart attack. He had lived long enough to see his ambition realized, his ideas accepted, and his conclusion based upon a single tooth confirmed. He did not, however, live to see the bulk of the fossils and artifacts which were to come from the Choukoutien area.

The man who succeeded Black at the Peking Union Medical College was another anatomist and physician, Dr. Franz Weidenreich. Weidenreich, who was born in Germany in 1873, had an unhappy penchant for losing positions through no fault of his own. After Germany's defeat in World War I, the French dismissed him from a teaching position at the University of Strasbourg. Hitler's rise to power resulted in his ouster in 1933 from a professorship of anthropology at the University of Frankfurt.

Soon after his arrival in Peking in 1935, Weidenreich prepared a series of thorough studies of Peking man. Everything he wrote pointed to the same conclusion Black had reached: *Sinanthropus* was a human, albeit a primitive one. What made the "China man" a human? Most important, in Weidenreich's opinion, was his ability to walk on two legs. "Apes, like man, have two hands and two feet, but man alone has acquired an upright position and the faculty to use his feet exclusively as locomotor instruments." The jaw and dentition were hominid. The dental arch was arcuate, there were no projecting canines, and the teeth were quite human in all other features. The relatively large and rounded braincase had a capacity more than twice that of a chimpanzee. Finally, there were tools and proof that Peking man had used fire.

The tools were not recognized as such during the first years of excavation in the Choukoutien region, according to Dr. Kenneth Oakley. Black and his assistants may have been a bit naive archaeologically; but many of the artifacts were, in Oakley's words, "lacking in form." Had they been discovered apart from definite evidence of hominid fossils or activities, several of the stone implements "would not have been recognized as of human origin." Those stone artifacts that were identified (now known as the Choukoutien industry) consisted mainly of crude chopping implements and flake tools. The latter were pieces knocked off pebbles to form chopping tools; they were not deliberately shaped.[8]

Before work in the Choukoutien area ceased, parts of more than forty individuals were found in the limestone fissures and caves. Several layers of fossil-bearing strata were exposed, to a depth of 160 feet. At the lower levels was evidence of alternating occupation of the caves by large carnivores and hominids. Toward the top, the hominids took over permanently. Their artifacts and fossils, along with charcoal fragments and burned bones, showed up in several of the upper layers. Also in association with other materials were remains of some sixty species of animals Peking man presumably ate, ranging from small rodents to camels and elephants. Judging from the number of fossils, deer were the most common source of meat.

Operations at Choukoutien were halted late in 1941. The Japanese, who had taken over North China in 1937, showed a mounting interest in the world-famous fossils. Convinced that difficulties were ahead, Weidenreich took a set of plaster casts to New York (the fossils themselves were the property of the Geological Survey of China). While Weidenreich was gone, the director of the Geological Survey became fearful that the Japanese were going to confiscate Peking man's remains, so he asked for and received American assistance. The bones, boxed and classified as secret materials, were put on a special train that left Peking on December 5. The train was supposed to rendezvous with an American liner at a small Chinese port.

On the day of rendezvous, December 7, 1941, Pearl Harbor was bombed. The crew of the American liner grounded their ship to keep the Japanese from making immediate use of it (the Japanese later refloated and used the ship as a transport). The Marine guards who accompanied the fossils were captured and put in prison camps. These things are known. What is not known is what happened to the fossils. They were never received by Japanese officials, nor have they turned up in American or Chinese collections.

And so it was that Franz Weidenreich lost another position. Fortunately, he and the casts had arrived in the United States before World War II erupted in the Pacific.

A NEW SPECIES

With the discovery of the North China fossils, the enigmatic status of *Pithecanthropus erectus* began to be resolved. Similarities between *Sinanthropus* and *Pithecanthropus* were pointed out as early as 1929 by Marcellin Boule. Neither Dubois nor Black, however, accepted Boule's judgment. So far as Dubois was concerned, there was only one Ape-man. He rejected the possibility that similar forms could have evolved in different areas. Black acknowledged a great resemblance between the skulls of Java man and Peking man, but he stressed their differences rather than their likenesses when he prepared his description of *Sinanthropus*. Since he had created a new genus on the basis of a single tooth, he had to legitimize his creation.[9]

Weidenreich was more objective. Within a year after he took Black's place, he wrote: "I think that the Pithecanthropus skull cap has the same morphological and phylogenetical character as Sinanthropus. . . . The difference between the two skulls can be due at most to racial variation."[10] A few years later he compared the *Pithecanthropus* skullcap with the calvaria (the braincase minus facial bones and the lower jaw) of an adult female *Sinanthropus*. The latter was a bit better developed in the frontal area; the former, in the parietal area (the parietal bone forms part of the top and back of the braincase). Otherwise, the two skulls were quite similar.[11]

Weidenreich's diagnosis was supported by the discovery, in 1937, of another Java specimen, *Pithecanthropus II*. The specimen, a skull more complete than the *erectus* skullcap, was found by a young German pale-ontologist, G. H. R. von Koenigswald, near Sangiran (about forty miles west of Trinil). It came from the same stratum (the "Trinil layer") as Dubois' find. *Pithecanthropus II* was complete enough to show the for-ward position of the foramen magnum, an almost certain index of upright posture.[12] When the two Java specimens were compared, they were strikingly alike. They agreed, von Koenigswald later wrote, "even in what might be considered purely individual traits." [13] The major dif-ference—a sexual difference, von Koenigswald suggested—was in cranial capacity. The 1937 find had an estimated cranial capacity of only 775 cc.[14]

Sinanthropus had been readily accepted into human company. As it became evident that differences between Java man and Peking man were slight, the former was also accorded hominid status. Since each of the Asian hominids was a "true man," Weidenreich suggested in 1940 that they be called *Homo erectus javensis* and *Homo erectus peki-nensis*.[15] Such designations would indicate that they were of the same species but not of the same subspecies, or race.

Many scientists were willing to recognize the Asian forms as members of the genus *Pithecanthropus*, but not of the same genus as modern man. Weidenreich's suggestion found little support until 1950, when Ernst Mayr proposed that all fossil and recent hominids be tentatively classified as a single genus, *Homo*. Peking and Java man, Mayr said, would have to be considered a separate species from modern man; their species "must be called *Homo erectus*." [16] Articles and books published during the 1960's seemed to indicate that Mayr's proposal was generally accepted.

Homo erectus: Dates and Locations

The fossil evidence collected prior to World War II suggested that *Homo erectus* had existed only in the Far East. In addition to the speci-mens discussed above, von Koenigswald and his assistants made some other discoveries in Java between 1936 and 1941. All of these came from a stratum that underlies the Trinil deposits (the "Djetis layer"). Two were identified as members of *Pithecanthropus: Homo modjokertensis*, an infant skull found near Modjokerto (about eighty miles east of Trinil); and *Pithecanthropus robustus*, skull and jaw fragments uncov-ered at the *Pithecanthropus II* site.

The identity of some finds made just before war broke out in the Pacific is still uncertain. They consist of jaw fragments and teeth, which von Koenigswald initially thought came from a giant. Weidenreich, who believed the pieces were remains of an ancestor of *Pithecanthropus,* named the fossils *Meganthropus palaeojavanicus* ("large man of old Java"). J. T. Robinson compared the fossils with African specimens and concluded that *Meganthropus* was an Asian *Paranthropus.*[17] Phillip Tobias and von Koenigswald have made similar comparisons. They state that *Meganthropus* was more advanced than any of the australopithecines but not as advanced as *Homo habilis.*[18] To Le Gros Clark, the Java find is an unusually large individual of the same group as *Pithecanthropus I* and *II.*[19] Pilbeam and Simons do not think the fragments provide enough information for Clark to make such a judgment.[20]

Postwar discoveries and comparisons have altered earlier ideas about the geographic distribution of *Homo erectus.* It now appears that members of this species were located not only in Java and North China, but also in Africa and probably in Europe during the Middle Pleistocene.

Table 2. Subspecies of Homo Erectus *

LOCATION	FORMER CLASSIFICATION	SUBSPECIES DESIGNATION	APPROXIMATE AGE IN YEARS
Swartkrans (South Africa)	*Telanthropus capensis*	*capensis*	?
Olduvai (East Africa)	*Homo habilis*	*habilis*	1,000,000
Modjokerto, Java	*Pithecanthropus robustus* *Homo modjokertensis*	*modjokertensis*	710,000 or more
Chenchiawo, Northwest China	*Sinanthropus lantianensis*	*lantianensis*	700,000 or more
Trinil and Sangiran, Java	*Pithecanthropus I* and *II*	*erectus*	550,000
Choukoutien, China	*Sinanthropus pekinensis*	*pekinensis*	500,000
Olduvai (East Africa)	"Chellean man"	*leakeyi*	500,000
Mauer, Germany	*Homo heidelbergensis*	*heidelbergensis*	400,000
Ternifine, Algeria	*Atlanthropus mauritanicus*	*mauritanicus*	350,000

* Adapted from Bernard G. Campbell, *Human Evolution* (Chicago: Aldine Publishing Company, 1966); William W. Howells, "Homo Erectus," *Scientific American,* 215 (November, 1966), 46–53; and W. E. Le Gros Clark, *The Fossil Evidence for Human Evolution,* 2nd ed. (Chicago: University of Chicago Press, 1964).

The place of origin for the species, the available evidence suggests, was either South Africa or East Africa. The age of the South African specimen—originally *Telanthropus capensis,* now *Homo erectus capensis,* discovered by J. T. Robinson at Swartkrans—is not known. A possible member of *Homo erectus* from Olduvai Gorge is estimated by Phillip Tobias to be about a million years old.[21]

Table 2 summarizes the distribution and ages of fossils that have been identified as subspecies of *Homo erectus* by at least two authorities. This listing will have to be revised when and if more complete remains of some of these and other specimens are found and as better dates are established. At the moment, there appear to be two likely additions. The first, an African find of somewhat uncertain age—possibly late Lower or early Middle Pleistocene—is either a representative of *Homo habilis* or of *Homo erectus*, in Tobias' opinion. The find is an incomplete cranium discovered in 1960 in northern Chad by Y. Coppens.[22] Coppens initially considered it a new species, *Tchadanthropus uxoris* (*Tchad* because of the location; *uxoris* to honor his wife). More recently, in 1965, he decided that the specimen represents a hominid type intermediate between the australopithecines and *Homo erectus*.[23]

The second possible addition to the list of *Homo erectus* subspecies is a skull fragment found in Hungary in 1965. The discoverer, L. Vértes, has classified it as *Homo sapiens*. According to William W. Howells, however, the fossil dates back at least 500,000 years—well before the appearance of *sapiens*.[24] Bernard Campbell gives the same dating and lumps the Hungarian find with other *Homo erectus* finds.[25]

INTERPRETATIVE SUMMARY

At present there is no firm evidence that *Australopithecus* (all the Lower Pleistocene hominids) existed anywhere but on the African continent.[26] All fossil evidence of this group suggests that they were largely restricted to East and South Africa. If we assume that specimens now labelled as members of *Homo erectus* are correctly identified, the earliest known representative of this species is from either Olduvai Gorge or Swartkrans. The implication is that *Homo erectus* evolved from *Australopithecus* in East or South Africa.

The new species became distinguished as such roughly one million years ago, probably before the end of the Lower Pleistocene (see table of major divisions of the Pleistocene on the end papers). At the time, the northern latitudes were experiencing the First (Günz) Glaciation and there was supposedly considerable rainfall in much of Africa. When this glacial period ran its course, the Middle Pleistocene began.* The tool-makers moved north of the Sahara; some possibly crossed land bridges into southern Europe and Asia.

Why the dispersal? J. Desmond Clark believes that climatic change was probably a very significant factor. The drier conditions which fol-

* The glacial chronology we are using is that employed by Kenneth Oakley, Michael Day, and other writers who have published books and articles since 1959 or 1960.

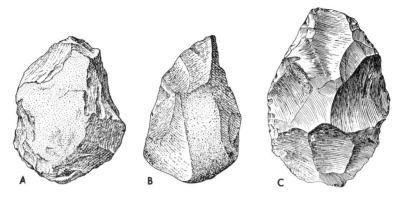

Figure 21. (A) Hand axe used by *Homo erectus* at Olduvai Gorge. Other Chellean (or Abbevillian) hand axes have been found in northern Africa (B) and in western Europe (C). (By courtesy of The Trustees, British Museum [Natural History].) Pieces of stone were probably knocked off two sides of a boulder with a hard hammerstone while the boulder was held on the edge of a heavy anvil stone.

lowed the glaciation made migration much easier; a decline in tropical vegetation probably "opened corridors and sometimes highways from north to south and from east to west." Food may have become more difficult to obtain for both animals and hominids, and both migrated northwards.[27] Clark thinks, too, that the less favorable living conditions stimulated "man's powers of invention toward improved methods of securing food and more comfortable living quarters." [28]

The kinds and extent of the "improved methods" are unknown and perhaps unknowable. It seems safe to assume that knowledge about environment increased, communication improved, and new technical and social skills were discovered or invented. Some groups probably learned to utilize animal parts, such as skins and sinews, for various purposes. New techniques for hunting and trapping may have been worked out. Evolving man acted upon his environment to increasingly bring it under control so that it would serve his ends. In short, there was an increase in culture.

The direct evidence for cultural growth, unfortunately, is quite limited. The quantity of deer and other large mammal remains in the caves at Choukoutien implies a higher level of social organization and hunting skills than *Australopithecus* possessed. At Olduvai, too, *Homo erectus* successfully hunted large animals, cutting them up and eating them where they were killed.[29]

Improvements in the manufacture of tools seem to have come about slowly; how slowly is impossible to determine. Fossils and tools have not always been found together. No artifacts at all were found in association with either of the Java subspecies (*modjokertensis, erectus*). Only one slightly worked pebble was found in association with the early Chinese subspecies (*lantianensis*).[30] In Africa, a number of Oldowan tools (or their equivalent) have been found separate from fossil deposits. It may be significant that when notable changes in tool-making did seemingly occur, they took place among the largest-brained (about 1,000 cc.) subspecies, *pekinensis* and *leakeyi*. The former, we noted earlier, were using crude chopping and flake tools about 500,000 years ago. At about the same time, the Olduvai *leakeyi* were learning to work pebbles to form biface hand axes. This innovation marked the dawn of the Chelles-Acheul culture or tradition that spread throughout Africa and into different parts of Europe.* [31]

The control of fire was, without doubt, one of the most significant discoveries or inventions made during the Middle Pleistocene. Although Peking man probably wore some sort of body covering, such as animal hides, it is unlikely that he could have endured the cold of the Second (Mindel) Glaciation without fire. Fire was of utility not only for warmth but also for light. The light was used to illuminate caves and possibly to hunt and keep animals away from habitation sites. Because of fire, women and children could safely remain in sheltered places while the men hunted. Some cooking of meat was likely performed, which may have sharpened the division of labor between the sexes.

How man learned to control fire, we do not know. He might have been attracted to fires created by lightning or volcanic action and noticed that they gave him warmth. With a little effort, he found he could keep such a fire going once it was started. Perhaps he discovered that sparks created while making tools caused dry materials to ignite or smolder.

It is tempting to think of fire-making and experiences associated with migration as causal factors in the expansion of the *Homo erectus* brain— to an average of 1,000 cc., according to Le Gros Clark.[32] But one of the largest brained specimens, *Homo erectus leakeyi*, was not a fire-maker; and he apparently never left Olduvai Gorge. Perhaps the major factor in increase in brain size was an increase in body size. (One estimate of the height or *Homo erectus*, based upon the femur found by Dubois, is around 5 feet 8 inches.) [33] An enlarging brain may have contributed to the control of fire, migrations, and improved techniques of tool-making.

CONCLUSIONS

A rather striking fact has emerged from the study of *Homo erectus* materials: By about 500,000 years ago, evolving man had acquired most of the physical characteristics which put him within range of modern

---

* The Chelles-Acheul tradition is often distinguished in terms of two phases, the Chellean (or Abbevillian) and the Acheulian. The latter is recognized by more finished forms of biface tools and a greater amount of flaking.

man. True, he had beetling brows, a retreating forehead, large neck muscles, often a heavily constructed jaw,* large teeth, and a skull thicker than that of the average living man. His brain was small by present-day standards, and he was prognathic. Still, from the shoulders down, *Homo erectus* appears to have been very much a modern man. And some of the characteristics above the shoulders are different only as to frequency of occurrence. The average cranial capacity, for example, is below the average for present-day man; but there are individuals today who have even smaller braincases than the *Homo erectus* average. Nor does skull thickness distinguish *Homo erectus* from *Homo sapiens*. According to Stanley M. Garn, cranial thicknesses in fossil men and contemporary white Americans overlap.[34] The teeth, though large, fall within the range of modern human teeth.[35]

As the fossil evidence mounts, it is becoming abundantly clear that there are no criteria which precisely delineate one form of man from another. Pilbeam and Simons state that *Homo erectus* "is barely distinguishable taxonomically from *Homo sapiens*." [36] Others, such as Phillip Tobias, point out that fossils once thought to be Australopithecinae are actually *Homo erectus* specimens, and specimens once considered to be *Pithecanthropus* are more advanced hominids.[37] The emerging picture, in short, is that man evolved gradually—like any other mammal. This has been known for years, of course. But there has often been a tendency in the past to force fossils, particularly hominid fossils, into neat taxonomic pigeonholes and to lose sight of the fact that change is continuous.

* Weidenreich found some *Sinanthropus* jaws to be "bulky and high, others slender and low." Not only was there considerable difference in jaws, but also in the size of teeth—"These differences are much greater than they usually are in recent man." He attributed such variations to sexual dimorphism. See "Sinanthropus Pekinensis and Its Position in the Line of Human Evolution," *Peking Natural History Bulletin*, Vol. 10, Part 4 (June, 1936), p. 283.

NOTES

1. Herbert Wendt, *In Search of Adam* (New York: Collier Books, 1963), pp. 317–332; Andre Senet, *Man in Search of His Ancestors* (New York: McGraw-Hill Book Company, Inc., 1955), pp. 40–41.

2. Our discussion of Dubois and his finds is based upon Aleš Hrdlička, *The Skeletal Remains of Early Man* (Washington, D. C.: The Smithsonian Institution, 1930), pp. 28–53. Statements made by Dubois are quoted from this book.

3. Eugene Dubois, "Pithecanthropus in Java," in Robert F. Heizer (ed.), *Man's Discovery of His Past: Literary Landmarks in Archaeology* (Englewood Cliffs, N. J.: Prentice-Hall, Inc., 1962), p. 130.

4. Wilfrid E. Le Gros Clark, *The Fossil Evidence for Human Evolution*, 2nd ed. (Chicago: University of Chicago Press, 1964), pp. 88–90.

5. Michael H. Day, *Guide to Fossil Man* (Cleveland: The World Publishing Company, 1965), pp. 222–223.

6. Except as indicated, materials in this section are drawn from the following: Ruth Moore, *Man, Time, and Fossils*, 2nd ed. (New York: Alfred A. Knopf, Inc., 1963), Chap. 14; F. Clark Howell and the Editors of *Life, Early Man* (New York: Time Inc., 1965), pp. 78–79; C. L. Brace and M. F. Ashley Montagu, *Man's Evolution* (New York: The Macmillan Company, 1965), pp. 176–179; Senet, *op. cit.*, pp. 48–51.

7. Davidson Black, "Interim Report on the Skull of *Sinanthropus*," *Bulletin of the Geological Society of China*, Vol. IX, No. 1 (Peping, 1930), p. 10.

8. Kenneth P. Oakley, *Frameworks for Dating Fossil Man* (Chicago: Aldine Publishing Company, 1964), pp. 233–236.

9. Marcellin Boule and Henri V. Vallois, *Fossil Men* (New York: The Dryden Press, 1957), pp. 141–142.

10. Franz Weidenreich, "The Sinanthropus Population of Choukoutien (Locality 1) with a Preliminary Report on New Discoveries," *Bulletin of the Geological Society of China*, Vol. XIV, No. 4 (1935), p. 435.

11. Franz Weidenreich, "The Relation of *Sinanthropus Pekinensis* to *Pithecanthropus, Javanthropus* and Rhodesian Man," *Journal of the Royal Anthropological Institute*, LXVII (January–June, 1937), 52–53.

12. Day, *op. cit.*, pp. 226–227.

13. G. H. R. von Koenigswald, *The Evolution of Man* (Ann Arbor: University of Michigan Press, 1962), pp. 81–82.

14. Day, *op. cit.*, p. 227.

15. *Ibid.*, pp. 221, 250.

16. Ernst Mayr, "Taxonomic Categories in Fossil Hominids," *Cold Spring Harbor Symposia on Quantitative Biology*, XV (Cold Spring Harbor, N. Y.: The Biological Laboratory, 1950), 113.

17. Day, *op. cit.*, p. 240.

18. P. V. Tobias and G. H. R. von Koenigswald, "A Comparison Between the Olduvai Hominines and Those of Java and Some Implications for Hominid Phylogeny," *Nature*, 204 (1964), 517.

19. Wilfrid E. Le Gros Clark, *History of the Primates*, 5th ed. (Chicago: University of Chicago Press, 1966), p. 84.

20. D. R. Pilbeam and Elwyn L. Simons, "Some Problems of Hominid Classification," *American Scientist*, 53 (1965), 247.

21. Phillip V. Tobias, "New Discoveries in Tanganyika: Their Bearing on Hominid Evolution," *Current Anthropology*, 6 (1965), 397.

22. Phillip V. Tobias, "Early Man in East Africa," *Science*, 149 (1965), 24.

23. Day, *op. cit.*, pp. 149–150.

24. William W. Howells, "Homo Erectus," *Scientific American*, 215 (November, 1966), 49.

25. Bernard G. Campbell, *Human Evolution* (Chicago: Aldine Publishing Company, 1966), p. 368.

26. Tobias, "Early Man in East Africa," p. 25.

27. J. Desmond Clark, "The Evolution of Culture in Africa," *The American Naturalist*, XCVII (1963), 20.

28. J. Desmond Clark, "Human Ecology During Pleistocene and Later Times in Africa South of the Sahara," *Current Anthropology*, 1 (1960), 309–310.

29. J. Desmond Clark, "The Evolution of Culture in Africa," p. 21.

30. Woo Ju-Kang, "Mandible of *Sinanthropus Lantianensis*," *Current Anthropology*, 5 (1964), 98–101.

31. Oakley, *op. cit.*, pp. 174–175.

32. Le Gros Clark, *The Fossil Evidence for Human Evolution*, p. 114.

33. *Ibid.*, p. 102.

34. Stanley M. Garn (ed.), *Culture and the Direction of Human Evolution* (Detroit: Wayne State University Press, 1964), p. 5.

35. *Ibid.*, p. 7; Brace and Montagu, *op. cit.*, pp. 233–234.

36. Pilbeam and Simons, *op. cit.*, p. 257.

37. Phillip V. Tobias, "Early Members of the Genus Homo in Africa," *Yearbook of Physical Anthropology 1962*, Vol. 10, pp. 259–269.

14

Upper Pleistocene Man: The Neanderthals

How a fossil is interpreted is a function of technical skills and existing knowledge, comprised, in part, of assumptions, ideas, and beliefs about the nature of man and how he came into being. Quite often an assumption or idea attains the status of a scientific fact because it is supported by some sort of authority. We have seen, for example, that a number of scientists rejected the Australopithecinae as hominids because it was assumed that even the earliest Hominidae had brains no smaller than an established minimum. This minimum, 750 cc., was set forth by Sir Arthur Keith, one of the most distinguished of British physical anthropologists.[1] Implicit in many analyses of the australopithecines was another belief or assumption—that a large brain either preceded or accompanied the evolution of bipedalism. Early man, it was generally believed, learned to walk on his hind legs because he was unusually intelligent; he possibly became brainier as he became more bipedal.

A plausible idea sometimes becomes accepted as fact because alternative explanations are unknown or are not considered. The widespread belief that Peking man was a cannibal—that is, ate others of his kind for nutritional reasons—may be a case in point. This notion seemingly derived from a deduction made by Weidenreich. When several skulls were found without skeletal parts, he reasoned that they had been brought to the cave as spoils or trophies. The manner in which the skulls were broken suggested that the brains were extracted and eaten,[2]

231

and it was assumed that this was done to satisfy nutritional needs. Observations of practices in preliterate societies offer quite a different explanation. In one society, the skull was broken and the brain eaten as part of the funeral rites for a deceased person, not to obtain nourishment. Those who ate the brain did so in order to assume the virtues and merits of the dead individual. The skull, which was detached after the body dried out, served as a kind of protective divinity for the dead person's family.[3]

Strangely enough, ideas and beliefs occasionally influence the interpretation of fossil evidence even though the ideas and beliefs are no longer accepted. Such seems to be the case with regard to fossils we shall discuss in this chapter, those of Neanderthal (or Neandertal) man.

EARLY NEANDERTHAL MAN FINDS [4]

At least three Neanderthal specimens were discovered before *The Origin of Species* was published. Two—a child's skull found about 1830 in caves near Namur, Belgium, and a skull found in a Gibraltar quarry in 1848—were not identified as Neanderthals until 1907 and 1935. Since man was thought to have been created in his present form, these and other hominid fossils were usually ignored. The third specimen, uncovered in 1856 in the little German valley of Neander near Düsseldorf, received more attention.

Discovery of the Neander Valley (*Tal* is the German word for "valley") remains was accidental, as many fossil finds have been. In the course of cleaning out a cave preparatory to excavating limestone, workmen came across some old "bear" bones. These bones were brought to the attention of Dr. Johann Carl Fuhlrott, a teacher of natural science who had been collecting geological and paleontological materials from the area for several years. When Fuhlrott examined the remains, he realized that they were not from a bear, but from a man. Further study of the fossils—a skullcap, thighbones, and fragments of several skeletal parts—convinced him that the man had been quite primitive, a beast-man.

Fuhlrott invited some other scientists to pass judgment on the fossils. Among them was Dr. Hermann Schaaffhausen, professor of anatomy at the University of Bonn. The professor shared Fuhlrott's views. In a paper published in 1858 he described the fossils as from "the most ancient races of man." "The forehead," he wrote, "is narrow and low, though the middle and hinder portions of the cranial arch are well developed." The skull showed an "extraordinary development of the frontal sinuses," but Schaaffhausen saw no reason to regard the sinuses as an "individual or pathological deformity." Rather, they were "unquestionably a typical race character . . . physiologically connected with the uncommon thickness of the other bones of the skeleton." [5]

Most European scientists did not accept the diagnosis made by Fuhlrott and Schaaffhausen. To their way of thinking, the Neanderthal specimen was a modern type—an old Dutchman, perhaps, or a fallen Cossack, or a member of the Celtic race. It certainly did not represent a primitive man. How, then, Schaaffhausen wanted to know, were the gross anatomical deviations from the modern form to be explained? The answer was obvious to a man of medicine, replied the dean of European scientists, Rudolf Virchow: The old fellow from Neander had suffered from rickets in childhood, from several heavy blows on the head in adulthood, and from arthritis in old age. Virchow's judgment that the anatomical deviations of the "old man" were pathological settled the matter so far as most people were concerned. Even two of the men most intimately associated with the theory of evolution gave Fuhlrott and Schaaffhausen no support. Darwin made only very brief and cautious reference to the Neanderthal specimen in *The Descent of Man*. Thomas Huxley, who saw a cast of the skull, concluded that although many characters of the skull were apelike, Neanderthal man was merely an extreme variant of the modern type of man and not a separate species or type.

One of Huxley's contemporaries, Dr. William King, professor of anatomy at Queen's College, Galway, Ireland, thought otherwise. "So closely," he wrote in 1864, "does the fossil cranium resemble that of the chimpanzee as to lead one to doubt the propriety of generically placing it with man. . . ." King therefore assigned the specimen to a new species, *Homo neanderthalensis*. Despite this classification, King did not believe the creature had resembled man in his outlook: "The Neanderthal skull is so eminently simian . . . I am constrained to believe that the thoughts and desires which once dwelt within it never soared beyond those of the brute." [6]

Arguments for the antiquity or separate species designation of Neanderthal man were weakened by the absence of artifacts in the cave in which the bones were uncovered. The manner in which the fossils had been excavated precluded any sort of dating. Nor did other fossil discoveries during the next quarter of a century or so alter conceptions and beliefs. Of a dozen or so fossil men uncovered, none resembled the Neanderthal find; they were all remarkably like modern man. Bits and pieces of what are now known to be remains of Neanderthal man were found, but none was complete enough to warrant much attention or analysis.

The picture was changed a bit in 1886. In that year two skeletons were disinterred at Spy, near Namur, Belgium, by Max Lohest and

Marcel de Puydt. In association with the hominid fossils were a variety of artifacts and the remains of animal species either extinct (such as the woolly rhinoceros and the mammoth) or no longer indigenous to the area. Great care was taken to observe and record all relevant data. Using the stratigraphic location of the materials and the nature of the flint tools as guides, Lohest assigned the discovery to the Mousterian period, so called because similar implements had been discovered near Le Moustier in southern France. Professor J. Fraipont, of the Liège University, identified the hominid fossils as Neanderthal man specimens.

There was no question that the specimens—Fraipont labelled them "Spy No. 1" and "Spy No. 2"—were older than the modern forms that had been found. The faunal remains and Mousterian artifacts were from a period in time which predated any hominid fossils known at the time, with the possible exception of the Neander Valley specimen. To some it became clear that the peculiar characters of the Neanderthal remains were not the result of disease or mechanical deformity; they were features of an earlier type of man.

Spy No. 1 had a skull resembling the initial Neanderthal find. The cranium of Spy No. 2 had a much higher vault and a less heavy brow-ridge than Spy No. 1 or the Neander Valley skullcap. Prehistorians should have learned from such differences that earlier forms of man varied morphologically, just as do members of our own species. Few apparently did. The usual practice for many years to come was to regard variations from a "type"—often the initial discovery—as evidence of a new species or even a new genus.

At least two factors limited the impact of the Spy materials upon scientific opinion in the years immediately following their discovery. One factor was Virchow's influence. Since he had judged the Neander Valley find to be pathological, there was a tendency to regard Neanderthal features in any specimen as abnormal or peculiar. According to C. L. Brace and Ashley Montagu, Virchow's ideas still carry weight. They find expression today among anthropologists who claim that the Neanderthals were too extreme or "specialized" to have been ancestral to modern man. The second factor which detracted from the importance of the Spy fossils was Dubois' discovery and the controversy which ensued concerning the status of *Pithecanthropus erectus*.

Another group of Neanderthal fossils which received scant attention for some years was found at Krapina in Croatia, now one of the republics of Yugoslavia. Most of the fossils were described in 1906 by K. Gorjano-vić-Kramberger, professor of geology and paleontology at the University of Zagreb. The bones represented the remains of perhaps twenty individuals of both sexes and varying ages. Features of the individuals exhibited, in Hrdlička's words:

a considerable variation, and that of a rather progressive tendency. Thus some of the foreheads approach closely those of some recent men; even the vault of these skulls has differed individually, in height, in breadth and other characters; and there is much of interest in this connection about the jaws and the teeth.

Between 1908 and 1912 a series of Neanderthal specimens was uncovered in southern France. One, a complete skeleton of a youth discovered at Le Moustier, was not satisfactorily described until 1925. Materials from another site, La Ferrassie, were yet to be described by the late 1960's. Hrdlička found fossils from another site, La Quina, to be of interest because "while distinctly neanderthaloid they present variants of the type, in the narrowness and lack of massiveness of the adult cranium" and in other ways. One of the jaws was also a "variant" in that it had "an approach to a chin." A skeleton from a fourth site, La Chapelle-aux-Saints, was to become the best known of all the western European, or "classic," Neanderthals. We shall examine this skeleton more closely below.

THE PROBLEM OF THE NEANDERTHALS

The entire group of hominids known as Neanderthals lived during most of the Upper Pleistocene, the beginning of which is marked by the Third Glaciation (see Table 3). All of the specimens mentioned in the preceding section have been dated, stratigraphically and through morphological comparison, to the Fourth (Würm) Glaciation, or the

Table 3. Upper Pleistocene Chronology *

NUMERICAL TERMS	ALPINE TERMS	APPROXIMATE NUMBER OF YEARS BEFORE THE PRESENT
Fourth Glaciation	Würm III Glaciation	24,000
	Würm II/III Interstadial	27,000
	Würm Glaciation	32,000
	Würm I/II Interstadial	45,000
	Würm I Glaciation	70,000
Third Interglacial	Riss-Würm Interglacial	150,000
Third Glaciation	Riss Glaciation	200,000

* Adapted from Michael Day, *Guide to Fossil Man* (Cleveland: World Publishing Company, 1965). © Dr. Michael Day.

last Ice Age.* Each of these western European specimens, according to Kenneth Oakley, lived no less than 35,000 years before the present. Most may have been alive between 35,000 and 70,000 years ago. Other Neanderthals lived in Europe about 120,000 years ago, and individuals with Neanderthal features—"early Neanderthaloids," Oakley calls them—could have been in existence some 250,000 years before the present.[7] The total time span during which men with Neanderthal characteristics were on the scene—from about 250,000 to 35,000 years ago—pretty well bridges the temporal gap between *Homo erectus* and *Homo sapiens.*

Some anthropologists, anatomists, and paleontologists believe that Neanderthal man also bridged the morphological gap between earlier hominids and modern man. They agreed with Franz Weidenreich, who saw "a rather continuous line of evolution which begins with [*Homo erectus*] and ends with recent man." In the morphological sequence of human forms, Weidenreich said, *Homo neanderthalensis* was intermediate to *Homo erectus* (Java and Peking man) and *Homo sapiens.*[8]

Another linkage is provided by tools and other artifacts. The Mousterian cultures varied in time and from place to place, but many tools were obviously derived from the Chelles-Acheul (or Acheullian) tradition of *Homo erectus* groups. In at least some areas, artifacts used by Upper Paleolithic man (Old Stone Age *Homo sapiens*) appear to have developed out of Mousterian traditions.[9] The Neanderthal material culture was, without question, richer and more advanced than that of earlier hominids. Stone implements included not only hand axes and scrapers, but points, knives, burins (chisel-like tools suitable for engraving or incising), and borers. Mineral color, such as manganese dioxide and red ocher was used for some purpose, possibly to paint the body. The Neanderthals buried at least some of their dead, and color may have been used in connection with funerary rituals. (Thus far, however, no evidence has been found to suggest that any Neanderthals painted cave walls.) In short, "Mousterian peoples" attained a cultural level not unlike that of our first known *sapiens* ancestors.[10]

Not all prehistorians have reached the conclusion which the foregoing implies, that Neanderthal man was ancestral to *Homo sapiens.* Those who have objected to considering Neanderthal man our immediate ancestor have done so for varying reasons. The principal objections,

---

* The Fourth Glaciation (Würm Glaciation, in Alpine terms) lasted from approximately 70,000 to 10,000 years ago. But it was not one long period of extreme cold. Instead, there were at least two warm periods or "interstadials." The dating of fossils is complicated by these warm periods; that is, it has not always been possible to determine whether "warm" fauna lived prior to the glaciation or during one of the warm periods.

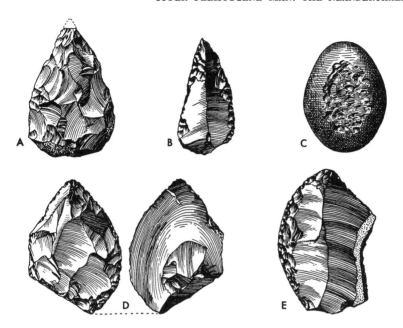

Figure 22. Some of the tools used by the Neanderthals of western Europe. (A) Hand axe; (B) point; (C) anvil stone; (D) and (E) scrapers. (By courtesy of The Trustees, British Museum [Natural History].) Long bones of animals were also broken and used as tools, and Mousterian industries included such implements as the burin and the stone knife (see Figure 24).

according to Henri V. Vallois, are based on two interrelated arguments: "A first group of arguments rests on *the specialization of Neanderthal man*"; the second group "turns on the fact of *the lack of morphological continuity between the European Neanderthals and the first Aurignacians* [the first *Homo sapiens*]." [11]

In other words, the Neanderthals—particularly those of western Europe—evolved nonhuman features ("specializations") of such a nature as to rule them out as ancestors of our species. This idea is quite evident in a description of the "classic Neandertals of Europe" which appeared in a 1965 anthropology textbook. According to this description, Neanderthal man had a large, heavy skull atop a "massive and relatively short spine." The "elongated form and low vault (platycephaly)" of the skull "give an appearance of primitiveness, as does the low, narrow, and retreating forehead." Both the supraorbital and occipital areas are large. "The foramen magnum is farther back than in modern man." Although the cranial capacity is large (from 1300 to 1600 cc.), "the forebrain is smaller than in modern man."

The Neanderthal face is long and projecting. "The upper jaw is markedly prognathous (forward projecting), and the lower jaw is

237

heavy and powerful, with only the beginnings of a chin." The dental arch is not fully human; it is "intermediate in shape between that of modern man and that of the apes." Wear on the teeth "shows a backward-and-forward chewing habit, rather than the side-to-side chewing of modern man."

Curves of the neck and lumbar region, the size and shape of the thigh bone, a widely separated toe, and other features suggest kinship with the apes rather than with modern man. It is hardly surprising, therefore, that "The characteristics described for the classic Neandertal fall outside the range of variation found in modern man. . . ." [12]

Another major reason for the rejection of the Neanderthals as genetic antecedents to our own species has been a persistent belief that modern forms—"presapiens," Gerhard Heberer called them—predated or were contemporaneous with Neanderthal man. The number of these early modern types has fluctuated. The most enduring "presapiens" candidates since the 1930's have been Swanscombe man (England), Steinheim man (Germany), and Fontéchevade man (France). Dr. Leakey has maintained for several years that fossils he discovered at Kanjera, Kenya, show that "by the end of the Middle Pleistocene *Homo sapiens* was already evolved." He once held similar ideas about another of his East African discoveries, a jaw from Kanam; but he revised his opinion about the jaw when *Zinjanthropus* was found. [13]

Heberer mentioned only one "presapiens," Fontéchevade man, in a paper he presented in 1959. This 1947 discovery, he said, gave support to his hypothesis that "a line leading to typical *Homo sapiens* can be traced back into the Pleistocene without postulating the Neanderthalians as ancestors, even in their early form of the last interglacial, the *Pre-Neanderthalians*." [14] Vallois, the man who described the Fontéchevade fragments, admitted that there was a considerable time lapse between Fontéchevade man and the appearance of *Homo sapiens*. But he, too, contended that the "presapiens," not the Neanderthals, were the ancestors of modern man. [15]

The "Pre-Neanderthalians" and the Classic Neanderthals

The "Pre-Neanderthalians" to which Heberer referred have also been known as "early," "progressive," "transitional," and "generalized" Neanderthals, Neanderthalers, or Neanderthaloids. Thus, they are distinguished from the "classic" group both temporally and morphologically. They were supposedly "early" in that they appeared at least 100,000 years ago—perhaps up to 200,000 years ago—during the warm period that preceded the last Ice Age, the Third Interglacial, or during the Third (Riss) Glaciation. They were "progressive," "transitional," or "generalized" in that they exhibited more modern features and fewer "specializations" than did the "classic" Neanderthals.

F. Clark Howell, who has made comparative studies of the "early" and "classic" Neanderthals, says that the latter were confined to the western and southern parts of Europe during the earlier part of the last glaciation. Their remains have been found in France, Belgium, Germany, Spain, and Italy. The distribution of the early Neanderthals was more widespread, "extending from south-central and western Asia into, and throughout, Europe." The major finds of early Neanderthals come from Mount Carmel, Palestine (now Israel). Other finds include specimens from North Africa and eastern Europe.[16]

When Howell compared skulls, he found that the presence of "many modern features" in the early Neanderthal crania was "striking." The skull vaults, for example, are more highly arched; the facial skeletons are small compared with the classic facial structure. Like the skull of modern man, the early Neanderthal braincase is relatively short and narrow; it is not widened and "bun-shaped" in the rear like the classic skull. Modern features are particularly noticeable in some of the crania found in caves at Mount Carmel.[17] Later, Howell noted that the postcranial skeleton of the early Neanderthals "exhibits features which are in general more anatomically modern than was the case in the distinctive classic Neanderthal group." The long bones, for instance, are relatively more slender and relatively straight.[18]

Howell's comparative studies satisfied him that the classic Neanderthals resembled one another and that they differed from their immediate ancestors and from *Homo sapiens*. Why were they different? Howell reasoned that the classic Neanderthal features were a consequence of genetic change and generations of close inbreeding. Close inbreeding resulted when glacial conditions isolated a small number of early Neanderthals in western and southern Europe from other groups. As often happens in any small breeding population, unique mutations and unusual gene combinations became part of the gene pool. Thus, in time, these Neanderthals became not only rather homogeneous in appearance, but also genetically and physically distinct from their forebears and relatives in other parts of the world.[19]

Howell believes that the immediate ancestors of the classic Neanderthals, the early Neanderthals, were also ancestral to modern man. He sees no reason to accept the idea that *Homo sapiens* evolved from yet another group, the "presapiens"; specimens labelled as such were actually early Neanderthals. Steinheim man, for example, was, without question, an early Neanderthal; and the Swanscombe fragments are similar to the Steinheim skull. Although the fragmentary condition of the Fontéchevade skull makes reconstruction difficult, "there is no strong evidence to preclude its being of this general [that is, early] type." The fossil record, in other words, gives no indication of peoples other than the Neanderthals prior to the appearance of unquestionable *Homo sapiens* specimens. At the same time, Third Interglacial individuals from Mount Carmel were "in many respects practically at the modern level although a number of general morphological features linked [them] to the other early Neanderthals." Therefore, Howell concluded,

> From the early Neanderthal group, the earliest possible representative being Swanscombe, evolved the classic Neanderthals . . . , a peculiar localized development in western Europe as a result of isolation of that region in the beginning of the Fourth Glacial. Further to the east, from the Mount Carmel population and similar groups, modern man evolved.

Like several other prehistorians, Howell tended to favor the notion that the classic Neanderthals "had either become extinct prior to, or were killed off by the arrival of, modern types from the more easterly European regions." This conclusion was suggested by the absence of any evidence of classic Neanderthals in western Europe after the appearance of *Homo sapiens*.[20]

Today, more than a century after the Neander Valley find, there is still uncertainty as to Neanderthal man's position in the evolutionary scheme. As we have indicated, some prehistorians believe that the Neanderthals as a total population represented a stage or phase of human evolution, a stage immediately preceding the appearance of modern man. Others accept as valid Vallois and Boule's declaration that "no modern human type can be considered as a direct descendant, even with modifications, of the Neanderthal type." [21] A number of other prehistorians believe that *Homo sapiens* and the classic Neanderthals were both descendants of an earlier Neanderthal group. An essential element in the controversy and confusion that has surrounded the Neanderthals for more than fifty years is a specimen discovered at La Chapelle-aux-Saints, in southern France.

THE "TYPE" SPECIMEN

The La Chapelle-aux-Saints specimen has only two teeth, but it was the first Neanderthal to be found with a whole braincase, including a complete face. Discovered in 1908 by a group of priests, the skeleton was turned over to Marcellin Boule, an outstanding paleontologist and natural scientist. Boule set to work and turned out three weighty tomes of description and analysis which were published between 1911 and

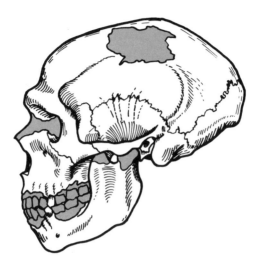

Figure 23. Skull of the La Chapelle-aux-Saints Neanderthal specimen.

1913.[22] A free translation of a sentence from the last of these volumes gives some idea as to what Boule thought of Neanderthal man:

> What contrast with the men of the next geological and archaeological period, with the men of the Cro-Magnon type, who had a more elegant body, a finer head, an upright and spacious brow, and who have left, in the caves which they inhabited, so much evidence of their manual skill, artistic and religious preoccupations, of their abstract faculties, and who were the first to merit the glorious title of *Homo sapiens!* [23]

As the result of Boule's publications, Brace and Montagu tell us, "the cartoon image of Neanderthal man was foisted upon an all-too-receptive world." [24] This image was partially depicted in a 1957 article by William L. Straus, Jr. and A. J. E. Cave:

> Neanderthal man is commonly pictured as but incompletely erect; as an almost hunchbacked creature with head thrust forward, knees habitually bent, and flat, inverted feet, moving along with a shuffling, uncertain gait. According to this view, he was a thoroughly unattractive fellow who was but imperfectly adapted to the upright, bipedal posture and locomotion characteristic of the modern type of man.[25]

Boule helped perpetuate the "cartoon image" in editions of his book *Fossil Men (Les Hommes Fossiles)*. In a 1923 edition, for instance, he let it be known that despite the large cranium of the La Chapelle skull (1600 cc., according to his estimate), "the brain of Neanderthal Man more resembles the brains of the great anthropoid apes or of microcephalic man." He said that the crudity of the brain structure and other physical characters

> are quite in agreement with what archaeology teaches us as to his bodily capacity, his psychology, and his habits. As we have already pointed out, there is hardly a more rudimentary or degraded form of industry than that of our Mousterian Man. His use of one simple material only, stone (apart probably from wood and bone), the uniformity, simplicity, and rudeness of his stone implements, and the probable absence of all traces of any pre-occupation of an aesthetic or of a moral kind, are quite in agreement with the brutish appearance of this energetic and clumsy body, of the heavy-jawed skull, which itself still declares the predominance of functions of a purely vegetative or bestial kind over the functions of the mind.[26]

The 1957 edition of *Fossil Men* (edited by Vallois; Boule died in 1942) carries some of the same ideas, as may be gathered from a summary statement: "That *Homo neanderthalensis* is a species with archaic characteristics is clearly evident from its general morphology. The numerous simian traits which it has retained are so many relics, still strongly in evidence, of an ancestral state." It was Boule's continuing belief that the Neanderthals disappeared abruptly.[27]

Boule's opinion carried considerable weight, both in Europe and in America. It is hardly surprising that few persons seriously considered the Neanderthals as ancestors to *Homo sapiens* after Boule typed them as he did. With their many "simian traits," the Neanderthals were a rather unsavory lot. They appeared to have been evolving *away* from modern man rather than in the human direction.

Seeds of Doubt

Boule's conception of Neanderthal man prevailed, almost without challenge, until the 1950's. There were, however, a few writers who directly or indirectly raised questions about the validity of his description or his conclusions. Dr. Dudley Morton, for example, wrote in 1926 that the Neanderthal foot was human in form; the big toe was not separated from the other toes (an ape character), as was commonly believed.[28] L. H. Dudley Buxton and G. R. de Beer announced in 1932 that there is considerable similarity between the adult *Homo sapiens* skull and the skull of a young Neanderthal. In their opinion, the resemblance suggests that *Homo sapiens* descended from *Homo neandertha-lensis* by neotony, or pedomorphosis, "the progressive retention into adult life of characters present in the young stages in the ancestor." [29]

Some of the anthropologists, paleontologists, and taxonomists who published during the 1940's seemed to be somewhat undecided about the prevailing image of the Neanderthals. Hooton, for instance, in 1940 accepted Boule's description of "the typical Western European Neander-thaloids," conceding that they had "many peculiarities which recall anthropoid apes." Still, Hooton wrote, these peculiarities are only sporadic. "The skeletons delineate a type wholly human, though primitive." Although the *Pithecanthropus-Sinanthropus* specimens "may have had straighter and modernesque thigh bones," the dentition and size of braincase of "these Neanderthalers are far more highly evolved and specialized in the human direction." [30]

One of the few men to directly attack prevailing views during the 1930's and 1940's was Franz Weidenreich. In a 1943 article, he wrote:

> Thirty years ago it almost became a sport of a certain group of authors to search the skeletal parts of Neanderthal Man for peculiarities which could be proclaimed as "specialisation," thereby proving the deviating course this form had taken in evolution. I wrote and referred to such an endeavour in 1939: "There is not one single peculiarity which has not been taken by some author to represent a unilateral specialisation, beginning with the strong development of the supraorbital ridges and ending with the conditions of the molar roots. Yet, evidence proving the correctness of such statements is lacking in all of the cases." A good example of the absolutely arbitrary handling of these speciali-sations is the so-called "taurodontism."

Weidenreich pointed out that taurodontism, a dental condition involving enlargement of the pulp cavities and reduction of the roots, was not a peculiarity of the European Neanderthals. "Spaciousness of the pulp cavity" of molar teeth occurs not only among apes but also among "certain races of modern mankind, as for instance, Eskimos and Bushmen." "There, indeed," Weidenreich stressed, "is not one among the suspected peculiarities of the Neanderthal skulls which would stand firm against a thorough comparative scrutiny." [31]

A revision in notions about Neanderthal man was hinted at in papers presented at the 1950 Cold Spring Harbor Symposium, "Origin and Evolution of Man," by Professor Theodore D. McCown of the University of California, Dr. T. D. Stewart of the United States National Museum in Washington, D. C., and Dr. Ernst Mayr of the American Museum of Natural History in New York City.

In his paper Professor McCown questioned the rather pervasive idea that there was a lack of evolutionary continuity between the Neanderthals and *Homo sapiens*. There is admittedly a distinctive Neanderthal "pattern," even with the addition of "early" (specifically, Palestinian) materials to the European materials. Nonetheless, McCown said, "it seems to be impossible to hold any longer to the view of a morphological hiatus between modern man and the Neanderthal population." Rather, the striking variability among them "seems similar in kind to racial polymorphism among *Homo sapiens*." To regard the Neanderthals as a subspecies of *sapiens*, therefore, "better represents a genetic interpretation of the phenotypic characters of the Neanderthal group." [32]

Dr. Stewart implied that a realistic evaluation of the Neanderthals' place in human evolution called for greater objectivity in the interpretation of data. The people who study and write about fossil man, he said in effect, are subject to a common human failing—they are likely to see what they want to see; their conclusions are often shaped by "psychological elements." Thus, authors and investigators who believe *Homo sapiens* descended from a presapiens group readily perceive *sapiens*-like features in some Middle and Upper Pleistocene specimens, especially specimens—like those from Swanscombe and Fontéchevade—which are represented by a few fragments. On the other hand, the same authors and investigators tend to ignore or minimize *sapiens*-like features in more complete specimens of the same relative age; they "for the most part are granted Neanderthal status," presumably because the more complete the specimen, the more likely it is to exhibit or suggest Neanderthal characteristics. So far as Stewart was concerned, "The '*sapiens*'-like forms [or presapiens] of the Middle and Upper Pleistocene were not widely different from the 'progressive Neanderthals'; and the latter are but natural variants of the classic Neanderthal." The "progressive" and classic Neanderthals, in other words, were not separate and distinct species or genera; rather they comprised a single, variable species. Differences between "progressive" Neanderthals and classic Neanderthals were no greater than differences found among populations of *Homo sapiens*.[33]

Ernst Mayr's paper dealt with the subject of the taxonomic categories for all fossil hominids. As Howell was to do, Dr. Mayr interpreted the Steinheim, Swanscombe, and Fontéchevade fossils "as remains of populations of *Homo* that were ancestral both to *sapiens* and to 'classical' Neanderthal and from which these forms evolved by geographical variation." It seems best, Mayr concluded, to include all the Neanderthals—both the early and the classical—within the same species, *sapiens*.[34]

244

A New Image

The year 1955 seems to have been a fateful one so far as the interpretation of Neanderthal man is concerned. In an article published that year, Adolph H. Schultz commented in a foonote that he "could never understand how any creature can be 'nearly upright' in the manner in which Neanderthal man has sometimes been reconstructed with his trunk leaning forward and taking a long step forward to prevent his falling." Neither a child learning to walk nor any ape standing on its hind legs maintains such a posture. "Even in the beginning stages of upright posture the trunk must already have been held *fully* erect, to be most easily balanced. . . ." [35] A second 1955 article, written by Camille Arambourg, carried this conclusion further. Since bipedal erectness must be total—there can be no "nearly upright" posture—Arambourg reasoned that Neanderthal man's anatomy was such as to permit the posture characteristic of modern man. [36]

A third 1955 publication, by Étienne Patte, was a compilation and interpretation of the literature dealing with Neanderthal man. Patte also concluded that modern and Neanderthal man were alike in posture. He denied that the foramen magnum was farther back in the classic Neanderthal skull than in the modern skull, as Boule had claimed. [37]

Another event of 1955 was a reexamination of the La Chapelle-aux-Saints specimen by William L. Straus, Jr. and A. J. E. Cave. What Straus and Cave found was that Boule's reconstruction was not completely accurate and his interpretation was somewhat biased. The specimen may not have stood and walked like a normal *sapiens* when he was alive—but then he was afflicted with spinal osteoarthritis. "Notwithstanding," Straus and Cave concluded, "if he could be reincarnated and placed in a New York subway—provided that he were bathed, shaved, and dressed in modern clothing—it is doubtful whether he would attract any more attention than some of its other denizens." [38]

The combined reports by Arambourg, Patte, and Straus and Cave left little doubt that Boule had read many apelike features into the La Chapelle remains. Why did Boule distort the evidence? And why were his description and interpretation accepted so uncritically? C. Loring Brace provides at least a partial answer to the second question. An assumption carried over from the nineteenth century, he says, was that early populations were small and geographically isolated and through interbreeding became pretty much alike. Therefore one individual served as a "type," a representative, for the entire population. There was, in other words, no awareness of the variability possible within small populations. "With the expectation of relatively uniform populations, the picture presented by a single fairly complete skeleton has been sufficient to satisfy many authors that the characteristics of the human populations immediately prior to the Upper Paleolithic were well known and that they corresponded to a single, easily recognizable 'type.' " [39]

Why Boule saw so many apelike features in the Neanderthal specimens he examined may never be known. Two biasing factors evident in his description were a belief that a *sapiens* type was the contemporary of the Neanderthals and his consideration of Piltdown man as a possible early ancestor of modern man.[40] The *sapiens* type, whose remains were found at Grimaldi, was later found to be from the Upper Paleolithic, that is from the period in time when *Homo sapiens* became definitely established. Boule was possibly influenced by Virchow's belief that Neanderthal characters were pathological and by anti-evolutionary views. As Brace points out, Boule and other French paleontologists trained in the nineteenth century were thoroughly grounded in Cuvier's ideas, some of which were anti-evolutionary. Boule's belief that the Neanderthals were suddenly replaced by *Homo sapiens* during the Upper Paleolithic, Brace observes, is remarkably similar to Cuvier's theory of catastrophism. Later forms—in this case, modern man—did not evolve from forms found in lower strata; they moved into an area and replaced those forms (the Neanderthals).[41]

Hrdlička pointed out, with little apparent effect, that Boule's notions had not been proved; they were simply assumptions. "If the given assumptions are true, then we are confronted by some strange major phenomena, vis., a long double line of human evolution . . . ; a sudden extinction of one of the lines; and evolutionary sluggishness or pause in the other." Why and where did *Homo sapiens* develop his superior makeup? If he evolved in Africa or Asia, where is "the evidence of his ancient dominion in those regions"? "Or, if he lived in Europe, coexisting with the Neanderthaler, where are his remains, and why did he not prevail sooner over his inferior cousin?" Why did the invaders, "a new, superior species, strong and able enough to completely do away with the Neanderthaler, take over the poor Neanderthaler's caves and sites, and live in them exactly, except for technical differences in stone-chipping, as did their crude predecessors?" Hrdlička was puzzled, too, that invasion was effected "during the last ice encroachment, an unfavorable period, when man might logically be expected to move from, rather than into, such a territory." [42]

HRDLIČKA'S ARGUMENT [43]

Hrdlička had several other things to say about the "problem of Neanderthal man" and his place in human evolution. With regard to the "problem," he warned that there were a number of uncertainties. When Neanderthal man lived, the area he had occupied, or who he actually was had not been definitely established as of 1930. There were no guides, no criteria, for determining these matters. Faunal indices employed in dating, for instance, gave no clear-cut time period for the Mousterian culture or for the Neanderthals. "Neanderthal man did not come in with any special fauna, nor did he go out with any. . . ."

The principal argument advanced by Hrdlička was that there was no known reason to rule out the Neanderthals as possible ancestors to *Homo sapiens*. The culture and habits of the former did not cease with the appearance of the latter; they were carried forward. The Neanderthals occupied caves and rock shelters—but early *sapiens* occupied them more extensively. Both groups also had sites in the open. No sudden change in tool-making is evident, and Mousterian implements are often difficult to distinguish from tools made by Upper Paleolithic men. In short, "the coming of a distinct and superior species of people ought to have left a very tangible record on the sequence and nature of the cultural levels of the two stocks"—but there is no such record. If the *sapiens* were a conquering race, they brought no tools or weapons with them— none, that is, which can be distinguished from Mousterian artifacts.

Hrdlička tackled the matter of morphological characters by considering all the Neanderthal specimens arranged in an order, "beginning with those that show the most primitive or old features and advancing gradually towards more modern standards." One fact which emerges from such an ordering is that each skeleton has primitive parts and features and "parts and features that are practically modern; and every skeleton is found to differ in these respects." Even in the most nearly related specimens—Neander Valley, La Chapelle, Spy No. 1, Le Moustier—"there is in evidence a considerable variability, with more or less advance in various parts in the direction of later man." The remaining, presumably more recent skeletons, exhibit increased variability and a considerable increase in the number of modern characters.

As we might suspect, Hrdlička found the physical differences between Neanderthal man and modern man less decisive than most writers:

About the most distinguishing and important marks of difference of the typical Neanderthaler from later man are, we may repeat, the lowness of his head, with low receding forehead and a peculiar protruding occiput; a heavy, supraorbital torus; a heavy, chinless jaw; and, as determined from intracranial casts, a low type of brain. It will be well to see how these characters stand the light of our present knowledge. Lowness of the vault, low and receding forehead, and projecting occiput, all show in the series of the Neanderthal skulls known today a large range of gradation, the lower limits of which are well below, but the upper grades of which are well within, the range of variation of the same characters in later, and even present, man. There exists today a whole great strain of humanity, extending from Mongolia deep into America, which is characterized by low vault of the skull. Low foreheads are frequent in prehistoric America. The pronounced Neanderthal occiput, such as shown by the La Chapelle, La Quina and La Ferrassie skulls, would be difficult to fully match in later man; but on the one hand the character is not present or marked in all the Neanderthalers, while on the other there are decided approximations to it among recent skulls.

Hrdlička went on to emphasize that the heavy supraorbital torus, the ridge above the eyes, shows up to some degree in later skulls. In fact, there is "in the civilized man of today" perceptible evidence of a reduction in this torus. Some of the heavy jaws are not known among later specimens, but some Neanderthals are "very much more advanced morphologically toward the present human type. . . . Let us add to this the various huge, nearly chinless, and even receding jaws that occur now and then in the Australian, Melanesian, Mongolian, American Eskimo, and Indian, and the picture loses much of its discontinuity. Much the same may be said also of the teeth."

In sum, "the Neanderthal man is now known to show wide morphological variation, leading in the direction of later man; and there are individuals among later men, even to this day, who show transitional features reminiscent of the Neanderthalers." Since there is no evidence for a separately evolving *Homo sapiens* line, there is reason to assume that Neanderthal man evolved into modern man. Until evidence to the contrary is found, "there appears to be less justification for the conception of a Neanderthal *species* than there is for that of a Neanderthal phase of Man."

CONCLUSIONS

Books and articles published since 1960 indicate that there is still a Neanderthal problem. From such publications it is evident that assumptions, beliefs, and ideas of earlier generations continue to affect our thinking about the Neanderthals. Such is inevitable, for the interpretation of past events is not an exact science. The data with which the prehistorian must work are, as we have seen, incomplete and biased samplings in time. The subjective element can—and must—play an important role in reconstructing human evolution.

Our impression is that Neanderthal man, in some form, is now widely accepted as the ancestor of our species. This is an impression based upon what is not written, as well as what appears in print. As an example of the latter, one writer commenting upon an article by Brace said: "Brace publicly points to what many paleo-osteologists already privately accept— Neanderthal forms are direct ancestors of modern man." [44] Bernard Campbell lists all Neanderthal specimens, including the classic forms, as members of *Homo sapiens*.[45] John Buettner-Janusch also believes the "Classic" Neanderthals can be assigned to "the population that is our own direct ancestor." [46] Brace and Montagu treat all the Neanderthals as a "stage" of human evolution.[47]

A number of writers now accept as *sapiens* ancestors the "generalized" or "progressive" Neanderthals, but not the "classic" type. Such writers agree with von Koenigswald, that the latter was a "terminal type" that had "no direct genetic connection" with *Homo sapiens*.[48] Le Gros Clark, who offers a "provisional statement" to the effect that a generalized Neanderthal type gave rise to modern man, goes so far as to assign the classic type to a separate species of *Homo*.[49]

The idea that a modern type of man—the "presapiens"—was more ancient than any of the Neanderthals apparently has few avid supporters today. But the idea has not been abandoned completely. Le Gros Clark, for one, has not ruled out the possibility that Swanscombe, Steinheim, Fontéchevade and other specimens predate the Neanderthals. He says, in fact, that "it now seems probable that *Homo sapiens*, or at least a type of Man not markedly different from *Homo sapiens*, had already appeared during the second or third interglacial period . . . in Pre-Mousterian times." [50] Michael Day believes it is possible that the "more sapient groups represented by Steinheim and Swanscombe man" were contemporaneous with Middle Pleistocene ancestors to Neanderthal man.[51]

Reference to "early" Neanderthals is quite common in the literature of the 1960's, as is suggested by a statement by Bertram S. Kraus: "There is general agreement that the *chronologically earlier* Neanderthaloids are *morphologically closer* to *Homo sapiens*." [52] The absolute dating of Mount Carmel specimens and of fossils discovered in Iraq between 1947 and 1960 casts considerable doubt upon the content of such agreement. The Mount Carmel materials date back only 39,000 to 42,000 years before the present; the Iraqian fossils, to 48,000 years ago at most.[53] It would appear that the structurally more modern Neanderthals were roughly contemporaneous with the classic Neanderthals, if we assume that estimated dates for the latter are fairly accurate.

The ultimate fate of the classic Neanderthals of Europe is still unknown. Few writers seem to accept the earlier view that our murderous *sapiens* ancestors exterminated them. But there is as yet no evidence which definitely proves that they were absorbed by invaders through interbreeding or destroyed by disease, or that they experienced mutations in the *sapiens* direction. More precise—and probably more accurate—datings of fossil and archaeological materials might possibly eliminate at least one of these alternatives. An important, as yet unanswered question is, Was there time enough for the classic Neanderthal face to become modern? Boule, of course, saw no temporal distance between the classic Neanderthals and *Homo sapiens*, and this belief still persists. There is, however, no firm evidence that such was the case.

The peculiar face of the classic Neanderthals, according to Carleton S. Coon, was due primarily to a large, projecting nose. The importance of the nose as "the prime architect of the Neanderthal face" has been generally overlooked because the nasal bones are missing in the two skulls with faces. The large projecting nose caused the face to protrude, and it gave the individual an unbroken brow ridge (the supraorbital torus of the "progressive," or early, Neanderthal was not continuous; it projected only over the eye orbits). Coon believes this nose contributed to survival in an extremely cold climate. Because of its size and construction, arteries near the nasal passages were protected from the cold. There was, therefore, no chilling of blood that went to the brain—a critical factor, since the brain cannot tolerate much variation in temperature.[54] Another function of the large nose was to warm and moisten cold, dry air before it went to the lungs.

Boule's image of Neanderthal man seems to have been modified, at least to some extent; yet, as the textbook description cited earlier suggests, there is still some tendency to depict or imply a number of apelike features in the classic skeleton. An occasional author uses Boule's diagrammatic reconstruction of the La Chapelle-aux-Saints skeleton, a drawing Boule employed in *Fossil Men*, to illustrate the poor posture and backward positioning of the foramen magnum.

Continuing Uncertainties

None of the "uncertainties" to which Hrdlička referred in 1930 is yet an absolute certainty. As we have implied, most of the Neanderthal specimens are not definitely located in time. The geographic distribution of the Neanderthals has not been determined, but it is evident that they were a far-ranging group. Remains identified as Neanderthals have been found in a number of European countries, from England to the U.S.S.R.; in the Near East (Israel, Lebanon, Iraq, Iran); the Far East (China, Java); and in various parts of Africa.[55]

When and where Neanderthal man lived is intimately related to who he was. Uncertainty as to the identity of the Neanderthals has probably increased during the past few decades. As several writers have had occasion to note, "Neanderthal" (or some derivative of the term) is a rather imprecise concept, not a taxonomic category. Too frequently, it is often lamented, a specimen is called "Neanderthal" simply because of the presence or suggested presence of heavy brow ridges or a low forehead. Hrdlička defined Neanderthal man and his period culturally, as "the man and period of the Mousterian culture." [56] Brace suggests a morphological corollary: "Neanderthal man is the man of the Mousterian culture prior to the reduction in form and dimension of the Middle Pleistocene face." [57]

No definition, cultural or morphological, is likely to be completely adequate. Neither man nor his early culture evolved by a series of discrete, readily identifiable steps—except in the classifier's mind. Beetle-browed *Homo erectus* gradually became beetle-browed Neanderthal man, and gradual modifications in the Neanderthal skull resulted in *Homo sapiens*. With a few alterations and additions, Mousterian cultures flowed into cultures of the Upper Paleolithic. These continua may be divided into as many or as few categories as we see fit, but the boundaries between the categories will be difficult to determine. There was no precise point in time when *erectus* ceased to be *erectus* or when *sapiens* became *sapiens*.

NOTES

1. C. L. Brace and M. F. Ashley Montagu, *Man's Evolution* (New York: The Macmillan Company, 1965), p. 221.

2. Franz Weidenreich, "The Sinanthropus Population of Choukoutien (Locality 1) with a Preliminary Report on New Discoveries," *Bulletin of the Geological Society of China*, Vol. XIV, No. 4 (1935), p. 455.

3. F. M. Bergounioux, "Notes on the Mentality of Primitive Man," in Sherwood L. Washburn (ed.), *Social Life of Early Man* (Chicago: Aldine Publishing Company, 1961), p. 114.

4. Except as noted, materials used in this section are drawn from the following sources: Roy Chapman Andrews, *Meet Your Ancestors* (New York: The Viking Press, 1945), Chap. 10; Aleš Hrdlička, *The Skeletal Remains of Early Man* (Washington, D. C.: The Smithsonian Institution, 1930), pp. 148–227; Herbert Wendt, *In Search of Adam* (New York: Collier Books, 1963), pp. 249–258; Brace and Montagu, *op. cit.*, pp. 128–158.

5. D. [Hermann] Schaaffhausen, "Discovery of the Neanderthal Skull," in Robert F. Heizer (ed.), *Man's Discovery of His Past: Literary Landmarks in Archaeology* (Englewood Cliffs, N. J.: Prentice-Hall, Inc., 1962), pp. 117–123.

6. Cited in Arthur Keith, *The Antiquity of Man* (London: Williams and Norgate, 1915), pp. 130–131.

7. Kenneth P. Oakley, *Frameworks for Dating Fossil Man* (Chicago: Aldine Publishing Company, 1964), pp. 295–301.

8. Franz Weidenreich, "Some Problems Dealing with Ancient Man," *American Anthropologist*, New Series 42 (1940), 380–381.

9. Karl W. Butzer, *Environment and Archaeology: An Introduction to Pleistocene Geography* (Chicago: Aldine Publishing Company, 1964), p. 385.

10. Francois Bordes, "Mousterian Cultures in France," in Joseph R. Caldwell (ed.), *New Roads to Yesterday* (New York: Basic Books, Inc., Publishers, 1966), pp. 78–88.

11. Henri V. Vallois, "The Origin of *Homo sapiens*," in William Howells (ed.), *Ideas on Human Evolution: Selected Essays, 1949–1961* (Cambridge: Harvard University Press, 1962), pp. 477–479.

12. Ralph L. Beals and Harry Hoijer, *An Introduction to Anthropology*, 3rd ed. (New York: The Macmillan Company, 1965), pp. 108–111. © The Macmillan Company, 1965.

13. L. S. B. Leakey, *Adam's Ancestors*, 4th ed. (New York: Harper & Row, Publishers, 1960), pp. xi–xii, 201, 212; Leakey, "East African Fossil Hominoidea and the Classification within This Super-Family," in Sherwood L. Washburn (ed.), *Classification and Human Evolution* (Chicago: Aldine Publishing Company, 1963), pp. 44–45.

14. Gerhard Heberer, "The Descent of Man and the Present Fossil Record," *Cold Spring Harbor Symposia on Quantitative Biology*, XXIV (Cold Spring Harbor, N. Y.: The Biological Laboratory, 1959), 242.

15. Vallois, *op. cit.*, p. 494.

16. F. Clark Howell, "The Evolutionary Significance of Variation and Varieties of 'Neanderthal' Man," *The Quarterly Review of Biology*, 32 (1957), 333–337.

17. F. Clark Howell, "The Place of Neanderthal Man in Human Evolution," *American Journal of Physical Anthropology*, New Series 9 (1951), 404–405.

18. Howell, "The Evolutionary Significance of Variation and Varieties of 'Neanderthal' Man," p. 332.

19. F. Clark Howell, "Pleistocene Glacial Ecology and the Evolution of 'Classic Neanderthal' Man," *Southwestern Journal of Anthropology*, 8 (1952), 377–410.

20. Howell, "The Place of Neanderthal Man in Human Evolution," pp. 409–412.

21. Marcellin Boule and Henri V. Vallois, *Fossil Men* (New York: The Dryden Press, 1957), p. 258.

22. Brace and Montagu, *op. cit.*, pp. 158–159.

23. William L. Straus, Jr. and A. J. E. Cave, "Pathology and the Posture of Neanderthal Man," *The Quarterly Review of Biology*, 32 (1957), 358.

24. Brace and Montagu, *op. cit.*, p. 160.

25. Straus and Cave, *op. cit.*, p. 348.

26. *Ibid.*, p. 358.

27. Boule and Vallois, *op. cit.*, pp. 255, 257.

28. William Howells, *Mankind So Far* (Garden City, N. Y.: Doubleday & Company, Inc., 1949), p. 169.

29. C. H. Dudley Buxton and G. R. de Beer, "Neanderthal and Modern Man," *Nature*, 129 (1932), 940–941.

30. Earnest Albert Hooton, *Why Men Behave Like Apes and Vice Versa* (Princeton: Princeton University Press, 1940), p. 75.

31. Franz Weidenreich, "The 'Neanderthal Man' and the Ancestors of 'Homo sapiens,'" *American Anthropologist*, New Series 45 (1943), 44–45.

32. Theodore D. McCown, "The Genus Palaeoanthropus and the Problem of Superspecific Differentiation Among the Hominidae," *Cold Spring Harbor Symposia on Quantitative Biology*, XV (Cold Spring Harbor, N. Y.: The Biological Laboratory, 1950), 87–96.

33. T. D. Stewart, "The Problem of the Earliest Claimed Representatives of Homo Sapiens," *Cold Spring Harbor Symposia on Quantitative Biology*, XV (Cold Spring Harbor, N. Y.: The Biological Laboratory, 1950), 97–107.

34. Ernst Mayr, "Taxonomic Categories in Fossil Hominids," *Cold Spring Harbor Symposia on Quantitative Biology*, XV (Cold Spring Harbor, N. Y.: The Biological Laboratory, 1950), 109–118.

35. Adolph H. Schultz, "The Position of the Occipital Condyles and the Face Relative to the Skull Base in Primates," *American Journal of Physical Anthropology*, New Series 13 (1955), 99.

36. Straus and Cave, *op. cit.*, p. 350.

37. *Ibid.*, pp. 361–362.

38. *Ibid.*, p. 359.

39. C. Loring Brace, "Refocusing on the Neanderthal Problem," *American Anthropologist*, 64 (1962), 729–730.

40. C. Loring Brace, "The Problem of the Neanderthals," in Peter B. Hammond (ed.), *Physical Anthropology and Archaeology: Selected Readings* (New York: The Macmillan Company, 1964), p. 110.

41. C. Loring Brace, "The Fate of the 'Classic' Neanderthals: A Consideration of Hominid Catastrophism," *Current Anthropology*, 5 (1964), 5.

42. Aleš Hrdlička, *The Skeletal Remains of Early Man* (Washington: D.C.: The Smithsonian Institution, 1930), pp. 344–345.

43. *Ibid.*, pp. 329–348.

44. George A. Agogino, Comments on "The Fate of the 'Classic' Neanderthals," *Current Anthropology*, 5 (1964), 19.

45. Bernard G. Campbell, *Human Evolution* (Chicago: Aldine Publishing Company, 1966), pp. 367–368.

46. John Buettner-Janusch, *Origins of Man* (New York: John Wiley & Sons, Inc., 1966), p. 151.

47. Brace and Montagu, *op. cit.*, pp. 244–251.

48. G. H. R. von Koenigswald, *The Evolution of Man* (Ann Arbor: The University of Michigan Press, 1962), p. 98.

49. W. E. Le Gros Clark, *History of the Primates*, 5th ed. (Chicago: University of Chicago Press, 1966), pp. 110–112.

50. *Ibid.*, pp. 100–103.

51. Michael H. Day, *Guide to Fossil Man* (Cleveland: The World Publishing Company, 1965), pp. 73–74.

52. Bertram S. Kraus, *The Basis of Human Evolution* (New York: Harper & Row, Publishers, 1964), p. 245.

53. Oakley, *op. cit.*, pp. 304–306.

54. Carleton S. Coon, *The Origin of Races* (New York: Alfred A. Knopf, Inc., 1963), pp. 532–533.

55. Oakley, *op. cit.*, pp. 295–309; Buettner-Janusch, *op. cit.*, pp. 148–149.

56. Hrdlička, *op. cit.*, p. 328.

57. Brace, "The Fate of the 'Classic' Neanderthals . . . ," p. 18.

15

Upper Paleolithic Man: *Homo Sapiens*

Hrdlička's comment in 1930 regarding Neanderthal man, "It is not yet properly known just where, when, and how he began," [1] applies equally well to the present state of knowledge with regard to modern man. For the moment, however, we shall deal with what *is* known—that is, with matters about which prehistorians are in general agreement. Our starting point is the discovery of early specimens of *Homo sapiens* that were identified as such. These, and other early representatives of our species to which we shall make passing reference, lived during the Upper Paleolithic.*

The Upper Paleolithic, the last phase of the Old Stone Age, began sometime during the last (Würm) glaciation, probably during the first interstadial (a relatively short warming period). It was originally distinguished in Europe from the Middle Paleolithic, or Mousterian com-

---

* "Paleolithic" (*paleo*, "old"; *lithic*, "stone") as used here refers to a cultural epoch; the term is also sometimes used to refer to traditions and industries which persisted beyond the epoch. All evidences of culture found in Pleistocene (a geological epoch) deposits are regarded as Paleolithic industries. The Lower Paleolithic began with the initial appearance of stone tools. We—but not all authors—regard the appearance of Mousterian industries as the beginning of the Middle Paleolithic.

254

plex, by what was thought to be a sudden change in tool-making traditions. It was believed that the characteristic tools of the Middle Paleolithic, hand axes and flakes, were suddenly replaced by a variety of blade tools. Unlike flake tools, which were by-products of the fashioning of hand axes, blade tools were intentionally split off from rocks with considerable precision. The change from one type of tool-making to the other was not sudden, however, and cannot be used to distinguish the Middle Paleolithic from the Upper Paleolithic period. In actuality, blade tools were used in some Mousterian cultures; and flake implements were more numerous than blades in some Upper Paleolithic cultures.[2] (See Figure 24, page 256.)

We shall use the term "Upper Paleolithic," as it is frequently used in the literature, to refer to a period in time. According to this usage, the Upper Paleolithic began with the first appearance in the fossil record of specimens of morphologically modern man and ended with the termination of the Pleistocene or the beginning of the present postglacial period. As a period, "Upper Paleolithic" is not limited to blade cultures or to peoples of Europe.

FIRST DISCOVERIES OF MODERN MAN [3]

The first fossil evidences of prehistoric modern man came to light when it was generally believed that the Bible contained the total history of mankind. As a result these fossil finds, like the initial Neanderthal finds, were not recognized for what they actually were for a number of years. How many specimens were found and lost or destroyed will never be known.

The first discovery of Old Stone Age modern man, as reported by Sir Arthur Keith in 1915, was of a specimen sometimes referred to as the "Red Lady of Paviland." Discovery of the "Red Lady"—who turned out to be a male—was a by-product of an interest in exploring caves to find extinct forms of animals. This interest developed in Germany during the latter part of the eighteenth century, then spread to other European countries. One of the caves explored was the Paviland cave on the south coast of Wales.

Animal remains found in the Paviland cave in 1822 brought Dean Buckland, of Oxford University, to the site. The Dean found not only an abundance of extinct forms of animals, but also a headless skeleton that had been colored red with ocher. In the same stratum with the skeleton were flint tools and ornaments and implements made from bone and ivory. Buckland explained the contents of the cave in a manner which satisfied himself and others. The extinct animals, he said, had been swept into the cave by the Noachian deluge. The human re-

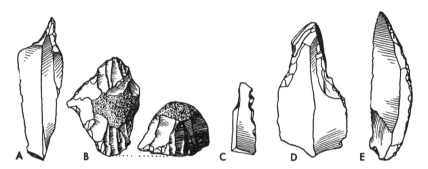

Figure 24. Examples of Upper Paleolithic blade tools made from flint found in western Europe. (A) Piercer or "hand drill"; (B) nosed scraper or "push-plane"; (C) fragment of saw blade; (D) burin or graver; (E) knife. (By courtesy of The Trustees, British Museum [Natural History].)

mains had been buried there by people who had settled in Britain after the Flood. In reporting this explanation, Keith commented: "It was then an article of faith that man did not exist in Western Europe before the flood."

Another specimen was discovered in 1830 by Dr. P. C. Schmerling while excavating the cave of Engis near Liège, Belgium. The specimen, a skull and skeletal fragments, was also associated with stone and bone artifacts and the remains of extinct animals. The braincase, according to Keith, was modern in every way; the estimated brain capacity was 1500 cc. The face was missing.

Except for Neanderthal finds, there appear to have been no fossil discoveries during the 1840's and 1850's—that is, none were reported. Nonetheless, a growing number of people began to realize that man was more ancient than was commonly believed. The major reasons for this realization were the frequent discovery of bone and stone implements and the insistence of a few men, such as Boucher de Perthes, that such implements could only have been shaped by early man. In 1859, Charles Lyell gave the case for ancient man a boost when he gave support to Boucher de Perthes' views in *The Antiquity of Man as Proved by Geology.*

Artifacts found in the Paviland and Engis caves and at various other sites were eventually known as the "Aurignacian culture." "Aurignacian" is a derivative of "Aurignac," the name of a village in southern France. Near this village, in 1860, Edouard Lartet uncovered implements and ornaments like those found in the caves. At the time, the men who had fashioned the artifacts were unknown. Buckland's find rested in a museum and was not definitely identified until 1912, and the status of the Engis skull was being debated as late as 1915.

Identification of the authors of the Aurignacian culture followed the recovery of materials from an old rock shelter at Cro-Magnon, not far from the village of Les Eyzies in southern France. The rock shelter was uncovered by workmen preparing road beds for a railroad and a highway. As excavation proceeded, chipped flints, broken animal bones, and human crania were exposed. Authorities in nearby Bordeaux were notified, and Louis Lartet, son of Edouard Lartet, arrived shortly to take charge of further excavation. The floor of the shelter, Lartet found, contained hearths and Aurignacian artifacts. Strata above the floor contained animal bones. At the back of the shelter, in conditions suggesting burial, were the remains of five individuals. The skull of one, the "Old Man of Cro-Magnon," was almost complete; only the teeth and part of the face were missing or deteriorated.

Keith described the Cro-Magnon individuals as

> . . . tall people; the men were about five feet eleven inches in height (1.8 m.)—tall, lanky fellows. . . . The proportion of their limbs was somewhat peculiar; their tibiae or leg bones were relatively long, their humeri or upper arm bones, short. Individuals with similar limb proportions still occur amongst negroid races, but no modern European race can show the negroid limb proportions of the Cromagnon race—men of the Aurignacian period.

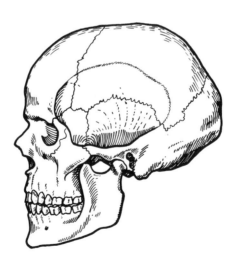

Figure 25. The skull of a Cro-Magnon male.

The Cro-Magnon crania seem to have puzzled Keith. They suggested "another race of men," different from any that were known. The skull of a Cro-Magnon was "massive," "much too large for the conventional modern frame," with a brain capacity of approximately 1660 cc.

> We have come across, in those large heads, a puzzling and unexpected fact; we are naturally astonished to find that men who have preceded us so long ago—men of a former geological epoch—should so far outstrip their successors of to-day who regard themselves as "the survival of the fittest," and believe the fittest to be the race with the biggest brains. We cannot quarrel with the facts, but how are we to explain them? The conclusion to be drawn is, not that brain mass, on the average, is to be rejected as an index of brain power, but that there are other virtues or characters which go to ensure success of a human race in the struggle of life—other than brain power. A philosopher may be miserable or die childless, when a brainless savage or an industrious labouring man may be happy and leave a large family.

The Cro-Magnon discovery did much to convince people that Virchow was right in proclaiming the Neanderthal fossils to be pathological. The "Old Man's" face exhibited a degree of prognathism, but his relatively smooth brow and large rounded skull attested to his affinity with nineteenth-century Europeans. His antiquity was indicated by the amount of debris that had buried the shelter, the animal bones, and the archaeological materials. Many became convinced that man was more ancient than had been formerly believed. But some prehistorians still questioned the age of the fossils. They could not believe that "fossil Men could have practiced the veneration of the dead"; [4] that is, they could not accept the idea that any creatures other than civilized man could have buried their dead.

Additional Finds

The Cro-Magnon individuals lived perhaps 20,000 to 30,000 years ago, during the last glacial period.[5] They may have been representatives of the first Upper Paleolithic "race" to invade—or evolve in—Europe. More likely, according to some prehistorians, they were preceded by another so-called race, members of whom were buried in the Grimaldi caves of Italy. To the present, no satisfactory dates have been established for remains found in the Grimaldi caves.

In one of the caves, which are located along the Mediterranean not far from the French border, skeletons of a young man and an old woman were found. Their stature was between 5 feet 1 and 5 feet 3 inches, considerably shorter than the typical Cro-Magnon height. Features of the remains convinced a number of paleontologists and anthropologists that the young man and old woman had been Negroid. According to Boule, one of the main reasons for regarding the fossils as Negroid was the proportional length of the limbs. The forearm, for example, was very long in proportion to the whole arm. Several features of the skull, such as its length and narrowness, and face (marked prognathism, for instance) were also Negro-like.[6]

Keith and others took exception to the Negroid interpretation of the "Grimaldi race." Those characteristics labelled as Negroid, Keith said, also occurred in white races. He believed it was a mistake to separate the Grimaldi individuals "as types of a new race indigenous to Europe. To me these characters suggest that they are only an aberrant Cromagnon form, perhaps primitive, but nevertheless true members of the Cromagnon race." [7] Most present-day authorities tend to agree with Keith. In support of this position, Le Gros Clark has pointed out that there are probably no racial types "in which the skull characters are more distinctive than Negroes and Eskimos; and yet experts fail to agree when faced with single skulls whose claim to these types are in question." It is even more difficult, and often impossible, "to identify, by reference to limited skeletal remains, minor racial groups with less distinctive characters." [8] Prehistoric racial types, in other words, cannot be identified with any degree of confidence.

Another specimen that has been interpreted in different ways is a skeleton found at Combe Capelle, not far from Le Moustier. When first described, the specimen was assigned to a new species (*Homo aurignacensis*). Keith considered it and the "so-called Grimaldi negroids" as the earliest representatives of Aurignacian man in Europe. To others, Combe Capelle was "a representative of a negroid people, a people showing a close affinity to the darker-skinned races of Northern Africa." [9] At least one anthropologist thought Combe Capelle man possessed Australoid characters; yet others looked upon him as a variant of the Cro-Magnon "race." [10] More recently, Brace and Montagu have stated that the skeleton possesses some of the features that members of a population intermediate in form between Neanderthal man and modern man might be expected to exhibit. They also note, as did Keith, that the Combe Capelle remains were situated at what might be considered the stratigraphic borderline between the Mousterian and early Aurignacian cultures.[11] Kenneth Oakley, who estimates the fossils to be about 34,000 years old, lists them as a *Homo sapiens* specimen.[12]

Somewhat similar to the Combe Capelle specimen are a number of fossils discovered near Predmost, Moravia (Czechoslovakia). These fossils have been variously designated as a separate species (*Homo predmosti*), a distinct race, a Cro-Magnon type, and a type intermediate between Neanderthal and modern man. Heavy supraorbital ridges and the shape of the occipital area of the male skull, in particular, are reminiscent of Neanderthal man. However, most writers now classify the Predmost people of some 26,500 years ago (Oakley's estimate) as *Homo sapiens*. Whatever their taxonomic status, it is known that they were successful hunters of large mammals (especially mammoths) and fairly competent artists.[13]

General Summary of Upper Paleolithic Finds

In addition to the discoveries referred to above, many other specimens of Cro-Magnons and other supposed "races" or types were located in Upper Paleolithic deposits of the Old World. The human populations that lived during the last phase of the Würm Glaciation, it became evident, were a heterogeneous lot. They varied as to stature, head and face form, and proportional length of limbs. Many were thought to exhibit Negroid, Ethiopian, or Eskimoid (or Mongoloid) features—a notion that still persists.[14]

Despite the variability of Upper Paleolithic peoples, prehistorians generally agree that it would be difficult to distinguish them from living populations. The human form has changed but slightly during the past 35,000 years or so. Bones and muscles have tended to become less heavy; the face, less rugged.[15] The major changes since the days of the Cro-Magnons and their contemporaries have been cultural, not physical.

An important factor in the physical variability of Upper Paleolithic peoples was geographic dispersal. The majority of fossils and artifacts uncovered thus far have been in western Europe. But like the Neanderthals, the habitats of the earliest modern men were far-flung—from England to China, from northern Europe to South Africa. In several instances, they occupied the same areas—even the same sites—as the Neanderthals. Caves, in particular, have yielded materials from both types of men.

UNCERTAINTIES

Where did the modern type of man originate? When did he appear? Satisfactory answers to these questions are yet to be provided. The whole question of the origin of our species (or subspecies, in some schemes: *Homo sapiens sapiens*), one anthropologist has observed, is the "worst present problem in our evolution." [16]

The problem exists, in part, because of dating difficulties. All the Upper Pleistocene evidence has yet to be ordered chronologically. Cultural and geologic sequences have been pretty well worked out for western Europe, but the majority of materials found in other geographic regions has not been dated. At the present time, there are no techniques for correlating sequences in one part of the world with fossil or cultural evidence elsewhere. Climatic and geologic events that serve as time markers for one area oftentimes did not affect other areas or affected them differentially. Nor did cultural changes of the same supposed magnitude occur everywhere at roughly the same time. In and around Egypt, for example, tools presumably used only by Neanderthals seem to have persisted for some time after the appearance in southwestern Asia of tools identified with early *Homo sapiens*.[17]

A number of specimens cannot be assigned relative dates with any precision, even if sequences are correlated. Several, especially in western Europe, were recovered during the last century with little or no attention having been paid to stratigraphic details. Materials found in caves are sometimes impossible to relate to natural strata outside the caves. Burials, inside and outside of caves, have proved particularly troublesome in working out sequences. Unless there are clear indications of burial, fossils may be considered to be older than they actually are. Such was the case, for instance, with regard to some of the individuals once thought to be "presapiens."

The ideal situation, of course, is for all specimens to be assigned absolute dates. This would give not only a better idea as to when *sapiens* evolved, but where. If the exact age of each specimen were known, it might be possible to track Upper Paleolithic man to the area of his origin. The few absolute dates we have are suggestive in this respect. In 1959 a skull was found in the Great Cave of Niah, Borneo, that appears to be the oldest known representative of *Homo sapiens*. According to a radiocarbon analysis, the owner of the skull died somewhere between 38,600 and 40,600 years ago (39,600 ± 1,000). The next oldest *sapiens* specimen lived in Europe more than 10,000 years later, between 26,680 and 27,180 years ago.[18]

These dates give some support to a rather persistent and widespread belief that modern man migrated to Europe from the east. More evidence is obviously needed to prove that *Homo sapiens* originated in Borneo—or even in southeastern Asia. There is a possibility that the radiocarbon readings are in error. Although it seems unlikely, the skull may not have been correctly identified. Again, specimens even older may yet be uncovered elsewhere, if they have not already been discovered.

An assumption implicit in the preceding remarks is that all living peoples descended from a common *sapiens* stock, that *Homo sapiens* evolved but once and in but one part of the world. This assumption has been neither proved nor disproved, but many people accept it as reason-

261

able. To accept the assumption that *sapiens* originated in a single geographic area requires acceptance of another assumption—that subsequent generations dispersed to such widely separate points as England, China, and Cape Province (Republic of South Africa). The latter assumption is not implausible. But these points were also places where Neanderthal finds have been made. Did *both* types of man, by chance, locate in these widely separated areas? If so, why? Were the factors which encouraged or forced migration at one period in time compelling factors thousands of years later?

Evidences of Neanderthals at or near locations occupied by early *sapiens* in different parts of the world suggest that the latter evolved from Neanderthals in more than one geographic area. It might even be argued that modern man evolved independently from two or more dispersed *Homo erectus* groups, for they, too, were situated in Europe, China, and parts of Africa. Indeed, such has been argued. Weidenreich, for example, envisioned a parallel evolution of four major groups—Australian, Mongolian, African, and Eurasian—going back to *Homo erectus* or beyond.[19] More recently, Carleton S. Coon has offered a detailed study in support of Weidenreich's main idea. The thesis of the study, Coon explains,

> is, in essence, that at the beginning of our record, over half a million years ago, man was a single species, *Homo erectus*, perhaps already divided into five geographic races or subspecies. *Homo erectus* then evolved into *Homo sapiens* not once but five times, as each subspecies, living in its own territory, passed a critical threshold from a more brutal to a more *sapient* state, by one genetic process or another.[20]

"One genetic process or another" included crossbreeding between members of the subspecies. Some of the early Caucasoids, for instance, very likely entered the homelands of the Mongoloids (who descended from *Sinanthropus*) and mixed with the local populations. "If the Chinese population had not yet crossed the *erectus-sapiens* barrier, this injection of genes could have given them the chromosomal equipment to initiate such a transition." [21]

Coon's methodology has been criticized,[22] and his thesis has apparently gained little backing from other scientists thus far. Le Gros Clark, for one, believes the Coon-Weidenreich view "certainly demands serious consideration." He himself is not inclined to accept the view, mainly because he considers it improbable that the various *Homo erectus* subspecies could have remained in complete isolation long enough to evolve into the five geographic races Coon postulates. Too, he believes there was time enough for *Homo sapiens* to migrate extensively, for he accepts as an established fact the presence of *Homo sapiens* in Europe some 200,000 years ago.[23]

The ideas advanced by Weidenreich and Coon receive tacit support from the growing tendency to classify Middle and Upper Pleistocene hominids as members of only two species, *Homo erectus* and *Homo sapiens*. One implication of this new classification is that our species *could* have evolved from dispersed *Homo erectus* groups. Whether this actually happened can be demonstrated only when and if the fossil record becomes much more complete than it now is.

If Coon and Weidenreich are essentially correct, the answer to the question "Where did *Homo sapiens* originate?" is "almost anywhere." This explanation, unfortunately, further complicates the already complicated problem of determining *when* our species evolved. *Homo sapiens* may have appeared at different times in different areas or at about the same time everywhere. Presently, the available evidence and interpretative techniques provide no definitive answer as to the approximate time modern man originated in even one area.

One complicating factor is a lack of consensus as to the features or capabilities early representatives of modern man are expected to exhibit or reflect. In order to answer the question of when *Homo sapiens* originated, the characteristics which distinguish *Homo sapiens* from his predecessors must first be established. Historically, the tendency has been to regard as non-*sapiens* any specimen that possessed Neanderthal-like traits. One effect of such a practice, generally speaking, has been to postpone by several thousand years the appearance of modern man in Europe and elsewhere.

The historical tendency, we have noted, is being countered somewhat by what appears to be a developing tendency to include some or all Neanderthals within the taxon *Homo sapiens*. More scientists are prone to stress the modern features of this group and to recognize that "Neanderthals who lived in western Europe are not so different from modern man as has been supposed." [24] Even those who choose to regard the "classic" Neanderthals as a distinct species or subspecies of *Homo* tend to agree with Dr. T. Dale Stewart, Curator of Physical Anthropology at the Smithsonian Institution, that the "progressive" Mount Carmel Neanderthals are representatives of "an early variety of modern man." [25]

If Dr. Stewart is right, it appears that *Homo sapiens* was established in the Near East (Palestine) and the Far East (Borneo) at about the same time, roughly 40,000 years ago. Contemporaries of these two were specimens from the Transvaal and Cape Province, listed by Oakley as "*Homo sapiens* Neanderthaloids and Related Forms." Also of the same age were "Neanderthaloids" who lived in North Africa (Libya). A somewhat doubtful dating of materials from Kenya places *Homo sapiens* in East Africa 60,000 years ago.[26] These dates suggest that modern man is at least 40,000 years old and perhaps as ancient as 60,000 years. It should be noted, however, that relatively few of either the Neanderthaloid specimens from North Africa and the Far East or the *Homo sapiens* fossils found outside of Europe have been dated. If they can be dated, one or several may prove to be much older than 60,000 years. Indeed, if the estimated ages of a few Neanderthaloids of Europe [27] ("presapiens," in some schemes) can be verified, there may be good reason to believe that modern man was on the scene no later than 200,000 years ago.

Before leaving the subject of where and when our species appeared, it should be noted that cultural categories, such as "Mousterian" and "Upper Paleolithic," carry implicit assumptions about the emergence of modern man. "Mousterian" is normally associated with only the Neanderthals, and "Upper Paleolithic" is a cultural synonym for Old Stone Age *sapiens*. Thus, by implication, all peoples who manufactured or used Mousterian implements had to be Neanderthals, while those who fashioned blade implements had to be *sapiens*. In actuality, we have seen, there was no point in time when Middle Paleolithic cultures ceased and Upper Paleolithic cultures began. The former merged into the latter, at least in some areas.

Another factor to be considered when relating cultural levels to types, races, or subspecies of man is the raw materials that were available to peoples in various parts of the world. The Upper Paleolithic blade-tool assemblage was mainly limited to groups that occupied parts of Europe and Asia. Comparable tools are absent or almost absent from traditions in most of Africa and in southern and eastern Asia.[28] This does not necessarily mean that those who manufactured blade tools were morphologically more modern than those who did not. Blade-tool assemblages were developed where flint and other raw materials were readily accessible. In Africa chopping tools persisted in some parts simply because quartz and quartzite, which make good pounding implements, were at hand, while materials for making cutting tools were not.[29]

Problems connected with the origin of *Homo sapiens* appear to be somewhat analogous to those associated with the differentiation of primitive Hominidae from other hominoids. Answers to such questions as "What is a hominid?" and "What is a representative of *Homo sapiens*?" vary according to the supposed diagnostic characters. If a hominid is defined as a tool-maker, a bipedal creature that did not make tools (which could be identified as such) cannot be classified as a hominid regardless of its morphological similarities to man. Similarly, if the criteria for *sapiens* status include a smooth brow or a particular manufacture of implements, a large-brained fossil man who had a prominent brow or who made less complicated tools cannot be regarded as a representative of *Homo sapiens*.

THE TRANSITION TO MODERN MAN

How did our ancestors acquire those characters which distinguish the *sapiens*? More specifically, since members of *Homo erectus* were apparently like us from the shoulders down, what brought about transformations in the head and face?

Changes in the Head

The major alteration in the hominid head between *Sinanthropus* and Neanderthal man was an expansion of the braincase. There were other changes, of course, but the skull remained relatively low-vaulted and elongated. Heavy ridges at the front and rear of the skull were continued, and the classic Neanderthals had little more of the skull devoted to forehead than did their predecessors. With the Neanderthals, the hominid braincase seems to have reached its maximum capacity (on the average)—more than 1600 cc., according to some estimates. Since then, man has experienced no increase in cranial capacity; if anything, there has been a decrease.[30]

Why did the hominid braincase expand? Perhaps most of the increase in size of the brain and neurocranium was due to an increase in body size. Compared with *mammals* in general, J. N. Spuhler has pointed out, the human brain may be unusually large, both absolutely and relatively. However, when brain and body weights of *primates* are compared, the size of the human brain is less impressive. According to Spuhler, about 80 per cent of man's brain weight is due to the simple fact that he is a primate of large body size. The remaining 20 per cent or so "results from an evolutionary increase in the relative size of hominid brains."[31]

There is a likelihood, then, that a great part of the estimated 300 to 400 cc. increase in cranial capacity of European Neanderthals over late *Homo erectus* individuals was due to increase in body size alone. The latter were, on the average, not much more than 5 feet tall.[32] Classic Neanderthal individuals may not have been much taller, but they were heavier. Coon says that the La Chapelle-aux-Saints specimen and two other classic Neanderthal males stood between 5 feet 4 and 5 feet 6 inches tall; each weighed "probably a good 160 pounds or more."[33]

If greater body bulk did account for most of the Neanderthal braincase expansion, what would explain the "evolutionary increase"? The simplest explanation, as we saw in an earlier chapter, is neotenous mutations followed by selection for the enlarged brain. Pleistocene individuals with larger skulls may, for one reason or another, have been quite successful in transmitting their mutant genes. Perhaps, as one writer implies, sexual selection entered into the perpetuation of neotenous genes:

> Within the human family, females always tend to retain more foetal and infantile traits than males. Among European races, for example, the ideal feminine beauty is one in which a maximum of infantile traits has persisted—soft, silky hair, blonde hair, blue eyes, long eyelashes, and infantile facial features, e.g., in shape of forehead, nose and mouth.[34]

Studies by Bernhard Rensch suggest another kind of selection. Rensch, you will recall, found a relation between brain size and mental capacities. When animals of related species were tested, members of the larger-brained species were better able to remember and solve complex problems. If such a relation existed during human evolution, then factors selective for mental capacities may have been extremely important. Among these, very likely, were traits which allowed or facilitated social control and cooperation. The hunting prowess of the Neanderthals— their ability to kill large mammals with puny weapons—implies that such traits existed.

Cultural factors were probably of considerable importance in brain growth. As the hominid braincase expanded, so also did cumulated knowledge and skills. The full extent of Pleistocene advances in material and non-material culture is not known, but there is little question that the Stone Age tool kit gradually came to include better-made and more specialized implements. Tools were evidently employed for an increasing number and variety of purposes. It is quite evident, too, that means— technological and otherwise—were devised to allow groups to adjust to varied environments, including extremely cold regions. Paleolithic cultures came to include ideas, beliefs, and practices that might be termed religious. By the time of the Neanderthals, if not before, man buried his dead and oftentimes equipped them with implements and food, presumably to enable the deceased to pursue normal activities in an after-life.

In short, increasing cultural complexity—and, by inference, increasing social complexity—was an accompaniment of cranial expansion. This association suggests a cause-effect relationship or cultural selection for a larger brain or both. What could have been the "'cause"? Did increases in cortex result in cultural advances, or did cultural advances prompt brain growth? Ernst Caspari relates increase in brain size to increase in mental capacities and proposes an interactive cause-effect relationship. That is,

> in the evolution of man genetic change and cultural change have been in a positive feedback relation with each other; genic changes have caused an increased ability for active adaptation by cultural means, and adaptation by cultural means has changed environmental conditions in such a way that different selective pressures have arisen, giving rise to further genetic changes in the population.

Once evolving man began to adapt to environmental changes by exercising mental abilities, natural selection became a less potent mechanism. Man could "adapt actively to his environment"—even choose a variety of environments—and "actively change his environment by cultural activities." [35] Thus, conditions were created which fostered those kinds of genetic change that allowed groups to gain greater control over their environments. In the words of Ashley Montagu,

> Every new invention, every new discovery, had, as it were, a self-accelerating, an autocatalytic effect both upon the genetic and the cultural systems. It put a selective premium upon those who were able to take advantage of the new inventions and discoveries, and by both means facilitated further invention and discovery. Every cultural advance increased the selective advantage of those who were capable of utilizing it and of increasing the selective disadvantage of those who were incapable of using it. In this way the cultural pressures on the genetic evolution of man for increasing ability to adapt himself to the cultural environment have played a dominant role in the evolution of man. Without being aware of it man has produced the changing conditions of his own evolution, and has been selecting himself increasingly in relation to the cultural zone of adaptation.[36]

Conceivably, selection for larger heads was less complex. It has been suggested that man is quite intolerant of competitors, and that early groups may have exploited any superiority—mental, cultural, physical —to eliminate or absorb one another. Larger-brained hominids may have survived because they were more cunning, more capable of deviousness and guile, than their neighbors.[37] Again, mutations that resulted in brain increases may also have lengthened the life-span of those affected, thereby giving them a selective advantage over their smaller-brained kin.

The foregoing is speculation. There is no way in which the genes and many behaviors of evolving man can be resurrected. As Le Gros Clark and others have said, "nothing certainly" is known of the actual cause or causes of brain expansion.[38] Nor is there any certainty as to the adaptive advantage of more brains.[39] Presumably, however, there was some adaptive advantage, either for individuals or for groups; for there is no question that brain size did increase. There may also have been some selective benefit by reason of structural changes in the brain; but this, too, is uncertain. Some scientists have claimed that such changes can be read from endocranial casts, casts made of the interior of skulls. Others, such as Weidenreich [40] and Le Gros Clark,[41] have questioned the value and validity of many endocranial interpretations.

Changes in the Face

The human braincase attained its present-day size, if not its present-day form, by the time of the Neanderthals. The typically modern face emerged more slowly. Skulls complete enough to reveal facial features indicate that modern features, in combination, did not evolve until the appearance of the Cro-Magnons and their contemporaries.

When seen in profile, the most striking features of the earliest adult hominid faces are their prominence and their relatively large size. An adult australopithecine face sticks out from the rest of the skull and occupies a greater part of the skull than does the braincase. The brows jut forward and the areas below the orbits protrude. Throughout the Pleistocene there was a gradual, but often sporadic, shrinkage of the brows and a reduction in facial prognathism until, as Weidenreich said, "The nasal bridge, the anterior nasal spine, and the chin, jut out from the profile as the remaining foremost landmarks of the otherwise shrunken face." [42]

What brought about the "shrunken" face? Since reduction of the face was an accompaniment of cultural advances, another cause-effect relationship is implied. Comparative and experimental evidence suggests that the major causal factors were cultural changes which lessened the work of the masticatory apparatus and reduced wear on the teeth. So long as survival placed heavy demands upon the teeth and jaws (maxilla and mandible), these parts of the anatomy tended to be relatively large; the mandible was heavy. Since large teeth occupy more space than small teeth, facial prognathism was inevitable. Forces exerted by a powerful mandible created stresses in the skull, which were absorbed primarily by heavy brow ridges.[43]

Comparative studies have shown that the size of the molars or other teeth is related to the adaptive function they perform. For example, an animal that subsists primarily upon abrasive, fibrous vegetable materials requires larger, heavier grinding teeth than does an animal that eats only flesh or fruits. The greater the size of the teeth, the more space they occupy and the larger their roots. Larger teeth, therefore, require larger jaws. The size of the mandible and masticatory muscles is increased further, as experiments with animals have demonstrated, by heavy usage during the pre-adult period of life.[44]

Foreshortening of the face began rather early in hominid evolution. If Washburn's hypothesis is valid, the first decrease in jaw size resulted from a reduction in the canines. Washburn, you will recall, proposed that the use of tools and weapons eliminated a need for the large projecting canines that our hominid ancestors presumably possessed. There is, as we noted, no fossil evidence either to support or reject this hypothesis.

The fossil record, as it now exists, shows that the cheek teeth were the first teeth to undergo reduction. Between the time of the australopithecines and the appearance of *Homo erectus*, hominids experienced a sharp decrease in the size of the molars. The initially large cheek teeth, Campbell says, appear to have been an adaptation to the coarse vegetable diet available to plains-living animals that ate little meat.[45] As hunting implements and techniques were developed and improved, meat became a more important part of the hominid diet. The ingestion of protein foods, Brace and Montagu point out, requires less crushing and mixing with salivary enzymes than that of carbohydrates and starches. Thus, "it is reasonable to associate the significant increase of meat in the diet with a reduction in the amount of heavy duty mastication required." [46]

Subsequent reduction in the molars (and possibly other teeth), it is generally agreed, attended the cooking of food. The gradual acquisition of knowledge of heat-treatment of food, Albert A. Dahlberg has suggested, not only made for a greater range and variety of food sources; cooking may also have relaxed selective pressures on the dentition.[47] Or, as Brace and Montagu say, the "use of heat to break down the more resistant parts of the utilized foodstuffs [led] to a further reduction in the amount of required chewing, allowing the probable mutation effect to produce a reduction in the size of the molar teeth." [48] Preparation of food by cooking may account for the relatively small size of modern molars, particularly the third molar, and also for the fact that the third molar (called the "wisdom tooth") is sometimes missing altogether.[49]

While Pleistocene molars were becoming smaller, the incisors temporarily increased in size. The front teeth attained their maximum in gross dimensions and pattern complexity during the Middle Pleistocene, Brace tells us, from the time of *Sinanthropus* to the beginning of the Upper Paleolithic. Brace attributes this increase to great use being made of the "built-in tool at the front of the face." Great use is indicated by an unusual amount of wear on the front teeth. Somewhat similar wear may be found among living peoples who employ the "built-in tool" as a vise and as pliers.[50] Coon believes the classic Neanderthals used their teeth in dressing and softening skins, as do Eskimos today.[51] Activities of this sort often involve muscles of the neck as well as masticatory muscles, which may explain why *Homo erectus* and the western Neanderthals had heavy neck muscles.

As tools became more specialized, more versatile, during the Upper Pleistocene, the importance of unusually large incisors and heavy mandibles gradually declined. It became less and less essential to have teeth that, even when worn, could perform non-masticatory functions that were necessary for survival. Perhaps survival came to depend more upon being able to make and use implements, or to be associated with one or more individuals who possessed such knowledge and skills. With cultural advances, that is, the division of labor very probably became more complex. Positions were created which did not require technological or hunting skills—such positions, for example, as artists and religious practitioners (magicians, medicine men). Certainly, arthritic, near-toothless individuals, such as the man from La Chapelle-aux-Saints, managed to live despite their infirmities.

A reduction in heavy demands upon the masticatory apparatus meant that the skull architecture had fewer stresses to absorb. Consequently, the brow ridges became less prominent. Some amount of reduction in the supraorbital torus possibly occurred because of an elevation in the front part of the neurocranium. The entire forehead, rather than a limited buttress above the eyes, came to absorb stresses created by the exercise of masticatory muscles. Why the vertical forehead appeared is not known. Its appearance may have been related to a decrease in the size of the mandible and masticatory muscles that attended lighter usage of the jaws and teeth. Again, the skull of the infant chimpanzee suggests that we may owe our high foreheads to neotenous mutations.

Another modern feature, the chin, was produced by a shrinkage in the size and weight of the mandible. This shrinkage was sufficient, some writers believe, to produce the chin—a recession in the upper part of the mandible left the lower part jutting out. E. L. DuBrul and H. Sicher claim more was involved. The chin, they say, serves as a brace for the midline, or symphyseal region, of the mandible. A brace is needed in this region because considerable strain is exerted during rotary chewing; but for the chin, the two halves of the mandible could break apart. Earlier man did not need a chin, for the strain in the symphyseal region was taken by thick bone. The ape mandible is not only thick but is usually reinforced by a simian shelf, a bony plate on the inner surface of the symphyseal region.[52]

270

CONCLUSIONS

There are as yet no clear-cut answers to such questions as: Where and when did *Homo sapiens* originate? and what brought about the morphological changes in the skull that differentiate members of this species from *Homo erectus*? The search for answers to the first question is complicated by the "Neanderthal problem" and problems of dating and correlating much of the fossil and archaeological evidence. A definitive answer to the second question awaits a fuller understanding of genetic processes and of the adaptive significance of a relatively large brain.

If the Neanderthals and Neanderthal-like (Neanderthaloid) specimens are ruled out of human phylogeny, the present evidence—a single specimen—suggests that *Homo sapiens* originated in southeast Asia between 40,000 and 50,000 years ago. Should the "progressive" (early) Neanderthals and what Oakley terms "*Homo sapiens* Neanderthaloids" of Palestine, East Africa, and South Africa be accepted as members of our species, the antiquity of *sapiens* would not be appreciably increased; but other areas of origin would be suggested. In either case, the fossil gap between representatives of *Homo erectus* and *Homo sapiens* is considerable—about 300,000 years.

Inclusion of all Neanderthals and Neanderthal-like specimens within the species *Homo sapiens* does not eliminate the fossil gap, but it reduces it considerably. The time interval between *erectus* and *sapiens* specimens shrinks by roughly two-thirds, leaving a fossil void of about 100,000 years, according to figures supplied by Bernard Campbell. Campbell, who accepts all Neanderthal types as members of *Homo sapiens*, lists Swanscombe and Steinheim finds as the earliest representatives of modern man. These individuals supposedly lived between 150,000 and 200,000 years ago.[53] Le Gros Clark, who does not regard the Neanderthals as members of *sapiens*, also believes that the Swanscombe and Steinheim specimens are early representatives of our species that date back some 200,000 years.[54]

The second most ancient fossils, with estimated ages of between 70,000 and 150,000 years, come from France (Fontéchevade), Germany (Ehringsdorf), and Italy (Saccopastore). These, like the two specimens mentioned above, are variously regarded as Neanderthals, Neanderthaloids, and early varieties of *Homo sapiens*. It might be concluded from the total accumulation of evidence that our species originated in Europe no later than 150,000 years ago. Such a conclusion, though, would be based upon a limited and probably biased sample of relevant populations. Europe, especially western Europe, has been more thoroughly searched for evidence of early man than other parts of the world.

271

But even in western Europe new evidence is constantly coming to light. More than a dozen new sites have been located there since the end of World War II.[55]

Some day new evidence, improved dating techniques, or a new theory —or better utilization of what is now available—may allow scientists to confidently answer the when and where questions of modern man's origins. That answer might provide an entirely different picture of the time and place of such origins than any now being considered. We suspect that it will be eventually agreed that *Homo sapiens* did *not* evolve from a single, geographically restricted group. We do not intend to imply that the present races of man can be traced directly back to specific geographic fossil populations. In view of the frequent interchange of genes which characterizes human populations, it is unlikely, for example, that *Sinanthropus* was the sole—or even the major—ancestral group of the Mongoloids.

One objection to the hypothesis that *Homo sapiens* evolved from more than one group is the fact that all living peoples are members of the same species. It can be argued that since geographic dispersal— hence genetic isolation—among nonhuman animals has resulted in speciation, scattered pre-*sapiens* populations would also have evolved into new species. Therefore, if present-day populations were derived from such groups, there would now be two or more distinct species of *Homo*. In short, a number of species would have given rise to a number of species, not just one.

An argument of this sort is much less cogent today than it once was. Until recently, we noted in an earlier chapter, it was usually assumed that similar fossil forms that were separated by geographic distance or ecological barriers could not possibly be members of the same species. As a consequence, classificatory schemes listed several extinct hominid genera and species. Today, however, most of these genera and species are generally regarded as representatives of either *Homo sapiens* or *Homo erectus*. Increasingly, authorities list but one species, *Homo erectus*, as the immediate genetic predecessors of *Homo sapiens*. No scientist has yet established—or attempted to establish, so far as we know—that our species evolved from any particular *Homo erectus* group.

If *Homo sapiens* evolved directly from *Homo erectus*, no two species of *Homo* (with the possible exception of the classic Neanderthals, according to some writers) have lived contemporaneously for well over a million years. Most scientists apparently believe that there is no evidence to indicate that two or more hominid species have *ever* been contemporaries. Why not? Why did our prehistoric forebears fail to speciate like other animals? The obvious answer is that other animals did not share evolving man's evolutionary experiences. Evolving man early acquired a biological makeup that allowed him to do things beyond the capabilities of any other form of life. Relatively early in his history he could not only use tools but make them, he could subsist upon a variety of foodstuffs, and he appears to have been able to cooperate with his kind in the attainment of common goals. Somewhere along the evolutionary route, he gained a facility for communication through symbols; his brain enabled him to abstract and categorize the world about him. Evolving man, in short, was unique in that he was able to learn to adapt to his environment by means of culture.

By the time of *Homo erectus*, if not earlier, man's cultural achievements were sufficient to blunt—and perhaps eliminate—some of the selective factors which normally operate in the evolving of one animal species from another. The level of Middle Pleistocene culture was such that groups of hominids could adapt to a variety of environments without undergoing major morphological changes. Fossil specimens from China, Java, Europe, and different parts of Africa are by no means identical; but they are similar enough to be classified as members of the same species, *Homo erectus*.

Theoretically, then, the basic Weidenreich-Coon thesis has some validity. Early man controlled his environment through cultural means to the extent that survival was not contingent upon nonhuman-like biological modifications. Therefore, isolated *Homo erectus* groups, who could survive though isolated because they had culture, may very well have evolved—with genetic and cultural interchanges—into *Homo sapiens* populations. This thesis seems to gain validity, too, from the fact that subspecies, or races, were already in existence during the Middle Pleistocene.

It is often assumed that the living races of man evolved after *Homo* became *sapiens*. Whether 40,000 to 50,000 years—or even 200,000 years —would have been long enough for such to have occurred remains to be demonstrated. An assumption at least as plausible is that racial diversification began fairly early in the Pleistocene. Populations were smaller and more isolated then than later, so they were more likely to experience genetic drift and undergo hybridization when groups did exchange genes. Races of *Homo erectus*, or even Upper Paleolithic races, were probably not identical with present-day races. Factors which have altered and sometimes eliminated gene pools in more recent times—interbreeding, epidemics, warfare, migration into new environments—also affected prehistoric gene pools. Even so, it seems to us more likely that present-day races evolved from diversified populations than from a homogeneous stock. For the latter to have occurred, all but one of the Pleistocene subspecies would have had to be eliminated.

Why the relative size of the human brain came to exceed that of any other large primate (but not that of every small primate) is still somewhat of a mystery. Brain expansion began early in hominid evolution, for the australopithecines "were clearly, if only slightly, in advance of the level of brain evolution achieved by the anthropoid apes of our time." [56] It continued to expand as evolving man developed and elaborated cultural mechanisms of adaptation. A cause-effect relationship probably existed between social-cultural factors and cranial growth, but the nature of this relationship is not presently known. Caspari's hypothesis that cultural and genetic changes proceeded in an interactive positive feedback relation seems plausible.

Other major modifications in the skull are believed to be consequences of lightened usage of the teeth and mandible. Exactly how these and other structures were reduced is still somewhat of a mystery. Perhaps the simplest explanation—too simple, in the opinion of some [57]—is that offered by C. Loring Brace. Brace suggests that once selective pressures for a structure are suspended, the accumulation of random mutations that follows will eventually bring about reduction or loss of the structure. This follows, he believes, because mutations alter or delete enzyme chains which influence growth and development of the phenotype. "This, of course, is just a more complete expression of the long-standing observation that the great majority of mutations will be disadvantageous." The best illustration of structural reduction in man is in the face:

> As technology increasingly took over tasks formerly performed by the dentition, the adaptive advantage formerly inherent in the possession of large teeth decreased, and mutations affecting the face could occur without disadvantage to the possessors. Since the majority of such mutations will result in structural reduction, it is no surprise to find that the human face has become smaller as human culture has become a more complete means for adaptation. [58]

One major objection to Brace's explanation is that there is reason to suspect that the majority of mutations do not cause a reduction in the size of a structure. [59] It has also been argued that the employment of tools did not necessarily make tooth size "selectively neutral." "Rather," Howard L. Bailit and Jonathan S. Friedlaender state, "it is more consistent with modern evolutionary theory to postulate a positive process of natural selection for smaller anterior teeth." These writers do not know what the selective process for smaller teeth is, but they state:

> One of the most attractive hypotheses is that a nonfunctioning structure still requires a great expenditure of metabolic energy to create and

274

maintain, and hence will be selected against. This theory assumes that an organism expending energy for an unnecessary structure will be at a selective disadvantage compared with an organism in which that structure is reduced or absent. As a theoretical example, if the selection pressure for large tusks in pigs is relaxed because of changes in the environment, the pigs with smaller tusks will be more "fit" since they will have relatively more energy to expend on other processes and structures.[60]

Professor Alice M. Brues also rejects the idea that there is a "passive and automatic reduction of parts or organs with decreased function." She suggests that natural selection resulted in reduction of the size of the hominid face. The real disadvantage of a large face in an erect or semierect primate probably "lies in its interference with rotating movements of the head." A jutting muzzle decreases the efficiency of rotation because there is more inertia to overcome—the center of gravity of the head is more distant from the axis of rotation.

Now the ability to look over one's shoulder in case of possible threat from the rear, and to look back again, in case of threat from more than one side, requires not only quick initiation of head rotation, but quick termination of the motion so that the eyes may be fixated. The speed with which the environment can be visually scanned, therefore, will be increased by muzzle reduction.

Quick rotation of the head, it would appear, has high survival value under certain conditions. Therefore, "no causes other than ordinary natural selection need be invoked in the reduction in prognathism in the later stages of man's evolution." [61]

Some of the differences between modern and prehistoric *Homo* faces may be due less to selection for genetically-related changes than to differential usage of the masticatory apparatus. Such a possibility is suggested by at least two types of evidence. Wear and attrition on the occlusal surface (the surface in contact with an opposite tooth) will ultimately stimulate dentin-producing cells (odontoblasts) to produce additional dentin.[62] And experiments with weanling rats have demonstrated that differences in dental wear, weight of the mandible, and width of the dental arch follow rather quickly from a diet of hard, crunchy food.[63] Such findings may indicate that if prehistoric man had not used his mouth as a tool and for heavy-duty mastication, his teeth would have been smaller and his mandible less heavy. In other words, the lower part of his face might have been more like that of modern man—even if there were no mutations for changes in that area.

Our discussion has dealt primarily with typical representatives of

Homo types and species. We have not attempted to deal with the range of variability to be found in any population, living or extinct. In closing, we shall simply point out that there are peoples today who exhibit traits reminiscent of the Neanderthals—some amount of facial prognathism, large incisors, heavy brows, a slanting neurocranium. Neanderthal characteristics, on the other hand, were not shared to the same degree by even the classic Neanderthals, as is evidenced by the finds from Spy and Krapina. Due to the presence (or supposed presence) of modern features in some specimens, there is still disagreement among prehistorians regarding the status—and sometimes the dating—of all the known Upper Pleistocene individuals. Consequently, we find that the same fossils are variously labelled as "presapiens," "early Neanderthaloids," "Neanderthals," and "*Homo sapiens*."

Interpretation of the fossil record, we reiterate, is not an exact science. It is more so, however, than it was a few years ago. Not only do we now know more about our ancestors than has ever been known, but our knowledge is more solidly based upon rigorous scientific principles and procedures. Scientific facts are constantly replacing untested beliefs and assumptions. As interpretative techniques become increasingly more sophisticated, we can look for many of the problems which now hinder and complicate reconstruction of the story of man to be of historical interest only.

NOTES

1. Aleš Hrdlička, *The Skeletal Remains of Early Man* (Washington, D.C.: The Smithsonian Institution, 1930), p. 327.

2. Denise de Sonneville-Bordes, "Upper Paleolithic Cultures in Western Europe," in Joseph R. Caldwell (ed.), *New Roads to Yesterday* (New York: Basic Books, Inc., Publishers, 1966), p. 130.

3. Except as noted, materials in this subsection are drawn from: Arthur Keith, *The Antiquity of Man* (London: Williams and Norgate, 1915), Chap. 4; George Grant MacCurdy, *Human Origins: A Manual of Prehistory*, 1 (New York: D. Appleton and Company, 1924), 379–383.

4. Marcellin Boule and Henri V. Vallois, *Fossil Men* (New York: The Dryden Press, 1957), pp. 273–274.

5. Kenneth P. Oakley, *Frameworks for Dating Fossil Man* (Chicago: Aldine Publishing Company, 1964), p. 315.

6. Boule and Vallois, *op. cit.*, pp. 285–289.

7. Keith, *op. cit.*, p. 67.

8. W. E. Le Gros Clark, *The Fossil Evidence for Human Evolution*, 2nd ed. (Chicago: University of Chicago Press, 1964), p. 54.

9. Sir Arthur Keith, *New Discoveries Relating to the Antiquity of Man* (New York: W. W. Norton & Co., Inc., 1931), pp. 385–386.

10. Boule and Vallois, *op. cit.*, p. 298.

11. C. L. Brace and M. F. Ashley Montagu, *Man's Evolution* (New York: The Macmillan Company, 1965), p. 158.

12. Oakley, *op. cit.*, p. 314.

13. Grahame Clark, *World Prehistory: An Outline* (Cambridge, England: Cambridge University Press, 1962), pp. 54–58.

14. See, for example, Raymond Lantier, *Man Before History* (New York: Walker & Company, 1965), Chap. 4; Carleton S. Coon, *The Origin of Races* (New York: Alfred A. Knopf, Inc., 1963), Chaps. 8–12.

15. Brace and Montagu, *op. cit.*, p. 255.

16. William Howells, *Mankind in the Making*, rev. ed. (Garden City, N. Y.: Doubleday & Company, Inc., 1967), p. 215.

17. Robert J. Braidwood, "Near Eastern Prehistory," in Caldwell, *op. cit.*, p. 153.

18. Oakley, *op. cit.*, pp. 248–249, 312–324; de Sonneville Bordes, *op. cit.*, p. 133.

19. Franz Weidenreich, "Facts and Speculations Concerning the Origin of *Homo Sapiens*," *American Anthropologist*, New Series 49 (1947), 200–201.

20. Coon, *op. cit.*, p. 658.

21. *Ibid.*, pp. 521–522.

22. Joseph B. Birdsell, "The Origin of Human Races," *The Quarterly Review of Biology*, 38 (1963), 178–185.

23. Le Gros Clark, *op. cit.*, pp. 84–86.

24. Joseph R. Caldwell, "Introduction," in Caldwell, *op. cit.*, p. 6.

25. "Anthropological Notes," *Science of Man*, I (1961), 61.

26. Oakley, *op. cit.*, pp. 309–310.

27. *Ibid.*, p. 295.

28. Karl W. Butzer, *Environment and Archaeology* (Chicago: Aldine Publishing Company, 1964), p. 385.

29. John Buettner-Janusch, *Origins of Man* (New York: John Wiley & Sons, Inc., 1966), p. 353.

30. Gerhardt von Bonin, "On the Size of Man's Brain As Indicated by Skull Capacity," *Journal of Comparative Neurology*, 59 (February, 1934), 24.

31. J. N. Spuhler, "Somatic Paths to Culture," *Human Biology*, 31 (February, 1959), 7–8.

32. W. E. Le Gros Clark, *History of the Primates*, 5th ed. (Chicago: University of Chicago Press, 1966), p. 90.

33. Coon, *op. cit.*, p. 548.

34. W. C. Osman Hill, *Man's Ancestry: A Primer of Human Phylogeny* (Springfield, Ill.: Charles C Thomas, Publisher, 1953), p. 165.

35. Ernst Caspari, "Selective Forces in the Evolution of Man," *The American Naturalist*, XCVII (1963), 11.

36. M. F. Ashley Montagu, *The Human Revolution* (Cleveland: The World Publishing Company, 1965), p. 120.

37. Stanley M. Garn, *Culture and the Direction of Human Evolution* (Detroit: Wayne State University Press, 1964), pp. 12–13; Ernst Mayr, "Taxonomic Categories in Fossil Hominids," *Cold Spring Harbor Symposia on Quantitative Biology*, XV (Cold Spring Harbor, N. Y.: The Biological Laboratory, 1950), 116.

38. Le Gros Clark, *History of the Primates*, p. 119.

39. Garn, *op. cit.*, p. 12.

40. Weidenreich, *op. cit.*, p. 199.

41. Le Gros Clark, *The Fossil Evidence for Human Evolution*, pp. 96–97.

42. Franz Weidenreich, "The Trend of Human Evolution," *Evolution*, I (1947), 229.

43. Bernard G. Campbell, *Human Evolution* (Chicago: Aldine Publishing Company, 1966), pp. 212–213.

44. *Ibid.*, p. 182.

45. *Ibid.*, p. 197.

46. Brace and Montagu, *op. cit.*, p. 262.

47. Albert A. Dahlberg, "Dental Evolution and Culture," in Garn, *op. cit.*, p. 28.

48. Brace and Montagu, *op. cit.*, p. 262.

49. Campbell, *op. cit.*, p. 197.

50. C. Loring Brace, "Cultural Factors in the Evolution of the Human Dentition," in M. F. Ashley Montagu (ed.), *Culture and the Evolution of Man* (New York: Oxford University Press, 1962), pp. 347–348.

51. Carleton S. Coon, "Race and Ecology in Man," *Cold Spring Harbor Symposia on Quantitative Biology*, XXIV (Cold Spring Harbor, N. Y.: The Biological Laboratry, 1959), 155.

52. Campbell, *op. cit.*, pp. 185–186.

53. *Ibid.*, pp. 367–368.

54. Le Gros Clark, *The Fossil Evidence for Human Evolution*, pp. 67–70, 85.

55. Oakley, *op. cit.*, pp. 295–301.

56. Harry J. Jerison, "Interpreting the Evolution of the Brain," in Garn, *op. cit.*, p. 70.

57. See, for example, Timothy Prout, "Observations on Structural Reduction in Evolution," *The American Naturalist*, XCVIII (1964), 239–249; Ralph L. Holloway, Jr., "Structural Reduction Through the 'Probable Mutation Effect,'" *American Journal of Physical Anthropology*, 25 (1966), 7–12.

58. C. Loring Brace, "Structural Reduction in Evolution," *The American Naturalist*, XCVII (1963), 42–44.

59. Prout, *op. cit.*, pp. 244–248.

60. Howard L. Bailit and Jonathan S. Friedlaender, "Tooth Size Reduction: A Hominid Trend," *American Anthropologist*, 68 (1966), 665–672.

61. Alice M. Brues, "'Probable Mutation Effect' and the Evolution of Hominid Teeth and Jaws," *American Journal of Physical Anthropology*, New Series 25 (1966), 169–170.

62. Dahlberg, *op. cit.*, p. 22.

63. Edward E. Hunt, Jr., "The Continuing Evolution of Modern Man," *Cold Spring Harbor Symposia on Quantitative Biology*, XXIV (Cold Spring Harbor, N. Y.: The Biological Laboratory, 1959), 249.

Index

Adams, Frank Dawson, 22, 23
adaptation, 33, 69–72; arboreal, 127, 130n, 148–150, 197; through culture, 267, 273
adaptive radiation, 74
Aegyptopithecus, 160, 161
Aeolopithecus, 160
Agassiz, Louis, 11, 21
Agogino, George A., 253
alleles, 31n, 37
amniote egg, 138–139
amphibians, evolution of, 137–138, 139
Amphipithecus, 144–145
Andersson, J. G., 219
Andrew, R. J., 116
Andrews, Roy Chapman, 251
"anthropoid-ape hypothesis," 158–159
Anthropoidea, suborder of, 80, 84–88, 133; earliest evidence of, 159–161
Antiquity of Man as Proved by Geology, The, 256
apes, 86–88, 160, 161, 169, 195; compared with man, 89–94, 158–159; compared with monkeys, 89–91; *see also* Anthropoidea, chimpanzee, gibbon, gorilla, Hominoidea, orangutan
Apidium, 160, 161
Arambourg, Camille, 245
Archosauria, 141
artifacts, sequential changes of, 57–58; *see also* tools, Paleolithic

Ascenzi, Antonio, 61
Ascher, Robert, 195, 196–198, 208, 212, 213
Asimov, Isaac, 26n, 43
Atlanthropus mauritanicus, 224t
Atz, James W, 134
Aurignacian tradition/culture, 256–257, 259
Australopithecinae, 173, 182–184, 186, 189–190, 204, 209, 228, 231, 274; *see also Australopithecus, Homo habilis,* "Mrs. Ples," *Paranthropus*
Australopithecus, 167, 168, 173i, 179, 181, 184, 189, 190, 191, 207, 226
Australopithecus africanus, 174–175, 177, 181, 190
Australopithecus prometheus, 177, 181
Aves, evolution of, 126–130
Avis, Virginia, 95, 167n

baboons, 97, 101, 102, 103, 104–106, 196
Bailit, Howard L., 274–275, 278
Barth, Frederick, 157
Bastian, Hartmut, 134
Beach, Frank A., 115, 116
Beals, Ralph L., 252
Beck, William S., 22, 43
Beerbower, James R., 60, 142
Beg, Mirza Azhar, 115
Bergounioux, F. M., 251
Biegert, Josef, 213

Note: *n* indicates that the reference appears in a footnote; *t* indicates that the reference appears in a table; *f,* that it appears in a figure; and *i,* that it appears in an illustration.

Order	Suborder	Infraorde...
Primates	Prosimii	Tupaiiform...
		Tarsiiform...
		Lorisiform...
		Lemurforr...
	Anthropoidea	Platyrrhin...

Only those subclassifications pertinent to the text are s...